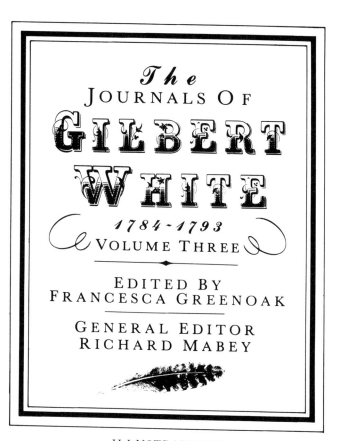

The JOURNALS OF GILBERT WHITE

1784~1793

VOLUME THREE

EDITED BY
FRANCESCA GREENOAK

GENERAL EDITOR
RICHARD MABEY

ILLUSTRATIONS
BY CLARE ROBERTS

CENTURY
LONDON · SYDNEY · AUCKLAND
JOHANNESBURG

Art Direction and Design by
Bob Hook

Introduction and Notes
Copyright © Francesca Greenoak 1989

First published in 1989 by Century Hutchinson Ltd,
Brookmount House, 62–65 Chandos Place,
Covent Garden, London WC2N 4NW

Century Hutchinson Australia Pty Ltd,
89–91 Albion Street,
Surry Hills,
Sydney, NSW 2010,
Australia

Century Hutchinson New Zealand Ltd,
PO Box 40-086 Glenfield, Auckland 10,
New Zealand

Century Hutchinson South Africa Pty Ltd,
PO Box 337, Bergvlei, 2012 South Africa

Set in Caslon Old Face and Caslon Open Face
Printed and bound in Great Britain by
Butler and Tanner Ltd, Frome, Somerset

British Library Cataloguing in Publication Data

White, Gilbert, 1720–1793
The Journals of Gilbert White, 1784–1793.
Vol. 3
1. Hampshire. Selborne. Natural history.
White, Gilbert, 1720–1793. Correspondence, diaries, etc.
I. Title II. Greenoak, Francesca
508'.092'4

ISBN 0 7126 2261 6

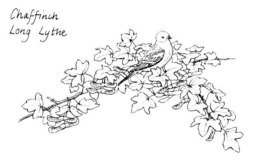

Chaffinch
Long Lythe

CONTENTS

Also from Century
by Richard Mabey
GILBERT WHITE
A biography

THE NATURAL HISTORY OF SELBORNE
A bicentennial edition

Acknowledgements

I should like to thank Robin McIntosh for her painstaking work in transcribing the hand-written manuscript, and Moyna Kitchin for copy editing. I should also like to thank Mr Tony Vincent of the Science Museum for conducting me around the vaults of the Science Museum and for giving me an introduction to 18th century barometers, and the British Museum (Natural History) for identifying some of the insects noted in the Journals. I am indebted to Mr Philip Hughes of The Society for the Protection of Ancient Buildings who illuminated some of the problems which Gilbert White had in the building of his new Parlour. My thanks also to Mr Jim Coles for his advice on some of the agricultural terms. Clare Roberts and I would both like to express our gratitude to Dr June Chatfield and David Standing of the Gilbert White Museum, Selborne, for their continued kind assistance. Clare Roberts would also like to give special thanks to Ludo Beumer, Steve Povey and Ann Mallinson. Finally, my thanks to the publishing team at Century Hutchinson for their support and to Bob Hook for his excellent design.

F.G.

F o r e w o r d

Gilbert White is often described as the founding father of natural history and his book *The Natural History of Selborne* is one of the most frequently published titles in the English language. Increasingly White is also being recognised as an important literary figure, who played a key role in the development of descriptive writing about place and nature.

Despite this, his *Journals*, which span more than forty years of observation, have never been published in full. As well as being the source of raw material for *The Natural History*, they are a unique record in their own right, and have a vividness and intimacy of style that was not to be seen again in English journal writing for another fifty years.

These three volumes cover the entire range of White's journals, from the early notes in a *Garden Kalendar* in 1751 to the final *Naturalist's Journal* entries in 1793. They are fully transcribed for the first time, and include all the detailed daily weather data of the original. As editor, Francesca Greenoak's chief aim throughout has been to make these remarkable manuscripts accessible to a wider audience. Annotation has therefore been kept to the minimum necessary for clarity and understanding.

In keeping with a tradition that has grown up around various editions of *The Natural History* of including illustrations of Selborne contemporary with the edition, these three volumes of *Journals* have been augmented by original drawings by Clare Roberts. Her pictures and field notes echo the detail and intimacy of White's writing, and were all drawn in the parish of Selborne and the surrounding countryside from 1985 to 1988.

Richard Mabey

INTRODUCTION

In 1750, Gilbert White's good friend and faithful correspondent John Mulso wrote to him:

> You are now I suppose to be found . . . ranging your Trees and nursing your Plants . . . I wish you joy of the arrival of the swallows and the swifts and the nightingales. I hope you will send me word how your nurseries go on, and the true state of Selborne Hanger . . .

By this time, at the age of thirty, a year after having been ordained, Gilbert had an evident interest in gardening and in the fauna and flora of his home village, and this was to be steadily extended and amplified throughout the rest of his life. Starting in 1751, he began to keep yearly journals in which he wrote perceptive notes on gardening and natural history, continuing this practice over forty-three years and ceasing to write entries only eleven days before his death. These journals prove his quite remarkable observational skills and, more clearly than any of his other writings, show a man whose scientific curiosity about the natural world incorporated a deep affection for plants and animals, particularly those of his native parish.

The journals fall into two distinct groupings, which differ more in form than content. The *Garden Kalendar*, continued between the years 1751 and 1767, comprise mostly but not exclusively gardening notes, written intermittently on blank quarto sheets. The *Naturalist's Journal* was a printed diary-notebook, each volume holding a year's observations, and Gilbert kept up these journals from the year 1768 to 1793. There was in addition a notebook-journal, the *Flora Selborniensis*, in which he wrote botanical observations during the year 1766.

Keeping regular notes of observations on horticultural, meteorological and natural history matters was a fairly widespread practice among gentlemen of Gilbert White's day. Robert Marsham, who corresponded with Gilbert after the publication of *The Natural History of Selborne*, wrote that he had kept a journal for more than fifty years. Coincidentally, Marsham seems to have been encouraged into the diary habit by Dr Stephen Hales, the notable scientist and botanist, Rector of Faringdon (a parish close to Selborne) and also a friend of the White family. Another friend of Robert Marsham was Benjamin Stillingfleet, in his latter years a gardener and botanist of considerable repute, who in 1759 published the influential *Miscellaneous Tracts relating to Natural History, Husbandry and Physick*. In the printed preface to the *Naturalist's Journal*, its originator Daines Barrington made several references to Stillingfleet's ideas, especially his recommendation of the keeping of daily records and observations. Thomas Barker of Rutland, who resided near Gilbert's uncle and aunt Mr and Mrs Isaacs at Whitwell Rectory, also kept a journal between the years 1736 and 1801. In its initial year, there were two spring-time notes initialled GW, one on wild geese flying northwards, and another on the sound of the cuckoo. It seems, however, that Gilbert did not keep a continuous journal of his own until he returned and settled back into life in his home village of Selborne, following his degree and ordination.

Gilbert White was a keen experimental gardener, and in 1747 bought for himself the most important horticultural work of the time, Philip Miller's great *Gardener's Dictionary*. Later he was to correspond with Miller, to meet him and exchange seeds. The Wakes, the family home of the White family, has its frontage right on the main street, with a considerable garden to the rear, backed by a field and the great beech hanger of Selborne. The garden was augmented and landscaped by Gilbert and his brothers and they adopted the Hanger itself into their schemes as part of the garden vista. Some of their work is still evident today: the lime trees to the front of the house, part of the fruit wall, the ha-ha at the end of the garden, and the two paths up the Hanger – the steep Zig-zag and the gentler Bostal.

The *Garden Kalendar* and the later years of the *Naturalist's Journal* give considerable detail about the plants in the garden of the Wakes. The cottage garden flowers which Gilbert grew in his borders are now once again in fashion – hollyhocks, larkspur, asters, lilies, fritillaries. He also planted trees and shrubs and several experimental crops such as sweet corn, sea kale and certain 'small beans' from Oxfordshire, 'never sowed but once in England'. In tune with the horticultural preoccupations of his time, Gilbert spent a great deal of energy maintaining hot-beds for melons and cucumbers. Yet the innovator, even one of dedication and skill, is, just like any gardener, at risk from the unpredictable English weather. Gilbert White's hot-beds sometimes reached baking point and burned the plants or lost heat completely so that they perished of cold. An entry for 1754 notes bleakly 'uncommon severe winter. Most things in the garden destroyed.'

The beautiful garden upon which his friend Mulso heaped high compliments in later years was won by hard labour and planning. The intractable Selborne soil was improved with cartloads of dung, and good loamy soil was brought over from nearby Dorton. Small parcels of land were bought bit by bit from neighbours, to enlarge the grounds. The 'picturesque' was the prevailing concept of the late eighteenth century, and entering into its spirit, Gilbert made a bastion and a mound. He hung a series of gates, artificially sized and placed to make a vista. He set up oil jars to mimic urns, and made up a two-dimensional board to look from a distance like a statue. He also built alcoves (small summerhouses) at places where the view was especially attractive.

Nearly all the observations in the *Garden Kalendar* are concerned with cultivated plants, but in the 1760s Gilbert was becoming increasingly interested in wild plants. He purchased an important botanical work: William Hudson's *Flora Anglica* in 1765, and amended the title page of the *Kalendar* of that year to include notes on the wild flora also. This was not entirely satisfactory, and in 1766 he kept both a *Garden Kalendar* and a notebook which he called *Flora Selborniensis*, which is a catalogue of his wild plant observations. This was a year of botanical groundwork.

In 1768, he received as a gift a journal devised by the

Honourable Daines Barrington and published by Gilbert's brother Benjamin. The *Naturalist's Journal* was a standardised diary for the kind of observations that gentlemen of a scientific inclination had been making informally on the subject of natural history. At first Gilbert observed the formalities of the columns, which designated set spaces for the first trees in leaf, flowers to bloom, birds appearing and so on, but it took only a few years for most of the information to be written all over the page in sometimes quite lengthy paragraphs. Towards the end of the 1770s, he began inserting blank pages on which to write pieces of more extended observation. The only records he continued to keep in columns were the figures for the barometer and thermometer readings, and notes on wind and rain.

Gilbert White has long been acclaimed for several important discoveries. It was he who first distinguished between the three leaf warblers, who gave us the first and still revealing description of the harvest mouse. He observed the yearly appearance and reappearance of a 'large bat', giving us the earliest notes on the behaviour of the noctule bat in Britain, and he made many pioneering observations on his favourites among the birds: swifts, martins and swallows.

Yet it is not for these achievements alone that Gilbert White is revered and regarded nationally with affection, and his *Natural History of Selborne*, never out of print. Under his serious and affectionate scrutiny, the parish, one of the most ancient units of human community in England, was extended conceptually to include plants and animals – presented not as specimens, but co-existing within an intimate landscape. A follower in White's footsteps will note obvious losses – kites, bustards, the playful ravens over the Hanger – and one has to search for glow-worms or wrynecks. Yet it is significant that walking around Selborne today one may see, as Gilbert White did, a nuthatch in the churchyard, marsh marigolds brightening the church meadow, toothwort on the hazel bank, hellebores in the hollow lanes and along the quiet country roads, and an astonishingly rich mixture of woodland plants: daffodils, golden saxifrage, ferns and even the shy rarity, herb Paris.

As a writer, Gilbert was far from flamboyant. Indeed, so great was his reticence that even in the journals the personal pronoun rarely intrudes itself. None the less, there is a strong sense of the man behind the observations. The arrival of swallows is accompanied in the journal by exclamation marks!! Snow is lying 'shoe-deep' or reaching to a horse's chest; and there are 'cracks in the ground deeper than the length of a walking stick'. These tell a story of the naturalist watching the skies, tentatively trying the snow or barging through drifts on horseback, prodding the dried-out ground enquiringly with his stick. He drew on the resources of English and classical poetry, prose and science as he wrote the apparently simple journal notes which read so vividly:

> May 2nd 1765: No vegetation seems to stir at present.
> May 3rd: This evening the vehement east-west wind seems
> to be abated; & the air is soft, & cloudy. Ground
> bound like stone.

As the years passed, Gilbert became more confident and relaxed. He was corresponding with and meeting some of the foremost scientists and naturalists of the period, and it is clear that he recognised the original contribution that he could make to the state of knowledge of the time. He wrote two papers which were read at meetings of the Royal Society, and had, by the mid-1770s, decided to write a book about the natural history of his native parish which was to be a distillation of his enquiries and observations. Gilbert White had a fine critical faculty, and one senses an impatience with headlong and insufficiently substantiated natural history writing. As early as 1770, he was writing to Daines Barrington:

> Though there is endless room for observation in the field of
> nature which is boundless, yet investigation (where a man
> endeavours to be sure of his facts) can make but slow
> progress; and all that one could collect in many years would
> go into a very narrow compass.

What sets Gilbert White apart from other naturalists is not simply a matter of unusual perception. The clear-sightedness of his observations arises from a continuous endeavour to strike through conventional interpretations or misleading appearances to reach the truth of whatever subject he was considering. He took immense pains with style, not just as a matter of pride, but because he rightly saw a fundamental correlation between precision of thought and exactness of expression. The *Naturalist's Journals* are both field notes and a working manuscript for *The Natural History of Selborne*. They are by no means hasty jottings, but already accomplished and polished notes, many of which were transposed to the published book with only minimal editing, and they provide a close insight into the life-long interests of this remarkable naturalist.

NOTES
ON THE TEXT

This is the first time that Gilbert White's journals have been printed in full. His forty-three years of notes and observations are published here in three volumes:

Volume   I   *The Garden Kalendar; Flora Selborniensis; Naturalist's Journal (1768–73).*
Volume   II   *Naturalist's Journal (1774–83)*
Volume III   *Naturalist's Journal (1784–93)*

Garden Kalendar

The manuscript of Gilbert White's *Garden Kalendar*, kept between the years 1751 and 1767, is at the British Library. It consists of quarto sheets of letter paper which were subsequently stitched together. The work has appeared in print in a facsimile edition with an introduction and notes by John Clegg (Scolar Press, 1975).

Flora Selborniensis

Flora Selborniensis was written by Gilbert White during the year 1766. It consists of a number of quarto sheets of notes principally about the wild flowers in the environs of Selborne. It is now owned by the Selborne Society. A facsimile *Flora Selborniensis* was published by the Society in a limited edition.

Naturalist's Journal

Between the years 1768 and the year of his death in 1793, Gilbert White made an entry almost every day in his *Naturalist's Journal*, taking it with him on his journeys away from home. The format for these annual journals had been devised by Daines Barrington and published by Gilbert's brother Benjamin White, and were in the form of blank diaries split into printed columns headed with items relevant to those with an interest in natural history. A selection of the entries, edited by Walter Johnson, appeared in 1931, but the complete journals have never been published in full. For this purpose, a transcription was made from the microfilm held by the British Library, where the manuscript journals are kept.

Any editor of Gilbert White's works begins with the immediate benefit of the orderliness of the author's method. The writing is clear copperplate, and there are very few indecipherable words. The arrangement of entries is generally easy to follow.

The two main principles behind the presentation and annotation of these manuscripts are maintaining the authenticity of the text, and endeavouring to present it in the way most accessible to the reader. Notes have been kept to a minimum and are intended simply to explain names or terms which would be unfamiliar to a present-day reader, or to indicate instances where the present status of plants and creatures mentioned by Gilbert White has changed dramatically. The variable spelling and the punctuation of the originals have been retained wherever possible, and most of the few crossings-out have been annotated. Gilbert sometimes used archaisms for effect and, as his interest in antiquities grew, drew also on vernacular Hampshire names for topographical details and for plants and animals. Interestingly, the English common names for plants have changed less than the scientific names over the last two hundred years.

Gilbert used the standard English flora of the early eighteenth century, John Ray's great work *Synopsis methodica stirpium Britannicarium* in its third edition of 1724 edited by J.J. Dillenius, and from 1765 he referred also to Hudson's *Flora Anglica*. He was familiar with the work of Linnaeus and, after 1768, many of the scientific names used are Linnaean ones. On the title-page of some of his journals he appends the information that 'the plants are named according to the sexual system [the Linnaean method], the birds according to Ray, the Insects according to Linnaeus'. Every attempt has been made in the glossary/index of this edition to identify the species noted by Gilbert White. Translations of Latin or Greek quotations are to be found under the note for that day.

In the course of putting Gilbert White's written notes into a printed form editorial requirements have dictated a kind of design which differs from the original. While the guiding principle has been to maintain the authenticity of the work, the aim has also been to achieve a result which is more accessible and easier to follow than the original, which was, after all, not intended for publication.

All scientific names have been italicised. Punctuation, including the use of colons where modern usage would dictate semi-colons or full stops, has been reproduced exactly as in the manuscripts. Gilbert White's short forms y^e and Bro^r have also been retained, as has the form *it's* for the possessive.

For the *Garden Kalendar* and the *Flora Selborniensis*, a simple format consisting of date, followed by notes, reproduces that of the originals. In the case of the *Naturalist's Journal* a different procedure has been adopted. The original pages were laid out in nine columns with printed headings. The first six columns of the original journals deal with data: place, date, barometric pressures, temperatures, rainfall, wind and other weather notes. These always relate to Selborne, someone else keeping the records while Gilbert was away.

While these notes are integral to the journals and most interesting when studied in the light of the miscellaneous observations which make up the main text, in themselves numerical and single-word records are by no means light reading. They have therefore been grouped together on the left-hand side of the page where, without interrupting the enjoyment of reading the main text, they may be consulted or ignored at the reader's wish.

Gradually, over the years, everything (except the weather data) comes to be written as 'observations', spreading more or less over the remaining space on the page, irrespective of columns. Sometimes, especially in the later years, notes have been continued over the top or bottom of a page or on to an inserted sheet. Some of these over-runs are dated, and their positioning usually indicates the date within the week to which they relate. Where the positioning is not clear or the comments are of a general nature, or entered retrospectively, the additional material has been placed with the entries for the nearest adjacent day and set in a different typeface.

Some of the barometer readings appear extremely complicated and their meaning is obscure. For instance, on 21st January 1774 the reading is 29½ ½/10.

When one examines barometers of this period, going through the physical process as Gilbert White would have done to make his daily readings, these figures, puzzling on paper, make sense. The mercury in the tube of the barometer, being very heavy, fluctuates only slightly, requiring minute calibration. Measurements are taken in two stages, the first on a large scale, ranged usually on the right side of the tube. In the example above, this would read 29½ inches. Then a more exact fraction is read from a more precise scale on the other side of the instrument, usually in tenths, sometimes hundredths. Gilbert White's small-scale calibration measured tenths but he could discern fractions of tenths: hence ½/10. So the barometer on that day stood at 29½ plus half of a tenth. It could have been expressed as 29 11/20, but he wrote it down in the same way as he read it from the barometer.

The way the columnar information has been interpreted in print is as follows:

Date and location – the month, year and place head each page and do not appear again unless there is a change. Each individual entry is dated.

Barometric pressures and any movements are next recorded. The end of this column is indicated by a semi-colon.

Temperatures in degrees Fahrenheit are shown next. The end of this column is again indicated by a semi-colon.

Wind direction and any changes are shown, as in the manuscript, by initial letters: SE, SW and a symbol @, denoting 'changeable'.

Weather conditions and their changes throughout the day are listed next.

Trees, plants in flower, fungi and mosses follow, preceded by a symbol ✿. Again the original column divisions are shown by a semi-colon, and the entry ends in a full stop.

Birds and insects encountered on that date appear on a fresh line.

Rainfall and snow measurements in inches and hundredths of an inch are recorded after 1778 and are entered last.

Gilbert White's comments and notes are reproduced in the right-hand column just as he wrote them.

Key to symbols

The Editor's notes on the text are indicated thus ¶ and the notes themselves are grouped at the end of the book under the relevant dates. They are also identified by date in the glossary/index.

Gilbert White's own notes are marked with asterisks, as in the manuscripts, and included in the text.

Editorial footnotes relating to the position or authorship of certain passages are indicated by a dagger sign†.

Comments or notes added by Gilbert White at a date later than the adjacent entry are set in a different typeface.

NATURALIST'S
JOURNAL

Thursday 1.
29 2/10; 27; N.
Dark, white fog.

SELBORNE
Snow in the night. Snow covers the ground.
Wagtails.

Friday 2.
29 ¾/10; 33; E.
Thaw, rain, swift thaw,
rain, rain, rain.

Snow almost gone. The ground floated with water.

Saturday 3.
29 5/10; 43; SW; 209.
Vast storms of rain,
sun, pleasant.

Snow gone: flood at Gracious street.

Sunday 4.
29 5/10; 43; SW; 87.
Rain, rain, rain.

Wagtail.

Monday 5.
29 8/10½; 42; NE.
Sun, mild, & pleasant,
frost.

Tuesday 6.
29 8/10½; 36; E.
Hard black frost.

Hoar frost lies all day.

Wednesday 7.
29 6/10; 36; SE.
Hard frost, dark &
still.
Full moon.

Hoar frost lies all day.
Frost comes in a door.

Thursday 8.
29 5/10; 32; NW.
Dark, hard frost, small
snow.

Some wild ducks up the stream near the village. Much wild-fowl
on the lakes in the forest.

Friday 9.
29 8/10½; 32; N.
Frosty, hard, dark &
still.

A grey crow ¶ shot near the village. This is only the third that I
ever saw in this parish.
Some wild-geese near the village down the stream.

Saturday 10.
30; 34; N.
Hard frost, dark &
still, haze.

Small snow on the ground.
Mr Churton left us.

Sunday 11.
29 9/10; 32; NW.
Hard frost, bright,
still, thaw.

Monday 12.
29 8/10; 39½; SW,
NW.
Fog, thaw, mild, deep
fog.

Walls sweat.

Tuesday 13.
29 6/10½; 43; W.
Dark & foggy, wet.

Wednesday 14.
29 3/10; 45, 47; SW.
Wet, blowing, & wet.

Walls sweat.

Thursday 15.
28 7½/10; 44½; W;
22.
Showers, & strong
gales, sleet, gales.

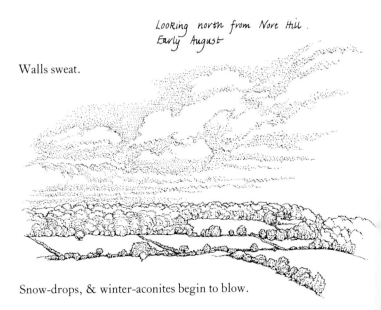

Looking north from Nore Hill.
Early August

Friday 16.
28 7/10; NW.
Showers, strong gales,
sleet, snow shower.

Saturday 17.
28 6/10; 36; NW.
Frost, sun, still, grey.

Snow-drops, & winter-aconites begin to blow.

Sunday 18.
28 3/10; 34, 33½; W.
Hard frost, sun, sharp,
bright, frost.

Clouds put up their heads.

Monday 19.
29 1/10; 31, 32; NW.
Severe frost, dark,
snow, driving snow,
D^o: D^o:, strong gales.

Sharp, driving snow.

Tuesday 20.
29 5/10; 27½, 29;
NW.
Fierce frost, sun,
driving snow, frost.

Drifted snow on the ground.
Ice in chambers.
Vast snows in Cornwall for two days past.

Wednesday 21.
29; abroad 26, 27, 29;
N, E, SE.
Fierce frost, grey &
sharp.

Ice in chambers.
Hares frequent the garden, & do much damage.

Thursday 22.
30, 31; NE, NW.
Hard frost, grey, snow,
sun, frost.

Much snow on the ground.
Snipes come up the stream.

Friday 23.
29 3/10½; 30, 32;
NW.
Hard frost, sun, paths
well trod, frost.

Saturday 24.
29 5/10; 29; NW.
Fierce frost, sun, frost.

The Thermom^r at Totnes in the county of Devõn abroad this
evening was, I hear, at 6.

Sunday 25.
29 6/10½; 30; NW,
SW.
Fierce frost, bright &
still, frost.

Much drifted snow still about.
The turnips that are not stacked, are all frozen & spoiled.

Monday 26.
29 7/10; 29, 32; NW,
N.
Fierce frost, sun, grey,
frost.

Made the seedling cucumber-bed with two cart-loads of hot
dung.
Cut my last years hay rick.

Tuesday 27.
29 5/10; 32; 34; NE.
Grey & still, snow,
snow, hazy & still.

Considerable snow in the night.
The hanger exhibits a very grotesque, & beautiful appearance.

Wednesday 28.
29 4/10; 33; N.
Severe frost, sun, sharp
wind, hard frost.

Snow covers the ground, & hangs on all the trees, & shrubs.

Thursday 29.
29 7/10; 29, 30½,
14½ abroad; N.
Severe frost, sun, &
sharp wind, bright with
hard frost.

Frost within doors. The dung & litter freezes under the horses in
the stable.
The hares nibble off the buds on the espalier-pear-treas.

Friday 30.
30; 21 abroad, 30; N.
Severe frost, sun, grey
& sharp.

Ice in close chambers.
A long-billed curlew has just been shot near the Priory. We see
now & then one in very long frosts. Two, I understand, were
seen.

Saturday 31.
30 1/10; 30½; N,
NW.
Sharp frost, sun, yellow
evening, frost.

Snow melts on sunny roofs.
Yellow wagtail. ¶
Much snow on the ground.
Hares frequent my garden, & eat the stocks.
Sowed some cucumber-seeds.

Rain in Jan: − 3 in: 18 h:

FEBRUARY 1784

Sunday 1.
29 9/10; 28; NW, W.
Severe frost, cloudless,
& sharp frost.

Snow melts under hedges.

Monday 2.
29 7/10; 32; N.
Hard frost, sun with
sharp air, bright.

Tuesday 3.
30 1/10; 28; N.
Fierce frost, sun, &
sharp wind, frost,
bright.

Much snow on the ground. Paths, & horse-tracks dusty.
Cucumber-seeds sprout.

A near neighbour shot at a brace of hares out of his window, & at
the same discharge killed one, & wounded an other. So I hope our
gardens will not be so much molested. Much mischief has been
done by these animals.

Wednesday 4.
30, 29 8/10; 30, 34;
NW, W, SW.
Hard frost, sun, paths
thaw, fleecy clouds, sky
muddled, halo.

Thaw in the sun.

Thursday 5.
29; 37, 39; SW; 31.
Rain, swift thaw, rain,
frost.

Snow almost gone.

Friday 6.
28 6/10½; 37; NW.
Hard frost, sun &
sharp air, hail, & sleet,
frost. Full moon.

Some snow remains.
Sowed 48 bushels of peat-ashes on the great meadow, which
covered more than half. 31 bush: were bought of my neighbours.

Saturday 7.
28 7/10; 32½, 34;
NW.
Hard frost, sun &
clouds, cutting wind,
snow.

Sleet, & hail cover the ground.

Sunday 8.
29 1/10; 33; NW.
Severe frost, sun, sharp
wind, bright, frost.

Snow covers the ground.

Monday 9.
29 1/10; 33; W,
SW, S.
Hard frost, dark, thaw,
snow, snow, snow.

Tuesday 10.
29 2/10; 33, 35; NW.
Hard frost, sun &
clouds, frost, snow.

Snow covers the ground.
No hares have frequented the garden since the man shot & killed
one, & wounded an other.

Wednesday 11.
29 2/10; 34, 35; NW.
Hard frost, sun, frost,
snow, frost.

Snow covers the ground. Hare again in the garden.

Thursday 12.
29 ½/10; 30½; NE.
Severe frost, snow,
snow, snow, wind.

Deep snow.

Friday 13.
29 2/10; 30½, 34; SE,
E, NE; Snow 5 in:
Sharp frost, snow,
grey, sun, bright, frost.

Very deep snow much drifted.
Frost all day.
This evening the frost has lasted 28 days.

Saturday 14.
29 2/10½; 32; NE, N.
Sharp frost, dark with
haze, small snow.

Sent Thomas ¶ as Pioneer to open the road to Faringdon: but
there was little obstruction, except at the gate into Faringdon
Hirn.

Sunday 15.
29 4/10½; 31; NE.
Fierce frost, sun, hazy
& sharp.

Snow deep, & drifted thro' the hedges in curious, & romantic
shapes.

Monday 16.
29 5/10; abroad 22,
31½; NW, N.
Hard frost, grey, small
snow.

Snow deep.
No hares frequent the garden.

Tuesday 17.
29 5/10; 31½; NE, N.
Dark, hard frost, small
snow, small snow, dark
& frosty.

Snow deep.

Wednesday 18.
29 6/10; 32; E, NE.
Hard frost, dark &
still, fog, dark & still.

Thursday 19.
29 6/10; 33½, 35½;
E.
Dark & still, grey, sun,
grey, fog.

Snow deep.

Friday 20.
29 2/10; 33½; SE.
Dark & blowing, snow,
snow.

Much drifted snow.

Saturday 21.
29 2/10, 3/10; 38,
39½; S, S.
White, warm fog,
thaw, small rain, thaw.

Snow much wasted.

Sunday 22.
29 3/10; 42, 43½; S,
SW.
Deep fog, swift thaw,
rain, rain.

Snow melts, & the country is flooded.
Flood at Gracious street.

Monday 23.
29 6/10; 43; 48; W.
Grey, & mild, sun,
pleasant starlight.

The tops of the blades of wheat are scorched with the frost.
Crocus's swell for bloom. Snowdrops blow.
Snow lies under hedges.
Aurora borealis.

Tuesday 24.
29 6/10½; S, SW; 25.
Fog, wet, grey, wet.

ALTON
The laurels, & laurustines are not injured by the severe weather.
Snow scarce passable in Newton-lane!

Wednesday 25.
29 8/10; 45; S. Wet,
clouds, sun & mild.

SOUTH LAMBETH
Little snow on the road.

Thursday 26.
29 6/10; 47; SW; 21.
Dark & mild.

Friday 27.
29 5/10½; 45; W.
Clouds, strong gale.

Filbert blows.

Thomas Hoar kept an account of the rain at Selborne in my
absence.

Saturday 28.
30 1/10; 38; NE.
Dark, & harsh.

Crocus's blow.

Sunday 29.
30 1/10; 34; NE.
Dark, frost & ice.

Rain in February . . 0 inc: 77 hund.

MARCH 1784

Monday 1.
30 1/10; 33; NW, NE.
Wh: frost, ice.

Brother Tho: found a grass-hopper lark dead in his out-let: it
seemed to be starved. I was not aware that they were about in the
winter.

Tuesday 2.
30 1/10; 32; E.
Frost, ice.

Wednesday 3.
30 ½/10; 33; E.
Strong ice, freezing.

Thursday 4.
29 6/10; 45; SW; 19.
Brisk wind, pleasant.

Friday 5.
29 3/10; 44; SW.
Fair, warm.

Saturday 6.
29 3/10; 50; SE; 65.
Rain, soft.

Sunday 7.
29 2/10; 48; SE.
Blowing night,
showers.

Monday 8.
29 2/10; 44; W; 40.
Blustering, hail,
showers.

Tuesday 9.
29 2/10; 38; E, N; 75.
Dark & moist, rain.

Wednesday 10.
29 6/10; 35; NW; 24.
Hazey, snow.

Thursday 11.
29 9/10; 30; NW.
Frost, ice, sun &
cutting wind.

Friday 12.
29 9/10; 33; NW.
Bright, hot sun, cold
wind.

Saturday 13.
29 9/10; 34; E.
Fog, sun.

Sunday 14.
30; 34; E.
Ice, sun & sharp wind.

Monday 15.
30; 33; E.
Ice, bright.

Tuesday 16.
30; 33; E.
Ice.

Wednesday 17.
30; 37; SE.
Wind, dark.

Thursday 18.
29 6/10; 39; NE.
Clouds & wind.

Friday 19.
29 7/10; 36; NE.
Cold, fair.

Saturday 20.
29 9/10; 29; NE.   Therm! 29: at 9 in the morning.
Thick ice, snow,
bright.

Sunday 21.
29 8/10; 34; SW; 12.   Deep snow at Selborne.
Frost, ice.

Monday 22.
29 9/10; 31; SW.   Roads very dusty.
Frost, ice, hazey, still.

Tuesday 23.
35; S; 24.   Dust.
Frost, fair.

Wednesday 24.
29 3/10; 37; W.   Snow gone.
Snow covers the
ground.

Thursday 25.
29 5/10; 44; SE; 45.
Rain, mild, louring.

Friday 26.
29 4/10½; 38; E; 78.   Great snow at Selborne.
Rain, snow, deep snow.

Saturday 27.
29 6/10; 34; NE.
Deep snow.

Sunday 28.
29 5/10; 33; NE.
Frost, ice, blustering,
severe.

Snow on hills & roofs.

Monday 29.
29 5/10; 34; NE.
Ice, blustering.

Tuesday 30.
29 5/10; 33; NE.
Dark & harsh.

† About this time a nightingale was heard at Bramshot.

Wednesday 31.
29 8/10; 33; NE.
Ice, dark.

Apricot begins to blow.
Rain in March . . . 3 inch: 82 hund:

APRIL 1784

Thursday 1.
30; 31; NW.
Frost, ice, sun, sharp.

Friday 2.
29 3/10½; 35½; SW.
Dark & harsh, thick ice
on lakes, & ponds,
rain.

SELBORNE
No snow 'till we came to Guild-down: deep snow on that ridge!
Much snow at Selborne in the fields: the hill deep in snow! The
country looks much dismally, like the dead of winter! A few days
ago our lanes would scarce have been passable for a chaise.

Saturday 3.
29 4/10; 38; S, E; 58.
Rain, dark, & thaw.

The crocus's are full blown, & would make a fine show, if the sun
would shine warm.
The ever-green-trees are not injured, as about London.

On this day a nightingale was heard at Bramshot!!

Sunday 4.
29 7/10; 38, 42; NE,
NW, SW.
Frost, sun, soft &
pleasant.

The rooks at Faringdon have got young.
Very little spring corn sown yet.
Wagtail.
Snow as deep as the horses belly under the hedges in the North
field. Snow melts.

A brace more of hares frequenting my grounds were killed in my
absence: so that I hope now the garden will be safe for some time.

---

† Entry crossed out.

Monday 5.
29 6/10½; 42½; NW,
S.
Grey & mild, small
rain, grey & mild.

My crocus's are in full bloom, & make a most gaudy show. Those eaten-off by the hares last year were not injured. Snow melts.

A very large fall of timber, of about 1000 trees, has been cut this spring in the Holt-forest: one fifth of which belongs to the Grantee Lord Stawel. He lays claim also to the lop, & top: but the poor of the parishes of Binsted, & Frinsham say it belongs to them: & have actually in a riotous manner taken it away. One man that keeps a team has carryed home near forty stacks of wood. Forty nine of these people his Lordship has served with actions: & provided they do not make restitution, proposes to sue them. The timber, which is very fine, was winter-cut: viz: before barking time.¶

Tuesday 6.
29 6/10; 45; N.
Rain, dark & wet, rain,
snow much.

Persian Iris's blow. Apricots promise for a fine bloom. Dogs violets bud for bloom.

Wednesday 7.
29 7/10; 41; NE; 40.
Snow melted, sun &
clouds, dry & cold.

Apricot begins to blow. Cucumber blows, female bloom without male.
Ever-greens little injured: about London several sorts are destroyed.
A farmer told Mr Yalden that he saw two swallows on this day at Hawkley!!

Thursday 8.
29 7/10¼; 41; N.
Grey, sun & pleasant,
red even:

Men open the hills, & cut their hops.
Many lettuces, both Coss, & Dutch, have stood-out the winter under the fruit-wall. They were covered with straw in the hard weather, for many weeks.

Friday 9.
29 3/10½; 41; SW, W.
Frost, sun, pleasant.

Swallow seen near the forest.

By a perambulation of this forest, in my possession, taken in the year 1635, being the 10th of Charles 1st, the Holt appears to have been very bare of timber, at that time.

Saturday 10.
29 3/10; 42; NE, N.
Rain, rain, rain.

Gentle rain.

Sunday 11.
28 9/10½; 42; W.
Wet & blowing, dark,
wet.

Monday 12.
28 7/10; 42; W; 57.
Snow, blowing, with
hail-storms.

Snow melted.
Polyanths begin to blow. Violets blow.

Tuesday 13.
29 4/10; 38; W.
Frost, ice, sun, hail-
storms.

Mutton per pound	5^d	
Veal	5	at Selborne
Lamb	6	
Beef	4	

Wednesday 14.
29 1/10; 40; S, S, SE;
87.
Rain, heavy snow!
snow, rain.

Wag-tail.
Much snow on the ground.
† No summer birds have been heard yet.

Thursday 15.
29 4/10; 47; NE.
Fog, sun, pleasant.

Dogs-toothed violets blow.
Showers about. Snow gone.
Crocus's make a splendid show. Bees gather much on the
crocus's.

Ivy-berries are full grown, & begin to turn black, & to ripen,
notwithstanding the length of frost, & severity of the spring.

Friday 16.
29 4/10; 42; E, N,
SW.
White frost, sun,
shower, thunder.

Showers about.
Crocus's begin to fall-off.
Nightingale heard in Maiden-dance.
Many swallows seen at Oak-hanger ponds:
perhaps they were bank-martins.

Saturday 17.
29 3/10½; 44, 50; SW,
NW; 31.
Shower, sun, pleasant,
& spring-like.

The buds of the vines are not swelled yet at all. In fine springs
they have shot by this time two or three Inches.
Peaches, & Nectarines begin to blossom.
Ring-dove builds in my fields.
Black-cap sings.

Sunday 18.
29 5/10; 45; NW, W.
Sun & clouds, pleasant,
grey.

Grass begins to grow a little on the grass-plots, & walks.
Bank-martins at Bramshot.

Monday 19.
29 3/10¾; 45, 50½;
W; 18.

Timothy ¶ the tortoise begins to stir; he heaves up the mould that
lies over his back.

---

† Entry crossed out.

Rain, grey & mild,
moist, fog.

Red-start is heard at the verge of the highwood against the
common.

Tuesday 20.
29 4/10; 47½; SW.
Grey & mild, rain,
rain.

No garden-crops sowed yet with me; the ground is too wet.
Artichokes seem to be almost killed.
The wall-trees are coming into good bloom.

Wednesday 21.
29 6/10; 50½, 56; W.
Rain, sun, mild, strong
gale, rain.

Crocus's in the shade still make a figure.
Two swallows about the street.
Daffodils begin to blow.

Thursday 22.
29 6/10; 56½; W; 31.
Fog, rain, strong gales,
sun, pleasant.

The spring backward to an unusual degree!
A house-martin at Newton-pond.
Some black snails come out.
Some swallows are come; but I see no insects except bees, & some
phalaenae in the evenings. Daiseys, & pile-worts blow.

Friday 23.
29 4/10; 50; SW.
Sun & clouds, windy,
shower.

Swallows about.
Timothy the tortoise comes forth from his winter retreat.

Saturday 24.
29 5/10; 47; SW; 24.
Shower, blowing, sun
& clouds, rain, hail,
bright.

Strong gales all day.
Planted ten rows of potatoes against the Wid: Dewye's garden.
Planted one row in the best garden.

John Carpenter buys now & then of Mr Powlett of Rotherfield a
chest-nut tree or two of the edible kind: they are large & tall, &
contain 60 or 70 feet of timber each. The wood & bark of these
trees resemble that of oak, but the wood is softer & the grain more
open. The use that the buyer turns them to is cooperage; because
he says the wood is light for buckets, jets, &c: & will not shrink.
The grand objection to these trees is their disposition to be shaky;
& what is much worse, cup-shaky: viz: the substance of these
trees parts like the scale of an onion, & comes-out in round plugs
from the heart.

   This, I know was also the case with those fine chest-nut-trees
that were lately cut at Bramshot-place against the Portsmouth
road. Now as the soil at Rotherfield is chalk, & at Bramshot, sand;
it seems as if this disposition to be shaky was not owing to soil
alone, but to the nature of that tree.

   There are two groves of chest-nuts in Rotherfield-park, which
are tall, & old, & have rather over-stood their prime.

   J. Carpenter gives only 8^d p^r foot for this timber on account of
the defect above-mentioned.

Sunday 25.
29 6/10; 44; SW.
Wh: frost, sun &
clouds, pleasant,
spring-like.

The Cuckow is heard in the hanger.
Wheat grows, & improves.
Grass grows. No barley seen at Faringdon.
Nightingale sings in my outlet.

Monday 26.
29 4/10; 49; SW.
Showers, dark &
mild, wet.

Wagtail about.
Crocus's out of bloom.
Sowed a crop of onions, & several sorts of cabbage: pronged the
asparagus beds.
Radishes grow.

Tuesday 27.
29 3/10; 49; SW; 23.
Dark & mild, wet,
rain, rain.

House-martins over my garden.
One swift.

Wednesday 28.
29 3/10; 52; SW; 23.
Sun, pleasant, clouds
about, sweet even:

Began mowing the grass-walks.
Grass-hopper-lark whispers.
Many house-martins. One swift.
Sowed a large crop of carrots in the great meadow.

There has been this spring a pretty good flight of wood-cocks
about Liss. If we have any of those birds of late years, it has been
in the spring, in their return from the West, I suppose, to the
Eastern coast.¶

Thursday 29.
29 6/10; 51; NE, E.
Very hoar frost, sun,
pleasant, sweet
afternoon.

The hoar frost was so great, that Thomas could hardly mow.
Sowed an other crop of carrots.
One swift.
Bats out for the first time, I think, this spring; they hunt, & take
the *phalaenae* along by the sides of the hedges.

Friday 30.
29 7/10; 54; NE, E.
Grey, sun, summer-
like.

Cucumbers set, & swell. Polyanths begin to blow well. Tulips
shoot, & are strong.
Sowed a pint of scarlet kidney-beans.
Goose-berry bushes leaf: quick-sets still naked.
Pile-wort in full bloom.

Rain in April . . 3 inch: 92 hund:

MAY 1784

Saturday 1.
29 6/10½; 51; N.

Cucumbers set apace. Men pole hops; sow barley, & sow clover

Celandines.
Zig - zag.
Late May.

Sun, cold, drying wind,
bright & cold.

in wheat.
Fine bloom on the wall-trees.
Two swifts.
Saw a cock white-throat.
Horse-chestnuts, & sycamores bud. Hyacinths blow.
Made an annual hot-bed for four lights.

Sunday 2.
29 8/10; 47, 54; NW,
N.
White frost, sun & cold
air.

Flies come out.
Two swifts: many house-martins.
Several swifts.

No ring-ouzels seen this spring: the severity of the season probably
disconcerted their proceedings.

Monday 3.
29 9/10; 50; NW, N,
NE.
White frost, sun, grey
& mild.

Roads dry very fast.
Wall-cherries blow. Earthed the annual beds.
Set up a copper-vane (arrow) on the brew-house.
Peaches, Nect, & Apricots finely blown.
The buds of hazles do but just open: so that the hedges are quite
naked.

Tuesday 4.
30 1/3/10; 51, 57: NE,
SE.
Fog, sun, summer
weather.

Ashes blow. Some beeches in the short Lythe are bursting into
leaf.
Timothy the tortoise weighs 6 pd 13 oun: he weighed at first
coming out last year only 6 pd 11 1/4 oun: He eat this morning the
heart of a lettuce.

Goody Hampton came to work in the garden for the summer.

Wednesday 5.
30, 30; 52, 62; NW,
N.
Sun, sweet summer, red
even:
Full moon.

Cut the first cucumber, a large one.
Apricots begin to set. Peaches & nectarines blossom well.
Sowed annuals in their frames.
The usual number of swifts do not yet appear.

Thursday 6.
29 9/10; 54, 64; SE,
SW.
Vast dew, cloudless,
summer, red even:

Sowed white cucumbers under an hand-glass.
Sowed green cucumbers in the annual bed.
Some beeches in the hanger begin to leaf.
Pulled the first radishes.
Golden weather.
Crown-imperials, & fritillaria's blown.

The polyanths blow finely, especially the young seedlings from
Bramshot-place, many of which will be curious.
Shot three green-finches which pull-off the blossoms of the
polyanths.

Friday 7.
29 7/10; 57, 66; SW,
SW.
Bright, summer, some
flisky clouds.

Beeches come out at a vast rate.
Vines shoot.
The number of swifts increased to 18, or 20.
The early tulips blow.
Vine-buds swell. Pears promise much bloom.
There is a ring-dove's nest in the American Juniper in the
shrubbery: but as that spot begins to be much frequented, the
brood will scarcely come to good.
Shot two more green-finches.
Apricots swell.

Saturday 8.
29 6/10¾; 56; SW, S.
Windy, dark &
louring.

Auricula's blow finely in the natural ground.
Mountain snow-drops, & polyanth-Narcissus in bloom.
The hanger almost all green. Many trees in the Lythe in full leaf.
Beeches on the common hardly budding.
Owls have eggs.

Sunday 9.
29 7/10½; 58, 68; W.
Brisk gale, sun, hot
summer, yellow even:

The hanger is very beautiful.
Asparagus-beds sprout.
Curran-trees much blown; goose-berries moderately.

Monday 10.
29 6/10; 60½, 66; SW,
NE.
Sun & clouds, dark &
hot, sprinkling.

The wild cherry, vulg. called the merris, begins to blow. Plums
blossom. Wallnuts promise for much blowing. Black-thorn
begins to blossom.
Fern-owl seen, but not heard.
Sowed dwarf kidney-beans, white: & one row of large white.
The ground is dry, & wants rain.

The black-birds, & thrushes are so reduced by the severe weather,
that I have seen in my out-let only one of the former, & not one of
the latter; not one missle-thrush.

Tuesday 11.
29 4/10, 6/10½; 64;

Sowed sweet Alyssum in basons on the borders.

Selborne Village
from the Hanger.

SN, NW; 23.
Showers, showers, sun,
bright gleam, cool.

Fine showers.
Wheat improves very much: the women weed it.
The leaves of some of the wall-trees begin to blotch already.
Peaches & nectarines set.

Wednesday 12.
29 9/10; 54; NW, W.
Sun, & brisk wind,
small showers, sun,
cold air.

The hanger seems to be quite in leaf.
Sowed an other row of large white kidney-beans.
There seem to be two, if not three nightingales singing in my
outlet.

Swallows nest in the village.
May.

Thursday 13.
29 9/10; 52; W, S,
SW.
Sun, hot sun, bright &
pleasant, cold air.

Cut the first bundles of asparagus.
Wind cold on the downs. Dark to the S:W. Daffodils, crown-
imperials, fritillaria's fade.

Friday 14.
29 9/10; 55; SW.
Dark, misty rain, sweet
afternoon.

Swallows build. They take up straws in their bills, & with them a
mouthful of dirt.
Fern-own churs.
The bark of felled oaks runs remarkably well; so that the barkers
earn great wages.
Vines shoot, & shew rudiments of bloom.
Pears & cherries have much bloom.

Saturday 15.
30; 57½; NW, N, S.
Grey & hot, sun,
summer, red even.

Cucumbers set apace: asparagus sprout.
Spring-corn wants rain.

Such is the vicissitude of matters where weather is concerned; that
the spring, which last month was unusually backward, is now
forward.
    The tortoise is very earnest for the leaves of poppies, which he
hunts about after, & seems to prefer to any other green thing.

Sunday 16.
30 ½/10, 30; 58½;
NE, E.
Great dew, sun, sultry,
summer, red even:

Apple-trees begin to blow.
Scarlet kidney-beans are up. Tulips blow.
So much sun hurries the flowers out of bloom!
Left off fires in the parlor.

Monday 17.
29 9/10; 61½ 70; E, S, SE.
Dew, sun, sultry, cloudless, red even:

Vast bloom of pears, & cherries!
The spring-corn wants rain.
Ground chops. Early tulips fade. Watered much.
Flesh-flies begin to appear.
Cherries set. The horses begin to lie out.

Tuesday 18.
29 8/10½; 62, 71½; NE.
Cloudless, hot summer, red even:

Watered the fruit-trees & crops.
Sycamores blow, & smell of honey; & are much frequented by bees.

Wednesday 19.
29 7/10⅓; 63, 74; NE, S.
Deep fog, cloudless, sweet even.

Fly-catcher returns. This is the latest summer-bird, which never is seen 'till about the 20th of May.
The Virginian creeper comes into leaf.
Flowers fade, & go-off very fast thro' heat.
There has been only one moderate shower all this month.

Thursday 20.
29 9/10; 62, 72; W.
Cloudless, clouds, hot sun, yellow even:

Bats very busy at a quarter past three in the morning.
Hops thrive; & have been tyed once to the poles.

Friday 21.
29 9/10½; 64, 66; NE, SE, W.
Bright, hot sun, sweet even, gale.

Laurel & lilac blossom.
Apis longicornis appears over the grass-walks, in which they bore holes.
Fern-own chatters.
Bees thrive.
Asparagus abound.
Many apple-trees covered with bloom.
Horse-chestnut begins to blow.

Saturday 22.
29 8/10; 63, 66½; NE, SE.
Cloudless, sun & gale, golden evening.

Columbines, & Monkshood blow.
Lapwings on the down.
Began to tack the vine-shoots.
Men bring-up peat from the forest.
The sycamores, & maples in bloom scent the air with a honeyed smell.
Lily of the valley blows.

Sunday 23.
29 5/10; 65½, 73; S, SW.
Sun, sultry, broken clouds, gale, lightening.

Field-crickets cry, & shrill in the short Lythe.
Thunder-like clouds from S:W. to NW.

Monday 24.
29 6/10½; 65, 70; SW,
NW, W; 19.
Gentle showers,
showers, cloudless, red
even:

Horse-chestnut finely blown.
Apple trees covered with bloom.

A pair of swifts frequent the eaves of my stable. These birds soon forsook the place, & did not build.

Tuesday 25.
29 5/10; 64½, 71½; S,
S, SE.
White dew, sun, sultry,
dark, shower, grey.

Planted out the white cucumber plants under the hand-glasses. Planted some green cucumber-plants in the frames among the bearing plants. Sowed some green cucumbers under the fruit-wall. Distant thunder to the SE.

Wednesday 26.
29 3/10½; 67½; S; 50.
Showers, cloudy with
gale, rain.

Thunder in the night with heavy showers & some hail.
Grasshopper lark in my outlet.
Hawthorn, berberry, laburnum, mountain-ash, scorpion sena, guelder rose begin to blow.

Thursday 27.
29 7/10; 59; W.
Sun & clouds, brisk
gale, bright gleam.

Distant thunder.
Young red-breasts.
S^t foin begins to blossom.
Honey-suckle against the wall begins to open.
Lime trees shew their bracteal leaves, & rudiment of fruit. Wall-nut trees shed their catkins and show rudiments of fruit. Maples shew fruit. My great single oak shews many catkins.

Friday 28.
29 7/10½; 55; W, SW.
Sun & clouds, showers
about, sun, & clouds,
red even:

Timothy the tortoise has been missing¶ for more than a week. He got out of the garden at the wicket, we suppose, & may be in the fields among the grass.

Timothy found in the little bean-field short of the pound-field.
   The nightingale, fern-owl, cuckow, & grass-hopper lark may be heard at the same time on any evening in my outlet.

Saturday 29.
29 6/10; 53, 61; S, SE.
No dew, dark, rain,
sun, grey.

Flag-Iris, & Narcissus blow.

Gryllo-talpa churs in moist meadows.
Aphides appear on the shoots of the wall-cherries.

Sunday 30.
29 6/10; 60; SE, S.
Wet, wet, dark &
moist.

Monday 31.
29 6/10; 60½; N; 60.
Rain, rain, dark.

Cinnamon-rose blows.
Rain in May . . . 4 inch 52 h:

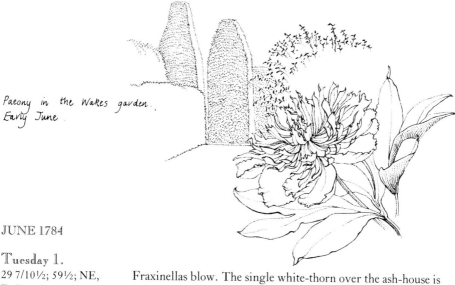

Paeony in the Wakes garden. Early June.

JUNE 1784

Tuesday 1.
29 7/10½; 59½; NE, E, E.
Deep fog, rain, rain, grey, red even:

Fraxinellas blow. The single white-thorn over the ash-house is one vast globe of blossoms down to the ground!

Wednesday 2.
29 9/10½; 58½; NE, E, N.
Sun & brisk gale, sun, sweet even.

Flag-iris, & orange lily begin to blow.
The forward wheat undulates before the wind.
Laburnums, berberries, &c: covered with bloom. Peonies in flower.

Thursday 3.
29 8/10¼; 58; N.
No dew, dark with gale, fine even: red.

Kidney-beans thrive, & are stuck.
Corn looks finely.
Turned the horses into Berrimans field.
White thorns covered with bloom every where.

Friday 4.
29 8/10; 60, 67; E, E.
Sun with gales, clouds & sun, sweet even:

Pricked-out some good celeri-plants.
Pricked out annuals.
A pair of fern-owls haunt round the zigzag.
Fiery-lily blows. Columbines make a fine show: this the third year of their blowing.

Saturday 5.
29 6/10½; 64½, 70; N, NE; 79.
Sun, sultry, vast drops, distant thunder, vast hail!!! fine even:

Blue mist.
Much damage done to the corn, grass, & hops by the hail; & many windows broken! Vast flood at Gracious street! Vast flood at Kaker bridge! Hail near Norton two feet deep.
Sowed endive, first crop.
Planted out annuals down the basons in the field.

Sunday 6.
29 6/10; 64; 66; NE; 10.
Rain, rain, sun, rain, thunder.

Nipped off all the rose-buds on the tree in the yard opposite the parlor window in order to make a bloom in the autumn.
No bloom succeeded.

The hail storm¶ which fell last Saturday was about a mile & an

Monday 7.
29 7/10½; 65; NE, W,
S.
Dark & close, showers,
heavy clouds.

Tuesday 8.
29 6/10¾; 59; S; 17.
Cloudy, gleam, dark,
small shower.

half broad, reaching from Wick-hill to the west end of the North-field. Had it been as extensive as it was violent, it would have ravaged all the neighbourhood. It seems to have originated in the parish of Harteley, & moved from N: to S. doing some considerable damage on Chilbury-farm. But the centre was over Norton farm, where of course most harm was done. Grange-farm which lies contiguous, to the S:, was much injured. Wick-hill farm on it's W: verge was pretty much cut. As the tempest advanced to the southward it soon spent itself: for the upper end of the village had scarce any hail at all; while the lower end, as far as the Plestor, sustained considerable loss from windows, & garden-frames. There fell at the same time prodigious torrents of rain on the farms above mentioned, which occasion'd a flood as violent as it was sudden; doing great damage to the meadows, & fallows by deluging the one, & washing away the soil of the other. The hollow lane by Norton was so torn & disordered as not to be passable 'till mended; rocks being removed that weighed 200 weight. The flood at Gracious street ran over the goose-hatch, & mounted above the fourth bar of Grange-yard gate. Those that saw the effect that the great hail had on ponds & pools say, that the dashing of the water made an extraordinary appearance, the froth & spray standing-up in the air three feet above the surface! The storm began with vast drops of rain, which were soon succeeded by round hail, & then by convex pieces of ice measuring 3 inches in girth. The rushing & roaring of the hail as it approached was truely tremendous. The thunder at the village was little & distant.

Tho' there was no storm that day at South Lambeth, yet was the air strongly electric, when the clouds were thin & light: for the bells of my Bro: Tho: White's electrical machine rung a great deal, & fierce sparks came from the machine.

Our storm happened about two o' the clock in the afternoon: & at half hour after three on the same day a still more destructive one befell in Somersetshire. It extended seven miles in length, & about 2 in breadth, covering 7000 acres of fertile country: beginning in the S:W: & passing on slowly to the N:E: The centre of the storm was seven miles W: of Taunton. The damage is very great!

Wednesday 9.
29 4/10¼; 61½; W, S;
22.
Shower, dark &
louring.

Continue to tack the vines. There is a show for much fruit.

Thursday 10.
29 2/10; 62; SW; 32.
Rain, rain, dark &
blowing.

Sold my St foin again to Timothy Turner; it looks well, & is in bloom. The 17th crop. The buyer to cut it when he pleases.

Friday 11.
29 6/10; 58; W, NW.
Sun & clouds, blowing,
pleasant, still.

Rain in the night.
The cherries against the walls begin to turn colour.
The walks covered with leaves.

Saturday 12.
29 4/10½; 59½; W,
SW.
Sun & clouds with
strong gale.

Men wash their sheep.
Some wood-strawberries eatable.
Finished tacking the vines.
Hoed carrots, parsneps, &c.
Received 5 gallons & a quart of French brandy from Mʳ Edmᵈ
Woods.

Sunday 13.
29 5/10; 64; W.
Sun, & showers with
strong gales, cool.

Few hirundines appear; they are sitting on their eggs.
Wheat comes into ear.

On this day arrived here from India Mʳ Charles Etty. In his passage
out, the ship he belonged to was burnt off the Island of Ceylon. He
came back from Madras to the Cape of good hope in the *Exeter*
man of war; & from thence worked his passage in the *Content*
transport, which brought him to Spit-head.
    The *Exeter* was so crazy, & worn-out, that they broke her up, &
burnt her at the Cape. Mʳ Ch: Etty brought home two species of
Humming birds which he shot at the Cape of good hope; & two
Ostriches eggs from the same place: two live tortoises from
Madagascar: several fine shells from Ioanna: & several turtle's
eggs* from the Isle of Ascension. Also the *Gnaphalium
squarrosum*, a curious Cudweed, from a Dutch-mans garden at
the Cape.
* Turtles-eggs are round, & white; a little variegeted with fine
streaks of red, & as large as the eggs of a kite; perhaps larger.

Monday 14.
29 7/10; 59½; SW, S.
Wet, wet, fog on the
hanger.

The Saint foin is in full bloom.
Hoed & weeded the potatoes.

Tuesday 15.
29 8/10; 61½; SW, S.
Wet, dark & still mist,
deep fog!!

Cherries on the wall turn very fast.
Apricots, peaches & nect: swell.
Continue to plant out annuals.
Some swallows have young.

Wednesday 16.
29 6/10; 62; SW, S.
Dark & moist, gale,
gleams of sun.

Pears in abundance.
Phallus impudicus, a stink-pot, comes up in Mʳ Burbey's
asparagus-bed.
Received an Hogsh: of port-wine, imported at Southampton.

Thursday 17.
29 5/10½; 60; W; 21.
Sun, blowing, shower,
blowing, sun & clouds.

Men sow turnips: a fine season.
Elder-trees blow.
Fine verdure on the down.
Thinned the crops of apricots, peaches, & nectarines, & pulled off many dozens.

Friday 18.
29 7/10½; 57; W,
NW.
Sun & clouds, blowing
with small showers.

Kidney-beans mount their sticks, & thrive.
Roses blow.

Saturday 19.
29 6/10¾; 57; NW, S.
Sun & clouds, dark &
moist, shower.

Men cut their S^t foin, & some clover.

Sunday 20.
29 6/10; 63; SW, S.
Sun & clouds, cool,
bright gleam.

Narrow-leaved iris, cornflag, & purple martagons blow.
Butterfly-orchis in the hanger.

Monday 21.
29 2/10; 60; S.
Dark & chilly, rain,
rain.

Standard honey-suckles in beautiful bloom.
Blowing. Cold & comfortless.

Tuesday 22.
29 ½/10; 60; 89.
Rain, rain, sun, strong
gales.

Heavy showers.
House-martins hatch.

Wednesday 23.
29 2/10; 56; S, SE, E.
Shower, blowing, rain,
rain.

S^t foin & clover lie in a bad state.

Thursday 24.
29 2/10; 56½; NW;
62.
Shower, dark & cold,
rain, bright even:

Wheat in bloom. Bad weather for the blowing of wheat. Wheat looks poorly in the N: field. Continue to take up tulips, & to plant-out annuals.

Towards the end of June they had snow in Austria, and the vines were frozen.

Friday 25.
29 6/10; 54!; W, W.
Dark, moist & cold,
strong gales, grey &
cold.

Very cold air: lighted a fire in the parlor.
Planted out annuals. Turned-out the white cucumbers from under the hand-glasses.

Saturday 26.
29 3/10½; 56; S, E.
Dark & wet, blowing,
cold & wet.

A brood of house-martins comes out.
No swifts to be seen this cold blustering weather.
Fire in the parlor.

Sunday 27.
29 4/10; 56½, 60; SW,
NW.
Sun, clouds, showers.

Monday 28.
29 6/10; 58; NW.
Grey, gleams, showers
about, sun, still.

Vines begin to blow.
The ears of wheat are small. Wheat in bloom.

Tuesday 29.
29 6/10; 56; NW; 39.
Dew, sun, dark & soft.

Cherries on the wall ripe & good.
Mʳ & Mʳˢ Richardson came.

Wednesday 30.
29 6/10, 7/10; 58½;
NW, N.
Grey, sun, showers
about, dark & mild.

The rain in June is – 3 in: 65 h.

Early morning mist
Looking towards Dorton
July

JULY 1784

Thursday 1.
29 9/10; 58½; N.
Grey, sun, dark, bright
in the N:W:

Backward Orange lilies, pinks, & cornflags, & backward honey-
suckles begin to bloom.
Men house their clover.
Young swallows come out.

Friday 2.
29 8/10½; 58; N, NE.
Dark & cold, sun,
yellow even:

Began to cut my meadow-grass: a good crop.
Mʳ & Mʳˢ Richardson left us.
Low creeping mists.
Stopped down the vines which are in bloom.

Saturday 3.
29 8/10; 58; SE, S.
Vast dew, sun & clouds,
warm, sweet even:

Continue to cut down the grass. Hay cut yesterday makes apace.
Rye turns colour, & barley in ear round the forest.
By the number of bank-martins round Oak-hanger ponds, I
should imagine that the first brood is out. Myriads of *ephemerae*
near the ponds.

Sunday 4.
29 7/10; 59½, 66;
NE, SW, S.
Dew, sun, sun &
clouds, soft even:

Wheat in high bloom.
Grass-hopper lark whispers.
Hemerocallis blows.
On this day my Godson Littleton Etty discovered a young
Cuckow in one of the yew hedges of the vicarage garden, sitting
in a small nest that would scarce contain the bird, tho' not half
grown. By watching in a morning we found that the owners of
the nest were hedge sparrows, who were much busied in feeding
their great booby. The nest is in so secret a place that it is to be
wondered how the parent Cuckow could discover it. Tho' the
bird is very young, it is very fierce, gaping & striking at peoples
fingers, & heaving up by way of menace, & striving to
intimidate those that approach it. This is now only the fourth
young cuckow that I have ever seen in a nest: three in those of h:
sparrows, & one in that of a tit-lark.
As I rode up the N: field-hill lane I saw young partridges, that
were about two or three days old, skulking in the cart-ruts; while
the dams ran hovering & crying up the horse-track, as if
wounded, to draw off my attention.

Monday 5.
29 7/10½; 62½, 70;
SE, S.
Vast dew, hot sun,
clouds, sun, red bank,
vast dew.

Scarlet kidney-beans blow. Hay makes finely.
White cucumbers, under hand-glasses, begin to set.
The garden looks gay with solstitial flowers.
Timothy Turner cuts Baker's hill, the crop of which he has
bought: His S^t foin run to seed, the 17th crop.

Tuesday 6.
29 7/10; 62, 73½; SE.
Vast dew, sun,
cloudless, red even:

Cherries ripe, & finely flavoured.
Ricked the hay of my great meadow in delicate order: six loads.

Wednesday 7.
29 3/10; 67, 79!; SE,
NE.
Vast dew, cloudless,
very sultry, dark &
threatning, lightening,
rain.

Finished my hay-rick in charming order: 1 load.
Thunder & lightening & much rain about.
By the manner of the swifts coursing round the church, it seems
as if some of their young were out.

Vast damage done in various parts of the kingdom by thunder-
storms & floods, from Yorkshire all across to Plymouth.

Foot-bridge at Dorton.

Thursday 8.
29 5/10½; 73, 60½;
NW; 23.
Dew, sun, hot, grey,
gloomy & heavy.

Much hay housed.
Cool gale. Pitch darkness.

Friday 9.
29 7/10; 67, 65; NW,
W, NW.
Grey, dark, wet mist,
gleams, cool air.

French marrigolds begin to blow.
Took away the cucumber-frames, & glasses.
Beautiful yellow, & purple clouds in the N: W.

Saturday 10.
29 8/10½; 63; N.
Grey, & pleasant gale,
sun, cool, red even:

The hops damaged by the hail begin to fill their poles.
Thatched my hay-rick.
Cherries very fine.
Grapes begin to set: vine leaves turn brown.
The young cuckow gets fledge, & grows bigger than it's nest. It
is very fierce, & pugnacious.

Sunday 11.
29 7/10; 60½, 68; S.
Dew, sun & cool gale,
backing S:W.

Much hay about.

My horses, which lie at grass, have had no water now for about 8
weeks; nor do they seem to desire any when they pass by a pond,
or stream. This method of management is particularly good for
aged horses, especially if their wind is at all thick. My horses look
remarkably well.

Monday 12.
29 6/10½; 65; S, SW,
NW.
Strong gale, sun, dark,
gale, fine gleam.

White lilies blow.
Hay makes finely. Lime-trees blossom.

Tuesday 13.
29 9/10½; 60½; 65;
NW, W.
Sun, great dew, sun, &
gale, strong gale,
yellow even:

Finished ripping, furring & tiling ¶ the back part of my house; a
great jobb.
Garden beans come in.

Wednesday 14.
29 9/10¼; 60½; W,
NW.
Sun, dark, sun, sweet
even:

Wheat turns colour.
Papilio Machaon in Mrs Etty's garden. They are very rare in these
parts.

Thursday 15.
29 9/10; 62, 69; N,

Tacked the wall-trees.

NE.
Sun, cloudless, golden
weather, red even:

Trenched-out two rows of Celeri.
Wood-straw-berries, & cherries delicate!

Friday 16.
29 7/10; 63½; N, SW,
NW.
Sun, bright, dark &
louring, gleams.

Much wall-fruit, many apples & pears.
Jasmine blows.
White cucumbers swell.
Made curran, & raspberry jam: the fruit is hardly ripe; but the
small birds will steal it all away.

Saturday 17.
29 6/10; 64; NW, SW,
NW.
Sun, gales & clouds,
sun, cool, red even:

Scarlet-kidney-beans show pods.
Vines are out of bloom, & the grapes appear.
Vine-leaves turn purple.
Cut two white Cucumbers. Sowed a crop of white turnip-
radishes.

M^r Ch: Etty has taken the young Cuckow, & put it in a cage,
where the hedge-sparrows feed it. No old Cuckow has been seen to
come near it.
  Mr Charles Etty brought down with him from London in the
coach his two finely chequered tortoises,¶ natives of the island of
Madagascar, which appear to be the *Testudo geometrica* Linn: &
the *Testudo tessellata* Raii. One of these was small, & probably a
male, weighing about five pounds: the other, which was
undoubtedly a female, because it layed an egg the day after it's
arrival, weighed ten pounds & a quarter. The egg was round, &
white, & much resembling in size & shape the egg of an owl. The
backs of these tortoises are uncommonly convex, & gibbous. Ray
says of this species that the shell was *"Ellipticae seu ovatae figurae
solida plus quam dimidia pars"*: & again, *"Ex omnibus quas
unquam vidi maxime concava."* Ray's *quadrup*: 260.¶
The head, neck & legs of these were yellow. These tortoises in the
morning when put into the coach at Kensington were brisk, &
well: but the small one dyed the first night that they came to
Selborne; & the other, two nights after, having received, as it
should seem, some Injury in their Journey. When the female was
cleared of the contents of her body, a bunch of eggs of about 30 in
number was found in her.

Sunday 18.
29 3/10½; 61, 66; N,
S, SW.
Sun, summer weather,
dark horison.

Hops look remarkably well, & clear from vermin.
The bar: has fallen for some days.

Monday 19.
28 9/10½, 29; 62; S,
SW; 51.

The garden is finely watered.

Dark & blowing, rain,
rain, sun, & clouds.

Tuesday 20.
29 4/10; 60, 62; S,   Strong gales all day.
SW.   Bro: Henry & his son Sam came.
Sun, showers, showers,   Saw an old swift feed it's young in the air: a circumstance which I
clouds.   could never discover before.

Wednesday 21.
29 1/10½; 58, 62; S,   Strong gales.
SW.   The cuckow in the cage dyed.
Dark, rain, rain, cold
& blowing.

Thursday 22.
29 4/10½; 55½, 55;   The wind broke-off a great bough from Molly White's horse-
SW, W; 52.   chestnut tree.¶
Cold & blowing,   Strong gales.
showers, showers,
gleam of sun.

Friday 23.
29 6/10¾; 55½; SW,   Pricked-out some rows of polyanths from their seed-box.
W.   Planted-out a bed of endive.
Sun, grey & mild,   Planted bore-cole, &c.
pleasant, dark heavy
clouds to SE.

Saturday 24.
29 7/10; 62; SW.   Bro: Henry left us.
Sun, dark & mild,
dark, yellow horizon.

Sunday 25.
29 6/10½; 63; SW.   Shower.
Dark, & moist, fog on
the hanger.

Monday 26.
29 4/10; 63, 64; SW,   Many swifts about.
S.   Heavy rain.
Dark & still, rain, rain.   Bottled-out the hogshead of port-wine: my two thirds ran 16
                               dozen & four of my bottles, some of which are Bristol bottles, &
                               therefore large.

Tuesday 27.
29 5/10; 61; N, W; 75.   Rain in the night.
Rain, sun, chilly, red   White cucumbers abound.
even: Mr & Mrs Mulso, & Miss Mulso, & Miss Hecky Mulso came.

Wednesday 28.
29 3/10½; 58; S, SE.
Vast dew, sun, clouds,
dark & louring.

First kidney-beans, scarlet.
Artichokes.

Thursday 29.
29 3/10½; 59; S; 37.
Heavy gales with rain,
wet & blowing.

Trenched-out two rows of celeri.
Drew-out from the port-wine hogsh: for my share, eleven bottles
more of wine: so that my proportion was 17 dozen, & three
bottles.
Thanksgiving for the peace.

Friday 30.
29 5/10; 60; SE, NE;
NW. Rain, showers,
gleams, dark & chilly.

Showers in the night.
Several swifts.

Saturday 31.
29 8/10; 60½; NW; 8.
Showers, showers, sun,
showers about.

Several swifts. Dark horizon.
Potatoes come-in: they are very fine.
Hops promise for a great crop; even those that were broken by
the hail are much recovered, & may bear well.
Rain in July . . . 240.

AUGUST 1784

Sunday 1.
29 9/10; 59½; 66; W,
SW. Vast cold dew,
sun, clouds, sun, sweet
afternoon.

Monday 2.
30; 61½; NE.
Great dew, cloudless,
hot sun, sweet even:

Wheat-harvest begins. Several swifts.
Wall-cherries, may dukes, lasted 'till this time: & were very fine.
Sowed a crop of spinage, prickly-seeded, to stand the winter: &
rolled the bed with a garden-roller.

Tuesday 3.
29 8/10, 7/10½; 62;
N. Deep fog, sun,
grey, yellow even:

Several swifts.
Vivid rain-bow.
Annuals now thrive: they never grew 'till lately.

Young swallows, & martins congregate on the tower, & on dead
trees.

Wednesday 4.
29 7/10; 65½; N,
NW, W.
Dark & hot, rain, rain,
dark & moist.

Skimmed my two pasture fields.
Hirundines congregate.
Some apricots begin to turn colour.

Thursday 5.
29 6/10½; 64; SW, S;
20.
Sun, clouds, soft air,
wet, dark & hot.

Vast numbers of young martins, & swallows.
Saw no swifts. Saw some nightingales in my outlet.

Friday 6.
29 2/10½; 64½; SW;
60.
Dark, rain, rain, rain.

There is fine aftergrass in my meadows.
Blowing with heavy showers.
Tremella ¶ abounds in the walks.

Several swifts flying round Colchester-castle in the county of Essex.

Saturday 7.
29 6/10½; 59; W,
NW.
Sun, & clouds, sun,
shower, red even:

Many hop-poles are blown down.
No swifts seen for some days.
Cool, autumnal feel. Days much shortened.

Sunday 8.
29 8/10; 59; W.
Cold dew, sun, &
clouds, showers about.

The wheat does not ripen: little of it cut: the reapers were stopped
by the rain.
Rain-bows. No swifts.
Kidney-beans do not thrive, especially the white ones.

Monday 9.
29 8/10; 56; N, E,
SW.
Cold dew, sun, dark &
louring, rain.

No swifts.

Tuesday 10.
29 8/10; 58½; SW,
W; 19.
Rain, showers, hot
gleams, dark & mild.

Harvest is interrupted by the wet.
A pair of swifts.
Mr & Mrs Mulso, &c: left us.

Wednesday 11.
29 9/10; 62; W, SW.
Grey, sun, clouds, sun,
sweet even:

Wheat-harvest becomes general.
Pair of swifts.
The crop of spinage comes-up finely.
Turnip-radishes grow.
Kidney-beans go off, & cucumbers do not thrive.
They want heat.

Thursday 12.
29 9/10; 63; W.
Gleams, moist, grey &
hot, grey & mild.

Wheat housing at Heards.
Apricots begin to turn colour & to look ruddy on the extremities
of the trees.

Friday 13.
29 9/10; 61½; W, NW.
Grey, sun, sweet afternoon.

The wheat that was smitten by the hail does not come to maturity together: some ears are full ripe, & some quite green. Wheat within the verge of the hail-storm is much injured, & the pease are spoiled.

Saturday 14.
30, 30; 63; N.
Grey, sun, hot, vast dew.

Ants (flying) come from under the stairs, & fill the rooms, & windows.
Much wheat housed this day.
Annuals improve much.
Plums show no tendency to ripeness. Scalded codlings come in.
Kidney-beans in general fail, & cucumbers do not succeed very well.

A puff-ball, *lycoperdon bovista*, was gathered in a meadow near Alton, which weighed 7 pounds, & an half, & measured 1 Yard and one Inch in girth the longest way 3 feet two inches. There were more in the mead almost as bulky as this.

Sunday 15.
30, 29 9/10½; 63½, 71½; N, NE.
Vast dew! Cloudless, sweet harvest weather.

Some wheat-ricks made; & much wheat in shock. Some wheat not ripe.
Thistle-down flies.
Women bring cran-berries, but they are not ripe.
Ant-flies in my house very troublesome: they come from under the stairs.

Monday 16.
29 8/10, 7/10; 66½, 71; SW, NW.
Dew, sun, brisk air, hot sun, sweet even:

Pease are housed.
Ripe apricots come in: very fine.
Young swallows, & h: martins swarm, & cluster on trees, & houses.

Tuesday 17.
29 6/10½; 64; N.
Dark & mild, chilly, rain.

Much wheat this day housed.
Pease are housed.
Farmer Spencer, & farmer Knight are forced to stop their reapers, because their wheat ripens so unequally.
No swifts seen since the 11th.
Fly-catchers abound.

Wednesday 18.
29 7/10½; 57; N; 8.
Dark & cold, sharp wind, chilly air.

Wheat housed.
The country is finely diversifyed by harvest-scenes.
Spinage very thick on the ground.
Men hoe turnips, stir their fallows, & cart chalk.

Thursday 19.
29 6/10½; 55, 57; N.
Dark, blowing & cold, wet, wet.

Strong gales in the night.
Cold & winter-like.
Sowed lettuces to stand the winter.

Friday 20.
29 6/10½; 57, 58; NE;
161.
Rain, rain, heavy rain,
dark & still.

Great rain all night.
Lighted a fire in the parlor: the weather is very cold.

On this day My Niece Brown was delivered of her 4th child, a girl, which makes the 41st of my nephews & nieces now living.

Saturday 21.
29 6/10; 56; NE, E;
26.
Rain, heavy showers,
hail, thunder, fair, sun.

The rain damaged the apricots.
Wheat lies in a sad wet state; there is much abroad.
Endives spread. Hops grow.
Trenched celeri grows.
Boiled up some apricots with sugar to preserve them.

Sunday 22.
29 3/10½; 57½; NW,
N.
Rain, dark & blowing,
rain.

Men have not housed half their wheat.
Apricots chop.

Monday 23.
29 4/10½; 56½; N;
20.
Sun & clouds, strong
gale, sun, calm, red
even:

Preserved more apricots.
Men turn their wheat in the grips.¶
No wheat bound, or housed.
Vast dew. Low, white mist in the meadows.
Fly-catchers still.

Tuesday 24.
29 4/10; 59; E, W.
Fog, shower, gleams,
dark, dark & moist,
heavy clouds.

The tops of beeches begin to be tinged.
Much wheat bound.
White turnip-radishes mild, & good, & large.
Spinage-bed thrives.

Wednesday 25.
29 5/10; 58½; N; 9,
21.
Shower, dark & moist,
fair, rain, dark.

Sad harvest weather.
My great apricot-tree appeared in the morning to have been robbed of some of it's ripe fruit by a dog ¶ that had stood-up on his hind legs, & eaten-off some of the lower apricots, several of which were gnawn, & left on the ground, with some shoots of the tree. On the border were many fresh prints of a dogs feet. I have known a dog eat ripe goose-berries, as they hung on the trees.

Thursday 26.
29 7/10½; 54, 55;
NW.
Dark & cold, gale, still
& milder.

Wheat begins to grow as it lies.
Tyed-up some endives, & planted-out some.
Wheat turned, but none bound.

This proves a very expensive, & troublesome harvest to the farmers.
Pease suffer much, & will be lost out of the pod.

Friday 27.
29 7/10, 8/10; 55; S,
S.
Sun & clouds, louring,
wet.

Field turnips grow. Celeri grows.
Wheat bound, & some housed.

Saturday 28.
29 2/10½; 58½; S,
SW; 10, 19.
Rain, grey with a gale,
rain.

Autumnal crocus, *colchicum*, blows.
Men house wheat.
Some thunder.
Preserved more apricots.
Young martins in a nest under the eaves of my stable.
Many wallnuts on the tree over the stable: the sort is good, but
the tree seldom bears.

Sunday 29.
29 4/10: 60; SW.
Sun & clouds, pleasant,
sprinkling, yellow
even:

Much wheat abroad.
Much *tremella* on the ground.
A Faringdon man shot a young fern-owl in his orchard.

Monday 30.
29 4/10; 55, 60; NE,
SE.
Vast dew, sun & clouds,
dark, rain.
Full moon.

Peaches & nectarines swell & grow; but want warm, dry weather
to ripen them, & give them flavour. Grapes are very backward.
Wheat carted all day.
Swallows gather on the tower.
Many pease abroad, that have lain for weeks.

Tuesday 31.
29 3/10¾; 60; SW, S;
15.
Rain, rain, sun &
clouds, sun, fine
afternoon.

Fly-catchers still.
No wheat housed.
Heavy clouds in the horizon.

The rain in August was . . . 3 inch: 88 h:

Walnut tree on Bakers Hill

SEPTEMBER 1784

Wednesday 1.
29 6/10; 60; NE, SE.
Deep fog, gleams of
sun, dark & mild, &
still.

Swallows gather on the tower.
Wheat housed.
Farmer Town began to pick his hops: the hops are many, but
small. They were not smitten by the hail because they grew at the
S:E: end of the village. Hopping begins at Hartley.

My Nep: Edm^d White & Mr Clement launched a balloon ¶ on our
down, made of soft, thin paper; & measuring about two feet & an
half in length, & 20 inches in diameter. The buoyant air was
supplyed at bottom by a cotton plug of wooll wetted with spirits of
wine; & set on fire by a candle. The air being cold & moist this
machine did not succeed well abroad: but in Mr Yalden's stair-case
it rose to the ceiling, & remained suspended as long as the spirits
continued to flame, & then sunk gradually. These Gent: made the
balloon themselves. This small exhibition explained the whole
balloon affair very well: but the position of the flame wanted better
regulation; because the least vacillation set the paper on fire.

Thursday 2.
29 8/10; 57½, 64;
NW, S.
Grey, mild, sun, &
clouds, fine harvest
weather, gale.
Harvest moon.

Timothy comes forth into the walks. The weather has been so
cold that he has not been out for some time.
Much wheat housed.

The two hop-gardens, belonging to Farmer Spencer & John Hale,
that were so much injured, as it was supposed, by the hail-storm
on June 5th shew now a prodigious crop, & larger & fairer hops
than any in the parish. The owners seem now to be convinced that
the hail, by beating off the tops of the binds, has encreased the
side-shoots, & improved the crop. Que: therefore, should not the
tops of hops be pinched-off when the binds are very gross, &
strong? We find this practice to be of great service with melons, &
cucumbers. The scars, & wounds on the binds, made by the great
hailstones, are still very visible.

Friday 3.
29 9/10¾, 29 9/10¾;
59, 63; SE, S.
Grey, mild, sun, hot
sun, sweet even:

China-asters begin to blow.
Saw a white-throat in the garden.
Sweet harvest weather. Wheat ricked, & housed.
Mich: daisies begin to open.
Many uncrested wrens still appear.

Saturday 4.
29 9/10, 8/10¼; 58½,
68; SE.
Fog, vast dew, sun,
cloudless, golden
weather, red even:

Wheat will be finished off to day pretty well.
Fly-catchers seem to be withdrawn.
Swallows cluster on the cherry-trees at the parsonage.
Tyed-up more endive: endive very large.
Ant-flies swarm.

Sunday 5.
29 8/10; 60, 70½;
NE, S, SW.
Vast dew, sun, sultry,
sweet afternoon.

No wasps yet: no mushrooms appear.
Heavy clouds about.
One fly-catcher at Faringdon.
Annuals begin to make a great show.

I saw lately a small Ichneumon-fly attack a spider much larger
than itself on a grass-walk. When the spider made any resistance
the Ichneumon apply'd her tail to him, & stung him with great
vehemence, so that he soon became dead, & motionless. The Ich:
then running backward drew her prey very nimbly over the walk
into the standing grass. This spider would be deposited in some
hole where the Ich: would lay some eggs; & as soon as the eggs
were hatch'd, the carcase would afford ready food for the maggots.
Perhaps some eggs might be injected into the body of the spider in
the act of stinging. Some Ich: deposit their eggs in the *aureliae* of
butterflies, & moths.

Monday 6.
29 8/10½; 63, 73; SE,
S.
Great dew, hot sun,
cloudless, sweet
afternoon.

Grapes begin to turn; but the bunches are small & mean.
Peaches & nectarines swell, & redden, & advance towards
ripeness.
Hopping becomes general.

Tuesday 7.
29 9/10¼; 64, 73; E,
S.
Deep fog, golden
weather, sweet
afternoon, red even:

The crop of apricots, which was very great, is over.
Ant-flies swarm from under the stairs.

Wednesday 8.
30, 29 9/10¾; 64½,
73; E.
Vast white dew, hot
sun, sultry, golden
weather, red even:

H: martins congregate in vast flocks.
Fine hopping: the poor earn good wages.
Men house barley in fine order.
No wasps are seen.

Thursday 9.
29 9/10; 66, 75½;
NE, SW.
Fog, sun, dew, sultry,
cloudless, sweet even:

Blanched endive comes-in.
Some peaches: but not fine:
Fern owl.

Friday 10.
29 9/10½; 65½; NE.
Dark & sultry, sun, red
even:

BRAMSHOT PLACE
Uncrested wrens seem to be withdrawn.

Mʳ Richardson's wall fruit at Bramshot-place is not good-
flavoured, nor well-ripened: & his vines are so injured by the cold,

black summer, as not to be able to produce any fruit, or good wood for next year. Mr Dennis's vines at Bramshot also are in a poor state.

Saturday 11.
29 9/10; 71, 68; NW.
Great dew, sun, sultry, fresh gale.

SELBORNE
Mr Randolph the Rector of Faringdon, came.

Sunday 12.
29 8/10; 63, 73; NE, E.
Dew, heat, cloudless, red even:

Peaches, & nectarines advance towards ripeness. Several hornets, but no wasps.
Ground dry, & heated.

Monday 13.
29 7/10; 63, 73; SE.
Vast dew, cloudless, sultry, red even:

Some few wasps.
Young martins in a nest under the Eaves of my stable.
Peaches, & nectarines come in.
Turned the horses in the little meadow for the first time since it was mowed. There is good after-grass.

Tuesday 14.
29 7/10; 66; NE.
Sun, fog, fog, cooler, grey.

The heats are so great, & the nights so sultry, that we spoil joints of meat, in spite of the care that can be taken.
My grapes turn very fast.

Wednesday 15.
29 7/10; 63, 68; E.
Grey, sun, hot sum: air, red even:

Peaches, & nectarines not delicate.
Mr Randolph left us.
Grass-walks burn.
The autumn-sown spinage turns-out a fine crop: but is much too thick. We draw it for use.

Thursday 16.
29 7/10½; 58½; E.
Cold dew, sun, hot sun, clouds.

Grapes come in. Grapes well-flavoured, the late, bad season considered. Nectarines good. Endives run up to seed. Tyed-up more endive.
Martins cling, & cluster in a very particular manner against the wall of my stable & brew-house: also on the top of the may-pole. This clinging, at this time of year only, always seems to me to carry somewhat significant with it.

Friday 17.
29 7/10; 59½; NE, SW.
Vast dew, sun, clouds, hot sun, grey.

Nep: Ben White left me: he stayed a few days.
Sweet autumnal weather.
Ivy begins to blow.

Saturday 18.
29 6/10½; 60; NE,
SE.
Deep fog, sun, broken
clouds, sweet even:

Nectarines very good.
Bees begin to devour the nectarines.
Endives very fine.

Sunday 19.
29 1/10½; 60½, 68;
SE, S.
Great dew, sun, sultry,
cloudless, heavy clouds.

The wind turns-up the leaves of the trees.
Dark weather to the S:W:

Monday 20.
29 1/10, 2/10½; 64,
63; S, W, NW.
Heavy showers,
showers, grey, yellow
even:

Uncrested wren still appears.
Hopping in general is finished, except in some few gardens.

Tuesday 21.
29 6/10; 56; W, S.
Dew, sun, clouds,
shower, louring.

Harvest mostly finished.
Gathered-in the early pippins, called white apples: a great crop.
Showers about.
Peaches, & nectarines are good.

Wednesday 22.
29 1/10½; 59; W; 35.
Rain, rain, gleams, hot,
rain, rain, blowing.

Wall-fruit falls off. We keep drawing the spinage, which is
grown very large, & much too thick.
Endives very large, & fine.
Many hirundines.

Thursday 23.
29 2/10½; 59½; W,
NW; 54.
Rain, rain, hot sun,
sun, warm, showers
about.

Showers about.
Hirundines, some.

Friday 24.
29 5/10; 57½; SE; 22.
Sun, showers, hot
gleams, dark & heavy.

Few hirundines.

Saturday 25.
29 2/10½; 60; S.
Sun, bright, vast
showers, rain.

Swallows.
Thunder.
Sister Henry White, & her daughter Lucy came.¶
Peaches & Nect: rot very fast.

Sunday 26.
29 2/10½; 60½; S,
SW; 75.
Showers, heavy
showers, showers.

Corn out at Faringdon & Chawton.
Mr Taylor took possession of Selborne vicarage.

Monday 27.
29 4/10; 56; W.
Sun, & clouds,
showers, sun,
moonshine.

Hirundines.

Tuesday 28.
29 4/10½; 55; NW,
N.
Grey, small shower,
sun, clouds, grey, cold
air.
Full moon.

Grapes good.
Hirundines.
Peaches & Nect: watry & rotten.

Wednesday 29.
29 6/10½, 54; N, NE.
Vast dew, sun, bright &
pleasant. Moon-shine.

Took possession of Selborne curacy.¶
Oats & barley much grown.
Hirundines.

Thursday 30.
29 7/10½; 51; NE.
White frost, sun,
pleasant. Moonshine.

Hirundines, a few. Some wasps.
Men house oats. Fire in the parlor.
Rain in September . . . 2 inch 51 h:

OCTOBER 1784

Friday 1.
29 9/10¼; 48; NE, E.
White frost, sun,
pleasant.

Gathered-in the Swan's egg, autumn-burgamot, Cresan-
burgamot, Chaumontelle, & Virgoleuse pears: a great crop. The
Swan-eggs are a vast crop.
Some swallows.

A wood-cock was killed in Black moor-woods: an other was seen
the same evening near Hartley-wood.

Saturday 2.
30½, 30½; 46½; NE,
SE, NE.
White frost, grey, grey
& mild.

Men house beans, & oats. Some swallows. Many house-
swallows.

Sunday 3.
30; 49; SE, E.

Some h: swallows.

No dew, grey, still &
cool.

Two young men killed a large male otter, weighing 21 pounds, on the bank of our rivulet, below Priory longmead, on the Hartley-wood side, where the two parishes are divided by the stream. This is the first of the kind ever remembered to have been found in this parish.

Monday 4.
29 6/10½; 50½; E.
No dew, grey, gale,
grey, cool.

Some swallows.

Tuesday 5.
29 5/10, 7/10; 51; SE.
No dew, grey, sun, soft
& still.

Swallows.
Gathered-in the knobbed russets, & the Cadilliac pears.

Wednesday 6.
29 8/10; 53½; NE.
Fog, sun, pleasant,
sharp wind.

The ground is very dry.
A vast flock of ravens over the hanger: more than sixty!

Thursday 7.
29 7/10; 51½; NE.
Dew, sun, sharp wind.

Some swallows.
The crop of pears is vast.
Pronged-up potatoes, & carrots, a fine crop.
Mrs Harry White, & Lucy left us.

Friday 8.
29 6/10; 52; NE.
Dew, sun, pleasant,
sharp wind.

Some few swallows.
Dug-up the carrots, & potatoes.
Mr Richardson came.

Saturday 9.
29 6/10; 51; NE.
Cold dew, sun, sharp
wind.

Some few swallows.
Mr R: left us.

It has been the received opinion that trees grow in height only by their annual upper shoot. But my neighbour over the way, Tanner, whose occupation confines him to one spot, assures me, that trees are expanded & raised in the lower parts also. The reason that he gives is this; the point of one of my Firs in Baker's hill began for the first time to peep over an opposite roof at the beginning of summer; but before the growing season was over, the whole shoot of the Year, & three or four joints of the body beside became visible to him as he sits on his form in his shop. This circumstance will be worthy of attention an other Year. According to this supposition a tree may advance in height considerably, tho' the summer-shoot should be destroyed every Year.

Sunday 10.
29 7/10; 50½; NE.
Dark, heavy & still.

Began to turn into the great mead, for the first time since it was mowed. The head of grass is great.

A person took a trout in the stream at Dorton, weighing 2 pounds, & an half; a size to which they seldom arrive with us, because our brook is so perpetually harassed by poachers.

Monday 11.
29 8/10½; 48½; N.
Cold dew, sun, gale,
sweet afternoon.

Men draw, & stack turnips.
This is the 14th dry day.
Ravens, many.

Tuesday 12.
29 9/10; 49½; NE.
Fog, sun, dark & still.

Grapes are very fine.
My well is very low in water.

Wednesday 13.
29 8/10; 50 ½/10; NE.
Dark, sprinklings, dark
& still.

Two or three swallows.
Gathered the dearling-apples in the meadow; a great crop.

Thursday 14.
29 7/10¾; 48; E, NE.
Grey, & cold, sun,
sharp wind, sun, bright
& sharp.

Finished gathering in the apples. Apples are in such plenty, that they are sold for 8d per bushel.
Planted coss-lettuce, & Dutch, in rows under the fruit-wall, to stand the winter.

Friday 15.
29 7/10; 45; E, NE.
White frost, sun, &
sharp air, bright, &
sharp.

Leaves fall. The foliage of trees is much tinged.
Potatoes, & carrots abound.
Timothy retreats under the laurel hedge.

Saturday 16.
29 8/10; 45½; NE.
Fog, sun, sun but some
haze, bright.

Wall-nuts on the best tree not good.
Mr Blanchard passed by us in full sight at about a quarter before three P.M. in an air balloon!!! ¶ He mounted at Chelsea about noon, but came down at Sunbury to permit Mr Sheldon to get-out: his weight over-loading the machine. At a little before four P:M: Mr Bl: landed at the town of Romsey in the county of Hants.
† *Extract of a letter from a Gentleman¶ in a village fifty miles S.W. of London, dated Oct. 21.*
"From the fineness of the weather and the steadiness of the wind to the N.E. I began to be possessed with a notion last Friday, that we should see Mr. Blanchard the day following, and therefore I called upon many of my neighbours in the street, and told them my

† Cutting inserted in the Journal from a newspaper or magazine.

suspicions. The next day proving also bright and the wind continuing as before, I became more sanguine than ever; and issuing forth, exhorted all those who had any curiosity to look sharp from about one to three o'clock, as they would stand a good chance of being entertained with a very extraordinary sight. That day I was not content to call at the houses, but I went out to the plowman and labourers in the fields, and advised them to keep an eye at times to the N. and N.E. But about one o'clock there came up such a haze that I could not see the hill; however, not long after the mist cleared away in some degree, and people began to mount the hill. I was busy in and out till a quarter after two, and in taking my last walk observed a long cloud of *London smoke* hanging to the N. and N.N.E. This appearance encreased my expectation. At twenty minutes before three there was a cry that the balloon was come. We ran into the orchard, where we found twenty or thirty neighbours assembled, and from the green bank at the end of my house, saw a dark blue speck at a most prodigious height dropping as it were out of the sky, and hanging amidst the regions of the air between the weather-cock of the Tower and the Maypole; at first it did not seem to make any way, but we soon discovered that its velocity was very considerable, for in a few minutes it was over the Maypole, and then over my chimney, and in ten minutes more behind the wallnut-tree. The machine looked mostly of a dark blue colour, but sometimes reflected the rays of the sun. With a telescope I could discern the boat and the ropes that supported it. To my eye the balloon appeared no bigger than a large tea-urn. When we saw it first it was north of Farnham over Farnham Heath, and never came on this (east) side the Farnham road; but continued to pass on the outside of Bentley, Froil, Alton, &c. and so for Medstead, Lord Northington's at the Grange, and to the right of Alresford and Winchester. I was wonderfully struck with the phaenomenon, and, like Milton's "Belated Peasant," felt my heart rebound with joy and fear at the same time. After a time I surveyed the machine with more composure, without that concern for two of my fellow creatures; for two we then supposed there were embarked in that aerial voyage. At last seeing how securely they moved, I considered them as a group of cranes or storks intent on the business of emigration, who had

       . . . . "Set forth
       Their airy caravan, high over seas
       Flying, and over lands, with mutual wing
       Rasing their flight" . . . . ¶

Sunday 17.
29 7/10½; 45½; NE.
Great dew, sun, still,
pleasant, dark.

Fine mackarel sky.

Monday 18.
29 5/10½; 47; NE.

This day the dry weather has lasted three weeks. Lightening.

Great dew, fog, sun,
still, pleasant.

Tuesday 19.
29 4/10; 47½; NE, W,
SW.
Sun, & clouds, pleasant
summer, sweet
afternoon.

Many spider's webs.

Wednesday 20.
29 7/10; 45½; N.
White frost, grey, dark
& heavy, bright
gleams.

Wall-nuts innumerable, but few good.
Foliage of the trees fades very fast, & becomes much tinged, &
dusky.

Thursday 21.
29 8/10½; 43½; W,
SW.
Frost, ice, sun,
pleasant, grey & mild.

This day at 4 o'clock P:M: Edm.d White launched an air balloon
from Selborne-down, measuring about 8 feet & ½ in length, &
16 feet in circumference. It went-off in a steady & grand manner
to the E. & settled in about 15 minutes near Todmoor on the
verge of the forest.

Friday 22.
29 7/10; 47½; W.
Clouds, some drops,
sun, mild, fine even:

Ash-trees are stripped of their leaves.
My hedges beautifully coloured.

Saturday 23.
29 2/10½; 50½; W.
Shower, sun & clouds,
showers.

Celeri comes-in.
Red-wings on our common.
Leaves fall very fast.
Rooks carry-off the wall-nuts.

I have seen no ants for some time, except the Jet-ants, which
frequent the gate-posts. These continue still to run forwards, &
backwards on the rails of gates, & up the posts, without seeming to
have anything to do. Nor do they appear all the summer to carry
any sticks or insects to their nests like other ants.

Sunday 24.
29 3/10; 42½; W,
NW; 20.
White frost, sun, cold
wind, dark & cold,
shower.

Leaves fall much.
Timothy retires under the laurel-hedge, but does not bury
himself.
Grapes very fine.

Monday 25.
29 6/10; 39½; N; 9.
Hard frost, thick ice,
sun, snow, snow! snow!

In my way to Newton I was covered with snow!
Snow covers the ground, & trees!!

Tuesday 26.
29 8/10; 38½; N.
Grey, sun, sharp wind,
shower, bright & cold.

Horses begin to lie within.
Compleated three rows of lettuces the whole length of the fruit-wall, to stand the winter.

Wednesday 27.
29 8/10; 39½; N.
Hard frost, sun, dark,
shower, bright.

Dunged, trenched, & earthed the asparagus-beds, & filled the trenches with leaves, flower-stalks, &c.
Timothy retires under the laurel-hedge, & begins to bury himself.

Thursday 28.
29 8/10; 40½; N.
White frost, dark &
moist, sharp wind,
bright.
Full moon.

Rooks carry off wall-nuts.
Mr John Mulso came.

Friday 29.
29 8/10¼; 41½; N.
Sun, grey & mild.

Grapes very fine.
Foliage turns very dusky: the colour of the woods & hangers appears very strange, & what men, not acquainted with the country, would call very unnatural.

Saturday 30.
29 7/10; 43; N, NE;
10.
Soft rain, grey, &
mild.

Bat comes out.

Sunday 31.
29 5/10; 46½; NW,
SW, S.
Grey, still, & soft.

Many people are tyed-up about the head on account of tooth-aches, & face-aches.
Rain in Octobr: . . . 0 inc: 39 hund.

NOVEMBER 1784

Monday 1.
29 3/10; 48; W; 10.
Rain, grey & mild, wet
& dark.

Mr John Mulso was shot in the legs.¶

Tuesday 2.
29 6/10; 50; NW, N.
Rain, mild, dark, &
wet, bright.

Leaves fall very fast. Grapes delicate.
Bats are out early in the evening, hunting for gnats, before moths begin to flie.

Wednesday 3.
29 5/10¾; 46; NE, E,
SE.

Timothy comes out.

Oak on Selborne Common.
28 September.

Grey & mild, sun,
shower, grey & mild.

Thursday 4.
29 4/10; 46; SE, E; 31.   Timothy out.
Grey & mild, sun,   Great meteor.
pleasant, fleecy clouds,
bright.

Friday 5.
29 2/10; 46; NE.   The deep, golden colour of the larches amidst the dark
Grey, mild & still, wet,   evergreens makes a lovely contrast!
misty.   Wood-pigeons appear.

Saturday 6.
29 3/10; 46; NE.
Dark & still, wet, dark
& moist.

Sunday 7.
29 6/10½; 44½; NE,   Timothy out.
N. Sun, & clouds, cold   Jet-ants still appear.
shower, grey & sharp.

Monday 8.
29 7/10½; 41; N.   The hanger almost naked: some parts of my tall hedges still finely
Hard frost, sun,   variegated: the fading foliage of the elm is beautifully contrasted
pleasant, bright, frost.   to the beeches!

Tuesday 9.
29 3/10; 39½; S, SW;   Leaves fall very fast.
32.
Frost, rain, rain, fair.

Wednesday 10.
29 2/10; 44; SW.   Mr John Mulso left us.
Sun, warm, haze, &   Blowing all night.
rain.

Thursday 11.
28 9/10¾; 53; SW, W.   Picked-up the beech-mast which fell from the trees of my
Rain, blowing, rain &   planting, & sowed it in the thin parts of the hedges of Baker's
wind, wind.   hill.
                            Trees & hedges are naked.
                            Jet-ants out still.

Friday 12.
29 2/10½; 51; SW; 94.   Much rain in the night.
Rain, rain, sun, wet.   Vines naked: many grapes left. Grapes delicate, but the vines
                            have lost all their leaves.

Saturday 13.
29 5/10; 47; SW.
Grey, sun, sun,
pleasant, grey & mild.

Gathered-in the remaining grapes: a large crop.
Timothy comes-out.

Sunday 14.
29 4/10; 49, 51; SW.
Dark & mild, wet, wet.

No acorns, & very few beech-mast. No beech-mast last year, but acorns innumerable.

Monday 15.
29 4/10; 53; S, W.
Rain, rain, rain.

Stormy in the night.

Tuesday 16.
29 6/10; 49; SW; 85.
Grey, & mild.

Wednesday 17.
29 5/10; 46; SW, W;
34.
Vast showers with hail,
bright & chill.

Thursday 18.
29 1/10½; 42½; SE.
Dark & mild, rain,
rain, rain.

Timothy out. In the evening he retired into the laurel-hedge, & has not been seen since. Very wet, & blowing.

Friday 19.
29 6/10½; 41; W; 74.
Frost, sun, pleasant.

Saturday 20.
29 8/10; 39; NW.
Hard frost, sun,
pleasant.

Large fieldfares appear.

Sunday 21.
29 9/10½; 35; N.
Hard frost, very white,
sun, cloudless, sharp
air.

Timothy is hid some where under the laurel-hedge.

Monday 22.
29 7/10½; 35½; S,
SE, NE, N.
Hard frost, swift thaw,
Rain, deep fog.

Finished sweeping-up the leaves in the walks.

Tuesday 23.
29 8/10; 37½; N.
Frost, deep fog, sun,
pleasant.

Brother Thomas & his daughter, & two sons came. The chaise that brought some of them passed along the king's high road into the village by Newton lane, & down the N: field hill; both of which have had much labour bestowed on them, & are now very safe. This is the first carriage that ever came in this way.

Wednesday 24.
29 7/10; 41; W.
Wet, grey, & mild,
wind.

Planted tulips again in the borders; & the small off-sets in a nursery bed.

Thursday 25.
29 6/10; 50; SW, W;
60.
Rain & wind, sun,
pleasant, grey.

The dew on the out-side of windows.

Friday 26.
29 9/10; 48; N, NW.
Grey, still & mild.

Haws in such quantities that they weigh down the white-thorns.

Saturday 27.
30; 48; S.
Grey & mild.

Flesh-flies come forth.
Beetles flie.

Sunday 28.
29 4/10½; 47; S.
Dark & mild, gleams,
dark & cold, rain.

Monday 29.
29 8/10½; 47; N; 50.
Rain, cold & wet, dark,
& raw.

Wood-pigeons in small flocks.

Tuesday 30.
29 6/10½; 42; NW,
SW.
Fog, sun, pleasant,
grey, stars.

Rain in November . . . 4 inch 70 hund:

DECEMBER 1784

Wednesday 1.
29 7/10; 40½; NW;
50.
Frost, ice, sun, cold air.

Rain in the night.

Thursday 2.
29 8/10½; 36; NW.
Hard frost, sun,
pleasant, frost.

Timothy is buried we know not where in the laurel-hedge.

Friday 3.
29 3/10; 39; SW.
Thaw, wet, grey, &
mild, rain.

Saturday 4.
29 1/10½; 42; SW; 21.
Grey & damp, stars.

Sunday 5.
28 6/10½; 41; S.
Dark, rain, rain.

Monday 6.
28 2/10½; 42; S; 102.
Dark, rain, rain, rain
& hail.

Dismally dark. No wind with this very sinking glass.

Tuesday 7.
28 5/10; 38; S; 30.
Snow, snow, snow.

Wednesday 8.
28 6/10; 36; NW.
Deep snow, snow,
snow.

Fierce driving snow all day.
Snow much drifted. Siberian weather.

Thursday 9.
29 1/10½; 32, 21;
NW, W; snow 12 inch.
Frost, bright sun.

Much snow in the night. Vast snow. Snow 16 inches deep on my grass-plot: about 12 inches at an average. Farmer Hoar had 41 sheep buried in snow. No such snow since Jan: 1776. In some places much drifted.

Friday 10.
29 3/10; Some what
below zero! 24, O-1.
Twenty-one degrees
below zero. Extreme
frost!!!! yet still, bright
sun.

Thomas Hoar shook the snow carefully off from the evergreens. The snow fell for 24 hours, without ceasing. The ice in one night in Gracious street full four inches. Bread, cheese, meat, potatoes, apples all frozen, where not secured in cellars under ground.

On the 9th & 10th of Dec: when my Therm: was down at 0, or zero: 18 degree below zero:- Mr Yalden's Therm: at Newton was at 19, & 22. Dec: 24, when my Therm: was at 10½ that at Newton was at 22, & 19. At Newton, when hung side by side, these two instruments accorded exactly.

Saturday 11.
29 3/10; 10, 26; E.
Grey, snow, still, sun,
haze.

My apples, pears, & potatoes secured in the cellar, & kitchen-closet; my meat in the cellar. Severe frost & deep snow. Several men, that were much abroad, made sick by the cold: their hands & feet were frozen.

We hung-out two thermometers, one made by Dollond, & one by B: Martin: the latter was graduated only to 4 below 10, or 6 degrees short of zero; so that when the cold became intense, & our remarks interesting, the mercury went all into the ball, & the instrument was of no service.

Sunday 12.
29 3/10; 26; N.
Strong frost, sun, sharp
wind.

Monday 13.
29 2/10½; 28; N,
NW.
Strong frost, sun,
pleasant, red clouds.

Shoveled out the bostal. ¶ Snow very deep still.
My laurel-hedge is injured by the cold.
Laurus-tines are also hurt.

Tuesday 14.
29 3/10; 25; NW.
Hard frost, grey &
still, small snow.

Finished shoveling the path to Newton.
Dame Loe came to help.

Wednesday 15.
29 6/10; 31; N.
Grey, & still, dark.

Deep snow still. Snow drifts on the down, & fills-up the path which we shoveled.

Thursday 16.
29 6/10; 32; N.
Snow, grey, snow.

Titmice pull the moss off from trees in searching for insects.

Friday 17.
29 6/10½; 25; E.
Hard frost, fog, sun,
fog.

Snow in the night.
Rime covers the trees. Snow still very deep.

Saturday 18.
29 4/10; 31, 33; N.
Fog, vast rime, snow,
snow.

Sunday 19.
29 5/10; 32; N.
Frost, still, grey, thaw,
hard frost.

Much snow on the ground.

Monday 20.
29 7/10; 25; N.   My laurel-hedge is scorched, & looks very brown!
Hard frost, sun, bright
& still, frost.

Tuesday 21.
29 5/10; 24; NW, W.
Hard frost, still, sun,
grey, some snow.

Wednesday 22.
29 4/10½; 26; N.   Much snow on the Ground.
Hard frost, sun, sharp   Farmer Lassam's Dorsetshire ewes begin to lamb.
wind.   His turnips are frozen as hard as stones.

Thursday 23.
29 6/10½; 24, 17; N.   Many labourers were employed in shoveling the snow, and
Vast rime, sun, still,   opening the hollow, stony lane, that leads to the forest.
pleasant, fierce frost.   Snow frozen so as almost to bear.

Friday 24.
29 8/10¼; 17, 22; N.   No wagtails since the snow fell.
Vast rime, deep fog,
still, & sharp.

Saturday 25.
29 9/10; 10½, 30; N,   Stagg the keeper, who inhabits the house at the end of Wolmer
W, SW.   pond, tells me that he has seen no wild-fowl on that lake during
Vast rime, sun, grey.   the whole frost; & that the whole expanse is entirely frozen-up to
                                  such a thickness that the ice would bear a waggon.
                                  500 ducks are seen some times together on that pond.

Sunday 26.
29 8/10½; 27; NE, E.
No frost, sun, deep,
freezing fog.
Full moon.

Monday 27.
29 7/10; 28; E.
Dark, & still.

Tuesday 28.
29 5/10; 27½, 26; E.
Grey, sharp wind, sun,
bright, & sharp.

Wednesday 29.
29 4/10; 24, 24; NE.

Severe frost, sun,
sharp, dark, sleet.

Thursday 30.
29 1/10¼; 31, 31½;
E.
Deep fog, thaw, dark,
& cold.

Friday 31.
29; 31; NE.
Fog, grey, & still,
thaw.

Much snow on the ground.
My laurel-hedge, & laurustines quite discoloured, & burnt as it
were with the frost.
Rain in Decemᵣ . . . 3 inch 6 hund.

Rain at Fyfield in 1784		Rain at Selborne in 1784		Rain at S: Lambeth in 1784	
	inc: h:		inc: h:		inc: h:
Jan:	2: 44	Jan:	3: 18	Jan:	2: 54
Feb:	1: 7	Feb:	0: 77	Feb:	1: 49
March	2: 24	March	3: 82	March	2: 63
April	2: 10	April	3: 92	April	2: 56
May	1: 57	May	1: 52	May	1: 36
June	2: 45	June	3: 65	June	3: 45
July	2: 80	July	2: 40	July	2: 26
Aug:	2: 79	Aug:	3: 88	Aug:	2: 84
Septᵣ	2: 7	Septᵣ	2: 51	Septᵣ	1: 65
Octᵣ	0: 17	Octᵣ	0: 39	Octᵣ	0: 83
Novᵣ	3: 14	Novᵣ	4: 70	Novᵣ }	5: 60
Decemᵣ	1: 72	Decᵣ	3: 6	Decemᵣ }	
	24: 60		33: 80		27: 21

Saturday 2.
28 8/10½; 32; NE.
Grey, frost, dark,
snow, snow.

SELBORNE
Much snow on the ground. Ponds frozen-up, & almost dry.
Moles work; cocks crow. Ground soft under the snow. No fieldfares seen: no wag-tails. Ever-greens miserably scorched; even
ivy, in warm aspects.

Sunday 2.
28 6/10½; 36; NE, E.
Fog, thaw, thaw, deep
fog.

Eaves drop.
This frost all thro' has been without any wind.

Monday 3.
28 9/10; 36; NE, E.
Deep fog, thaw, rain,
rain.

Began the new rick: the hay is very fine. Tho' my ever-greens are almost destroyed, M.ʳ Yalden's bays, & laurels, & laurustines seem untouched.

Tuesday 4.
28 8/10; 42; SE, S.
Swift thaw, rain, rain.

Berberries, & haws frozen on the trees. No birds eat the former.
Flood at Gracious-street.
Walls, & wainscot sweat.

Wednesday 5.
29; 48; SW; 112.
Swift thaw, rain, dark
& wet.

Snow much melted.
Brother Thomas & family left us.
Some insects about. Walls sweat.

Thursday 6.
29 4/10; 33, 25; N.
Snow, snow, snow,
bright, frost.

No snipes in the moors at the forest, or on the streams. No woodcocks to be found this winter.
Deep snow on the ground.

Friday 7.
29 6/10½; 17, 32; N,
W, SW.
Fierce frost, warm sun,
red, fleecy sky.

Shook the snow from the ever-greens, & shovelled the walks.
Snow-scenes very beautiful!

On this day M.ʳ Blanchard, & D.ʳ Jeffries rode in a balloon¶ from Dover-cliff & passing over the channel towards France, landed in the forest De Felmores, just 12 miles up into the country. These are the first Aëronauts that have dared to take a flight over the Sea!!!

Saturday 8.
29 7/10; 42; SW.
Swift thaw, snow melts,
rain.

Received five gallons, & seven pints of French brandy from M.ʳ Com.ᵈ Woods.

Sunday 9.
29 9/10½; 48; W; 71.
Dark & mild, soft, &
still, dark.

The dew on the windows on the outside. Walls sweat. Crocus's sprout.
Gnats play about in the air.

Monday 10.
29 9/10; 32; E; SW.
White frost, sun,
pleasant.

Snow gone, except under hedges.

Tuesday 11.
29 6/10½; 27; SE.
Frost, dark & still,
dark.

Men begin to plough again.

Wednesday 12.
29 5/10½; 31; E.
Frost, dark, & still,
fog.

Snow in the hollow lanes.

Thursday 13.
29 4/10½; 33; SE, E.
Dark, moist, & still.

Heaps of snow in shady places.

Friday 14.
29 3/10½; 37; E, E.
Deep fog, dark & still,
rain.

Saturday 15.
29 5/10; 38, 41; N,
NE.
Deep fog, dark & mild,
fog.

The air abounds with insects playing up & down.

Sunday 16.
29 5/10; 41; SE, S.
Deep fog, still & mild,
gleam of sun, wet.

Winter-aconites emerge, & bud for bloom.

Monday 17.
29 5/10½; 46; S.
Rain, rain, rain.

Tuesday 18.
29 5/10; 46; S; 39.
Wet, rain, rain.

Walls, & wainscot stream with water.

Wednesday 19.
29 3/10¾; 48; S.
Dark & wet, dark &
mild.

Wednesday 19.
29 3/10¾; 48; S.
Dark & wet, dark &
mild.

Thursday 20.
29 5/10; 49; S; 32.
Deep fog, sun, dark &
mild.

Snow-drops bud for bloom.

Friday 21.
29 7/10; 42; SE.
Deep fog, dark & still,
wet fog.

Made a seedling-cucumber-bed. The glazier mended the light of
the seedling-frame broken by the hail.
Finished dressing the vines, & laid-in the bearing-wood thinner
than of late.

Saturday 22.
29 8/10½; 44; S, SE.
Deep fog, sun,
pleasant, bright moon.

Planted in the border in the yard a row of tulips.
Ivy-trees cast their leaves.

Sunday 23.
29 9/10; 42; E, SE.
Deep fog, sun, spring-
like, bright.

Boys play on the Plestor at marbles, & peg-top. Thrushes sing in
the coppices.
Thrushes & blackbirds are much reduced.

Monday 24.
29 8/10; 42; SE.
Deep fog, dark, &
mild, spring-like.

Some snow yet in the hollow-lane.
Planted small tulip-roots in a nursery-bed.

Tuesday 25.
29 8/10; 42; SE.
Wet fog, deep, raw fog.

Wednesday 26.
29 8/10; 39; SE.
Dark & foggy, raw, &
cold.

Planted two rows of garden-beans.

Thursday 27.
29 7/10; 44; SE.
Wet fog, grey, sun,
spring-like, rain, rain.

Continue to trim the trees on the fruit-walls.
Bees come forth, & gather on the snow-drops.
Grass-walks that are rolled look beautifully.

Friday 28.
29 2/10; 43, 36; W;
30.
Rain, rain, gleams,
hail, moon-shine.

Saturday 29.
29 2/10½; 33; W.
Frost, sun, flight of
snow, clouds.

Sunday 30.
29; W.
Frost, rain, rain &
wind.

Monday 31.
29 7/10; 31, 26; N.
Frost, sun, & sharp
wind, hard frost.

Strong wind all night. Small flight of snow.
Sowed cucumber-seeds.
The wind blowed-off the fox's tail.
Rain in Jan: 2 inc: 84 hun:

FEBRUARY 1785

Tuesday 1.
29 8/10½; 28, 33; N.
Hard frost, sun, cold
air, frost, bright.

On this cold day about noon a bat was flying round Gracious
street pond, & dipping down & sipping the water,¶ like
swallows, as it flew: all the while the wind was very sharp, & the
boys were standing on the ice!

Wednesday 2.
29 7/10; 28, 33; N.
Hard frost, sun, grey,
thaw, red even.

Continue to trim the fruit-trees.
The scorched laurels cast their leaves, & are almost naked.

Thursday 3.
29 3/10; 28, 33; E,
SW, SE.
Hard frost, grey, &
still, mist, sleet, snow.

Friday 4.
29 1/10½; 28, 34, 31;
E, S, E.
Sun, cloudless, still,
bright.

Snow covers the ground.
Arbutus's Cypresses, Ilex's seem to be dead: even Portugal-
laurels are injured, & Cedars of Libanus.

Saturday 5.
28 6/10½; 32½; E.
Snow, dark & moist.

American, & Swedish junipers, & firs, Scotch & Spruce
untouched.
One black-bird in the garden.
Snow on the ground.

Sunday 6.
28 5/10; 29, 32; E, W.
Snow, snow, sun, frost.

Young sheep suffer much by the weather, & look poorly.
Deep snow.
Paths icy.

Monday 7.
29; 31½, 31; SW, W,
N.
Grey, thaw, rain, snow,
frost.

Snow on the ground.

Tuesday 8.
29 4/10; 28; W.

Paths icy. Snow covers the ground.

Hard frost, warm sun,
sun.

Wednesday 9.
29 7/10¾; 29; W, N.   Snow on the ground.
Frost, cold wind, sun.

Thursday 10.
29 7/10; 37½; S, E.   Deep fog on the hill. Dew on the windows on the outside. Warm
Rain, rain, rain, rain.   abroad.

Friday 11.
30 1/10; 35, 33; E;   This water fell at several times in snow, & rain.
NE; 141.   Potted cucumber-plants. Mezereon, & polyanths blow.
Grey, sun, dark, &   Snow gone.
harsh.

Saturday 12.
30 2/10; 31½, 32;   Ivy killed in many places. Furze is killed.
NE.   Few flakes of snow. Hollies in sunny aspects have lost their
Dark, still & cold.   leaves.

Sunday 13.
30 1/10½; 28½, 31;
NE.
Hard frost, dark, sun,
bright, frost.

Monday 14.
29 9/10½; 31½, 37;   Jasmine seems to be killed.
N.
Frost, dark, flight of
snow, dark & mild.

Tuesday 15.
29 8/10; 39; N.   Flocks of fieldfares.
Dark, & moist.

Wednesday 16.
29 6/10⅓; 38; N, W.   Men sow peat-ashes on their Grasses.
Dark, & still.   Winter-aconites make a gay show.

Thursday 17.
29 1/10; 20; W, N.   Sowed Celeri under a hand-glass.
Frost, sun, snow, frost.   Snow covers the ground.

Friday 18.
29 1/10; 20, 20; N.   Sharp wind.
Fierce frost, sun,   Cucumber-plants thrive.

clouds, bright.   Carried the apples, pears, & roots into the cellar.

Saturday 19.
28 9/10½; 15, 22; N,   Thick ice. Ice in warm chambers. Boys slide. Ground as hard as
SW, S.   iron. Snow on the ground.
Violent frost, sun,
bright & sharp.

Sunday 20.
28 8/10½; 19, 23; N.   Paths dusty.
Fierce frost, sun,
bright.

Monday 21.
28 7/10; 25; S, S.   Snow covers the ground.
Frost, grey, snow,
snow.

Tuesday 22.
28 6/10; 22, 23; E, N.   Deep snow.
Dark, & still, snow,
snow, dark.

Wednesday 23.
29 4/10; 22, 23; N,   Deep snow. Snow-scenes very beautiful.
NW.   Venus makes a most beautiful appearance.
Fierce frost, sun, sun,
bright.

Thursday 24.
29 5/10½; 35; W,
SW.
Frost, grey, thaw, swift
thaw, grey. Full moon.

Friday 25.
29 7/10½; 35, 45;   Crocus's bud for bloom.
SW, S.   Winter-aconites glow.
Small frost, sun, swift
thaw, wet.

Saturday 26.
29 8/10; 35, 45; SE, E;   Snow almost gone.
39.   Cucumber-plants thrive.
Grey & moist, dark &
harsh.

Sunday 27.
29 8/10½; 28, 31; E.   Snow covers the ground.

Hard frost, grey, &
sharp.

Monday 28.
29 8/10; 18½, 32; E.   Rain in February, 1 inc: 80 h:
Fierce frost, sun, sharp
wind, frost.

MARCH 1785

Tuesday 1.
29 9/10; 17½, 29;   Carted in six loads of hot dung for the cucumber-bed.
NE.   Cucumbers thrive.
Fierce frost, sun, sharp
wind, frost, bright.

Wednesday 2.
29 8/10¾; 28 37, 33;   Ground as hard as iron. Thick ice.
NE.
Frost, dark, sun, dark.

Thursday 3.
29 7/10½; 28, 31; N.   Sharp wind.
Dark, fog, rime, sun,
dark.

Friday 4.
29 7/10¼; 29, 32;   New worked-up, & mended the garden-lights broken by the hail
NE, E.   last summer.
Frost, dark, cutting   Thick ice.
wind, sun, sharp frost.

Saturday 5.
29 7/10; 31; E.
Frost, grey, sun, sharp
wind, sun, frost.

Sunday 6.
29 8/10; 30; NE.   Wheat looks sadly.
Frost, strong sun,
cutting wind, bright, &
sharp.

Monday 7.
29 6/10½; 30½; NE.   Crocus's bud for bloom.
Frost, dark, sun, sharp   Glazier's bill . . . £ 2: 5s 10d for garden-lights, & hand-glasses.
wind, dark.

Tuesday 8.
29 4/10½; 31; NE.
Frost, dark, sun,
pleasant, dark,
freezing.

Sowed radishes under the hot-bed screen.
Crocus's begin to blow.
Thick ice in water-tubs.

Wednesday 9.
29 2/10½; 3/10; 26,
30; NE.
Strong frost, dark &
sharp, & still.

Paths dry, & dusty.

On this day Mr Charles Etty sailed in the *Duke of Montrose* India-
man, Captain Gray, for Madeira, & Bombay.

Thursday 10.
29 6/10½; 35; NE.
Grey, sharp air, grey &
sharp.

Much beech-wood, & faggots carted home.
Roads dry.

Friday 11.
29 6/10; 21, 28; NE,
NW, W.
Fierce frost, sun,
cloudless, frost.

Saturday 12.
29 7/10½; 25; N.
Fierce frost, sun &
clouds, bright, frost.

Sunday 13.
29 8/10; 22; NE.
Fierce frost, sun &
clouds, sharp, bright,
frost.

Monday 14.
29 7/10; 21; NE.
Fierce frost, rime, sun,
sharp wind, dark.

Ice in Chambers.
Turned the dung for the hot-beds a second time.

Tuesday 15.
29 7/10; 37; N.
Grey, sharp, sun, small
showers.

Winter-aconites figure still.
Portugal laurels cast their leaves.

Wednesday 16.
29 9/10½; 41, 38; N.
Small rain, dark &
harsh.

Thaw. Men begin to plow.
Cucumbers thrive.

Thursday 17.
30 ½/10; 35; N.
Small frost, dark &
still.

Made the four-light bearing cucumber-bed with five dung-carts,
& ½ of dung.
Cucumber-plants thrive, & shew rudiments of fruit.

Friday 18.
30; 41; N.
Dark, still, & mild.

Crocus's blow. Bees gather on the crocus's.
Many Hepatica's killed: some in bloom.

Saturday 19.
29 9/10; 37, 51; NW,
N.
Grey & mild, spring
like.

Sowed a bed of spinage: the winter-spinage killed.
Tulips, & crown-imperials & hyacinths sprout. Portugal laurels
cast their leaves, & are much injured.
Planted eight larches in Baker's hill.
Cucumbers thrive. Insects frisk in the air.
Ice still in water-tubs.
Men plough: the frost pretty much out of the ground, wch is
mellow.

Sunday 20.
29 9/10; 39, 55; N, E,
S.
Grey, dark, still, &
mild.

Delicate spring weather.

Monday 21.
40, 50; W, NE.
Dark & mild, dark.

Mr Charles Etty sailed from the mother bank, near the Isle of
Wight, where they stopped to take in passengers.

Tuesday 22.
29 8/10¼; 31; NE.
Flight of snow, dark &
harsh, sun, sharp.

Wheat-fields look naked like fallows. The surface of the ground
is all dust.

Wednesday 23.
29 9/10; 25; NE.
Fierce frost, sun, flights
of snow, bright.

Thick ice. Colds & coughs frequent.
The garden-quarters, & borders all dusty.

Thursday 24.
29 7/10; 23; W.
Fierce frost, flights of
snow, dark & harsh.

Thick ice.
Earthed the bearing cucumber-bed. The cucumber-plants in the
pots large, & have fruit in bloom.

Friday 25.
29 8/10½; 32; NE.
Dark & harsh, dark.

Shoveled the alleys, & threw the mould on the borders, &
quarters. Ground all dust.

Saturday 26.
29 8/10; 32; N, W.

Turn'd-out the cucumber-plants into the hills of the bearing-bed.

Grey, sun, pleasant.

The plants are strong.
Sowed the great mead with ashes.

Sunday 27.
29 4/10; 34; W, N.
Rain, rain, snow, snow.

Soft rain.

Monday 28.
29 4/10½; 20; N; 30.
Fierce frost, sun, sharp
air, bright.

Thick ice: snow covers the ground. Long icicles.

Tuesday 29.
29 5/10; 22; N.
Fierce frost, sun, &
clouds, sharp.

Thick ice. Snow covers the Hill. Flight of snow.
Cucumber-plants blow, & look well.

My niece Clement was brought to bed of a boy. This child makes
my 42 nephew, & niece now living.

Wednesday 30.
29 4/10; 22; N, NW,
W.
Fierce frost, sun, &
clouds.

Thick ice: White frost.
Winter-aconites out of bloom: snow drops make still a fine†
Violets, & coltsfoot blow.

Thursday 31.
29 2/10½; 34½; N,
W, N.
Frost, ice, sun, grey,
dark & still.

Cucumbers thrive, & show fruit. Sowed cucumber-seed.
Sowed a bed of onions with radishes, & lettuce.

Rain in March . . . 0 inc: 30 h:

APRIL 1785

Friday 1.
29 ½/10; 29½, 42;
W, N, NE.
Hard frost, sun, dark,
sleet, snow, snow.

Snow covers the ground. Snow hangs in the trees, & makes a
perfect winter scene!

Saturday 2.
29 3/10; 21; N, N.
Fierce frost, bright sun,
snow showers, vast
clouds.

Thick ice. Snow deep on the ground.
Freezing all day. Snow melted in the sun.
Crocus's somewhat injured by the frosts.

Sunday 3.
29 7/10; 25; N, NW.

Thick ice. Snow covers the hill. Snow on roofs.

---

†Word missing.

Hard frost, sun & vast
clouds, snow-showers,
frost.

Monday 4.
29 8/10¼; 26; N, W;   Butter-fly.
17.
Hard frost, sun,
pleasant, grey.

Tuesday 5.
29 9/10½; 33, 49, 46;   Ring-dove coos: thrush sings.
N, SE.   Crocus's glow.
White frost, sun,   Sowed a large bed of carrots, with lettuce.
pleasant, dark & mild.   Cucumbers blow: one fruit seems to be set.
                              Bees gather on the Crocus's. Flies come-out.
                              Nightingale heard near Priory.

Wednesday 6.
29 9/10; 36; SE, NE.   Sowed parsnips with lettuce.
White frost, sun, sweet   All the winter-spinage is killed.
weather, cloudless.   Ice still in the water-tub.
                              Persian Iris's, dogs-toothed violets blow.

Thursday 7.
29 8/10½; 34; NE.   Crocus's make a beautiful show.
Frost, ice, fog, sun,   Hazels blow.
pleasant, dark & mild.   Brimstone, & brown butter-flies appear.

Friday 8.
29 9/10; 37; NE.   Cucumbers set, & swell.
Grey, sun, pleasant,   Apricot blows. Peach blows.
dark & still.   Many lettuces under fruit-wall have stood the winter: they were
                              covered with straw.
                              Men plant hops; & dress hop-grounds.
                              The bloom of the wall-fruit seems to be killed in the bud.

Saturday 9.
30 ½/10; NE, N.   Ground very dusty.
Grey, hot sun, wind
sharp, cloudless, red
even:

Sunday 10.
30 1/10¾; 37; N, S.
Fog, sun, cloudless,
sweet afternoon.

Monday 11.
30 1/10½; 37; S, S.   Farmers wish much for rain.
White frost, sun,   Ground dry & dusty.
cloudless, red evening.

Tuesday 12.
30; 35; SW, W.
Frost, sun, hot &
summer-like.

Wheat improves a little.
Halo round the sun.
Lined the cucumber-bed.
Swallow seen at Petersfield.
Swallow at Selborne.

Wednesday 13.
29 8/10¼; 42, 61; N,
NW.
Sun, sun & clouds.
❦ *Ficaria verna*.

Rain much wanted.

Thursday 14.
29 9/10; N, SW.
Wh: frost, sun, hot sun,
flisky clouds.

Vast halo round the sun.
Wheat mends.

Friday 15.
29 9/10; 39; N, SW.
Wh: frost, sun,
cloudless, hot sun,
muddy sky.

Goose-berries, & honey-suckles begin to bud, & look green.
Pronged the asparagus beds. Several honey-suckles seem to be
killed. My fine jasmine is dead.
The smallest willow-wren, the chif-chaf, is heard. In mild
seasons we used to remark them about the 20ᵗʰ of March.
Timothy the tortoise roused himself from his winter-slumbers &
came forth. He was hidden in the laurel-hedge under the wall-
nut tree, among the dead leaves.

Saturday 16.
29 8/10¼; 41; E, SW.
Sun, hot sun, summer,
red even:

Made the great annual bed for the 3 light frame.
Shell-snail comes-out.
Nightingale sings in my out-let.
Cut the first cucumber.

Sunday 17.
29 6/10; 41; E, S.
Wh: frost, hot sun,
cloudless, sweet even:

Several swallows. Hyacinths, frittillarias, blow.
Rain much wanted.

Monday 18.
29 4/10½; SE.
Dark & warm, sun,
dark, rain.

ALTON
A few drops.
Good shower.
The large shivering willow-wren.
The Cuckow is heard this day.

Tuesday 19.
SW, W.
Sun & clouds, flying
showers, hot & dusty.

S: LAMBETH

Wednesday 20.
30; 31; W.
Sun, & white frost,
clouds, harsh.

Thursday 21.
29 8/10½; 41, 45;
NW.
Cloudy, warm.

My brother Tho: planted his potatoes.
He sowed purple broccoli.

Friday 22.
29 8/10; 49; NW.
Cloudy & still.

Saturday 23.
29 8/10; 50; N.
Clouds & sun.

A little shower.

Sunday 24.
30; 42; N.
Wet mist, sun.

Wall-cherries, & plums blow. Black thorn in bloom.
My brother cut four cucumbers. His plants, & Benjamin's are
strong, & in good order.

Monday 25.
30 1/10; 36; N.
Bright, white dew, hot
& still.

Radishes dry, & hot.
Curran-bloom very great: cherries blow well.

Tuesday 26.
30 1/10½; 39; NE.
Bright, still, hot sun.

Regulus non cristatus medius, laughing wren, sings.
My brother Tho⁸ made melon-bed.
Red-start sings.

Wednesday 27.
30 2/10; 40; E.
White frost, hot sun,
cold wind.

Quickset-hedges look green. Roads are choaked with dust.
Horse-chestnuts shoot. Apricots swell.
Swallows frequent houses: some sit & dress themselves on trees,
as if wet, & dirty.
Vines shoot. Cut 2 brace of cucumbers.

Thursday 28.
30 2/10½; 35; E.
Strong frost, hot sun,
cold wind.

Spring-flowers of all sorts are hurried by the sun.
Cut five cucumbers.

Friday 29.
30 1/10½; 40; W, N.
Hot sun, still.

Saturday 30.
29 9/10½; 41; NE.
Overcast, misty rain.

Furze in bloom.
Rain in April . . 0 inc: 17 h:

MAY 1785

Sunday 1.
29 9/10½; 45; NE.
Sun, strong wind.

The dust on roads insufferable!
Saw one Swift. Two house-
martins in Fleetstreet.

Monday 2.
29 9/10½; 46; W.
Dark & still.

Standard-cherry blows.

Tuesday 3.
29 9/10½; 49; NW.
Bright & still.

Blanchard, & Miss
Simonet ascended.

Wednesday 4.
29 8/10; 51; W.
Bright & hot.

Thursday 5.
29 7/10½; 52, 66;
NW.
Fair, & hot.

Forward apples
in bloom.

Friday 6.
29 7/10½; W.
Bright, still & hot.

*Woodruff growing by the Bostal.
18 May.*

Saturday 7.
29 7/10; 50, 67; NW.
Bright, still, & hot.

Horse-chestnut in full leaf.
Pastures yellow with dandelions.
Meadow foxtail-grass, *alopecurus pratensis*, in bloom.

There is great want of rain in France as well as in England.

Sunday 8.
29 8/10; 52, 68; W,
NW.
Bright, & hot.

A cuckow haunts my brother's fields, so that probably there will
be a young cuckow hathed in the quickset-hedge.

Millions of *Empedes* or *tipulae* come forth at the close of day, &
swarm to such a degree as to fill the air. At this juncture they sport
& copulate: as it grows more dark, they retire. All day they hide in
the hedges. As they rise in a cloud they appear like smoke. I do not
ever remember to have seen such swarms except in the fens of the
Island of Ely. They appear most over grass-grounds.

Monday 9.
29 8/10½; 50; E.
Bright, & hot.

The grass in my Brother's fields burns, & does not look so well as it did when I came.

Tuesday 10.
29 9/10; 57; E.
White dew, bright,
strong cold wind.

Wednesday 11.
29 9/10; 48; E.
Bright, strong cold
wind.

Severe drying exhausting drought.
Cloudless days. The country all dust.
Timothy the tortoise weights 6 pd: 14¾ oun: He spoils the lettuce under the fruit-wall: but will not touch the Dutch, while he can get at any coss.

Thursday 12.
30 ½/10; 49; E.
Bright, warm, &
cloudless, brisk air.

Dragon-flies come forth out of their aurelia-state.
Great bloom of apples round S: Lambeth.

Friday 13.
NE.
Cold dew, mist, sultry,
hot sun.

ALTON
The country strangely burnt-up.
Fern-owl chatters.

Saturday 14.
29 9/10½; 67; NW.
Cold dew, cloudless,
hot sun, yellow even:

SELBORNE
My fields have more grass than my brother's at S. Lambeth, which burn. My S^t foin looks well, & is grown. Ponds in bottoms are dry.
Our down burnt brown.
A fine nightingale in my fields.

Sunday 15.
29 7/10; 67; N, NW.
Sun & clouds, cool
gale, sun, & clouds,
yellow.

Little apple, & pear-bloom: little wall-fruit.
My cucumbers bear well.

Monday 15 [16].¶
29 5/10½; 62; W.
Brisk gale, dark &
louring.

Fly-catcher. Fly-catcher appears: the latest bird of passage.

Tuesday 16 [17].
29 2/10; 57; W.
Strong gale, clouds,
sprinkling, dark,
sprinkling, cold wind,

Rain about London.

[84]

short shower, gale all
night.

Wednesday 17
[18].
29 5/10; 52; NW, SW.
Sun, & gale, sun,
clouds to the S.

Dust not laid.
Planted out China-asters in the basons.

Thursday 18 [19].
29 4/10; 54, 57; SW,
SW.
Soft showers, showers,
showers, dark & mild.

My wall-nut trees seem much injured by the frost. The laurels
shoot at the bottom of the boughs. Sycamores are injured.
Thunder, & more rain to the N:W:
Snails & worms come-out.
Scarce any rain since March 27: which was a wet day.

Chafers swarm about Oakhanger, & on the chalky soils, but not
with us on the clays.
    Rain all day at Fyfield near Andover.

Planted out some white cucumbers under hand-glasses. Planted
some green cucumber-plants, to fill the void spaces in the early
frames.

Friday 19 [20].
29 5/10; 57; W, NW;
20, 10.
Dark, sun, showers,
sweet even:

Pricked-out celeri. Planted some red cabbages from S: Lambeth.
Pricked-out China-asters upon a fresh bed.

Saturday 21.
29 6/10; 49; NW.
Much white frost, ice,
sun, dark, shower, sun,
showers about, cool air.

The kidney-beans are cut-down.
Potted several balsoms, a fine sort saved last year.
White-thorn blows.

Sunday 22.
29 8/10; SW, S
White frost, sun, cool
even.

Cut five brace of fine Cucumbers.
Hops are strong, & healthy.
Field-crickets cry round the forest.

Monday 23.
29 8/10; 53; S, SE.
White frost, sun, sweet
even:

Peonies blow.
Halo round the Sun.
Some chafers flie.
About nine brace of swifts as usual.
Swallows build. Fly-catcher builds in the vine.

Tuesday 24.
29 7/10; 64; SE, S.
Gray: no dew, sun,

Orange lilies blow.
Cut 5 brace of cucumbers.

grey, dark & soft. Full
moon.

Swifts copulate in the air, as they flie.

Wednesday 25.
29 8/10; 63; SW, W.
Shower, sun & clouds,
gale, bright.

Wood-ruff blows.
Many bank-martins over Oakhanger-ponds; & many swifts.

Tho' the stream has been quite dry for some time at Gracious street
quite down to Kimber's mead; yet, when it meets Well-head
stream at Dorton, it is little inferior to that. This shows that there
are several springs along at the foot of the Short Lithe, as well as a
constant one in Kimber's.

Thursday 26.
29 8/10; 65; SE, S.
Sun, clouds, fine even:

Rose-fly, a green scarab.
S! foin, fiery lily, & honey-suckles begin to blow.

Friday 27.
29 5/10½; 59; S, NW;
10.
Shower, dark, shower,
sun & clouds, show of
rain to the W: red.

Saturday 28.
29 3/10½; 59; W; 3.
Shower, blowing,
shower, sun & strong
gales.

Planted some basons of green early cucumbers from S: Lambeth
under the melon-screen.

Sunday 29.
29 4/10; 55; SW.
Grey, sun, vast clouds,
showers.

Thunder: heavy shower, & hail at Alton.
Many showers about.

The insects, known by the name of *Coccus vitis viniferae,*¶ annoy
the vine near the scullery again, & multiply under the loose bark,
where they stick to the wood, throwing out a cotton-like web,
among which they have laid innumerable eggs. Thomas has been
employed in killing them for many hours. Where they abound they
spoil the vines. I have observed the mischievous effects of these
animals for about four years on this vine: before which I never saw
any of the kind. The males, it seems, are small flying insects: but
the females stick motionless to the boughs, & look like large flat
wood-lice.

As I have always supposed that the *coccus vitis viniferae* was an
insect that belonged to the warmer parts of Europe, & not to the
island; I was surprised to find it on one of my vines in such
abundance, & especially after such a severe winter, which one
would have thought must have destroyed it. Unless I am assured

by enquiry that it does belong to England, I shall be much inclined to think that it came from Gibraltar among the many boxes and packages that I formerly received from thence: & especially as the vine infested grows under my study window, where I used to keep my specimens. True it is that I have received nothing from thence for above 12 years: but as insects, we know, are conveyed from one country to an other in a wonderful manner; & as this insect from it's sluggish nature can extend it's depredations but slowly, it may possibly have escaped our notice 'till lately, tho' brought long ago.

My Bro.^r John, in his excellent *Nat: History of Gibraltar*, which I have by me in M:S: gives the following account of the *Coccus vitis viniferae*.

"In the Year 1770 a vine, which grew on the E: side of my house, & which had produced the finest crops of grapes for years past, was suddenly overspread on all the woody branches with large lumps of a white fibrous substance, resembling spiders webs, or rather raw cotton. It was of a very clammy quality, sticking fast to every thing that touched it, & capable of being spun into long threads. At first I suspected it to be the produce to spiders, but could find none. Nothing was to be seen connected with it but many brown, oval, husky shells which by no means looked like animals: but rather resembled bits of the dry bark of the vine. The tree had a plentiful crop of grapes set, when this pest appeared upon it: but they were manifestly injured by this foul incumbrance. It remained all the summer, still increasing, & loaded the woody & bearing branches to a vast degree. I often pulled off great quantities by hand-fulls; but it was so slimy & tenacious, that it could by no method be cleared. The grapes never filled to their usual perfection, but turned watery, & vapid."

"Upon perusing the works afterwards of M: de Reaumur, I found this matter perfectly described, & accounted for. Those husky shells which I had observed were no other than the female *Coccus*, from whose sides this cotton-like substance exsudes, & serves as a covering, & security for their eggs."

Those boughs of my vine that have been infested with the *Coccus*, turn black in the autumn, & seem covered as it were with coal-dust. On this substance the flies swarm, & seem to feed eagerly. The shoots & leaves wither, nor does the fruit ever ripen. The ants resort much to the *Cocci* but do not seem to destroy them, as I could wish.

I am sorry to find that the insects on my vine were not suppressed by the severity of last winter: if that could not check them, we must not expect any assistance from cold.*

*Mr Lightfoot¶ has since informed me, that some years ago he observed the *coccus vitis* &c: infesting a vine in an extraordinary manner in the garden of M^r Le Coq at the town of Weymouth.

Monday 30.
29 6/10; 52; N; 17.
Grey, cold, sun &
clouds, cold air.

Tuesday 31.
29 6/10; 51½; W.
Grey & cold, dark
clouds, cold wind,
sprinkling.

Thomas persists in picking the *cocci* off the vine, & has destroyed hundreds.
Rain in May . . . 0 inc: 60 h:

JUNE 1785

Wednesday 1.
29 5/10; 60; W.
Clouds with cold wind.

The white cucumbers under hand-glasses thrive, & show fruit.
Columbines make a fine show: this is the third year of their blowing.

Thursday 2.
29 6/10½; 56½; SW.
Sprinkling, showers
about, sweet even:

Abram Loe came.
My well is very low.

Friday 3.
29 6/10; 64; N, SW.
Sprinkling, bright,
sweet even:

Saint-foin fly appears.
Fiery lilies glow.
Flesh-flies are troublesome.

Saturday 4.
29 4/10; 57; S, S.
White dew, hot sun,
soft rain, showers.

Several halos, & mock-suns this morning.
Flisky clouds about.
Wheat looks black, & gross.
Crickets sing much on the hearth this evening: they feel the influence of moist air, & sing against rain.
As the great wall-nut-tree has no foliage this year, we have hung the meat-safe on Miss White's Sycomore,¶ which she planted a nut; where it will be much in the air, & be well sheltered from the sun by leaves.

Sunday 5.
29 4/10; SW; 48.
Dark & moist, rain,
rain.

Fine rain in the night.
Dame's violets blow, & are very double.

Monday 6.
29 7/10¾; 57; S; 39.
Grey, sun, pleasant.

Fine showers in the night without wind. The ground is well-moistened. This is the first good rain that we have had all this spring. Growing weather.

Planted cabbages, & some annuals, & pricked-out more Celeri.

Tuesday 7.
29 4/10½; 59; S.
Showers, fog, dark &
moist, showers, warm
fog.

Cherries against walls begin to turn red.

Wednesday 8.
29 7/10; 60; SW, S;
27.
Showers, grey & mild,
rain, rain.

Planted the bank in the garden, & the opposite border with
China-asters all the whole length.
    More rain has fallen this week than in the last three months.

Thursday 9.
29 8/10½; 60½; 14.
Showers, dark, moist,
& warm, shower, sweet
even:

Showers in the night. My horses begin to lie out.
Field-pease look well, & begin to blow.
Planted-out all the annuals in general down Baker's hill, & in the
garden. The plants are strong, & vigorous, & the season very
favourable; the earth is well moistened, & the weather warm,
still, shady, & dripping.

Friday 10.
30¼; 61, 71; W.
Wh: dew, sun,
summer, sweet even:
dew.

The late severe winter, & spring seem to have destroyed most of
the black snails.
Began to dress, & tack the vines.

Saturday 11.
30, 29 9/10; 64; S,
SW.
Vast dew, fog on
hanger, cloudless, sweet
even:

The nightingale continues to sing in my outlet.
My potatoes do but just sprout above ground.
Sweet Williams blow.
Fraxinella blows.
While the hen fly-catcher sits on her eggs, the cock feeds her with
great assiduity, even on 'till past nine in the evening.

Sunday 12.
29 9/10½; 64; NE.
Vast dew, hot sun,
sultry, sweet even:

Wheat & pease look well: grass is very short.
Distant thunder-clouds to the E.

Monday 13.
30, 29 9/10½; 66, 75;
E.
Dew, bright, brisk air,
sweet even:

Established summer.
Corn-flag blows.
Watered the transplanted annuals, which suffer from the heat.
The yew-hedges at the vicarage half killed by the winter.

Tuesday 14.
29 7/10; 65; E.
Dew, sun, brisk gale,

Fly-catchers have young. Elder blows.
Kidney-beans promise well, & flourish.

sweet even:

Standard honey-suckles beautiful, & very sweet.
Bees swarm: men wash their sheep.
Clover in full bloom.

My tall hedges are much injured by the severity of last winter: many boughs are killed, & the foliage in general is thin.

Wednesday 15.
29 5/10; 66½; 73; SE, S, NW.
Grey, sun, blue mist, turbid, & red.

Roses begin to blow. Annuals want rain.
Watered the annuals.
Thistles bud for bloom.
Cut the tall hedge down Baker's hill, & the slope hedge.

Thursday 16.
29 6/10½; 64; NW.
Sun, & vast clouds, strong gales, thunder, red even: cold.

Some wheat in ear.
Showers about. Young martins hatched.
Hops fall-off, & seem to want rain.

Friday 17.
29 8/10½; 59; N.
Sun & cloudy, strong gales, yellow even:

Field-pease look well.
Rain is much wanted.
Strong gales again all day.
Vines begin to blow a little.

Saturday 18.
29 9/10¾; 65; N.
Sun & clouds, dark & mild.

Turned-out the white cucumbers from under their hand-glasses.

Sunday 19.
30 ¼/10; N.
Bright, summer, sweet even:

Wheat comes into ear.
Annuals die for want of rain.

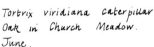
Tortrix viridiana caterpillar. Oak in Church Meadow. June.

Most of our oaks are naked of leaves, & even the Holt in general, having been ravaged by the caterpillars¶ of a small *phalaena*, which is of a pale, yellow colour. These Insects, tho' a feeble race, yet from their infinite numbers are of wonderful effect, being able to destroy the foliage of whole forests, & districts. At this season they leave their *aurelia*, & issue forth in their fly-state, swarming & covering the trees, & hedges. In a field at Greatham I saw a flight of Swifts busied in catching their prey near the Ground; & found they were hawking after these *phalaenae*. The *aurelia* of this moth is shining, & as black as jet; & lies wrapped-up in a leaf of the tree, which is rolled round it, & secured at the ends by a web, to prevent the maggot from falling out.

Monday 20.
30; 62; N.
Bright, grey & still, dark, soft even:

Men mow their clover, a very small crop.
In some parts the foliage of trees & hedges was much injured by swarms of chafers.

Tuesday 21.
30 ½/10; 64; NE.
Dark, soft rain, moist air, sun, sweet even:

Gathered the first cherries.

Wednesday 22.
30 ¼/10; 64; NE.
Sun, dark, & pleasant, sun, warm even:
Full moon.

Turbid sunset: the disk of the sun looked like three suns.

Thursday 23.
30 ½/10; 62; NE, E.
Sun, air, dark, cool, red even:

Fox-gloves blow.

Friday 24.
30; 62; NE.
Strong sun-shine with a gale, red even:

Netted the cherries.
Cherries well-flavoured.

Saturday 25.
29 9/10¾; 62; NE.
Sun, dark, cool air, red even:

Fallows dusty, & in mellow order. Young fawns in the Holt. My walnut-trees are almost naked, & half killed by the winter; while those at Rood are in full foliage, & shew fruit.

Mr Powlett of Rotherfield has no water for his cattle in the park, but what he fetches from Alton! He has a well for the house.*
    My well is low; but affords plenty of fine clear water. We draw great quantities for the garden. A constant spring runs into it.
    *Many years ago Mr Powlett's grandfather fetched water from Alton for all his cattles, deer & all, for three months together.

Sunday 26.
29 9/10; 70; NE, E.
Sun, cloudless, brisk
gale, red even:

Indian pinks, that stood the winter, blow.
Grass walks burn. Annuals die thro' heat.
Hops run their poles.
Young martins peep out of their nests.
Cuckow is heard.

Monday 27.
29 8/10; 64, 66; NE.
Sun, sultry, clouds,
sun, red even.

The Fly-catchers, five in number, leave their nest in the vine
over the parlor-window.
Stopped the vines, which are in full bloom.
Hemerocallis, day-lily blows. Late orange-lily, with dark leaves,
blows.
Chaffers fall dead from the hedges: they have served their
generation, & will be seen but little longer.

Tuesday 28.
29 6/10⅓; 64, 74;
NE, E.
Sun, hot sun, red even:

Distant heavy clouds to the N:E.
Clouds to the S. that look thunderous.
Annuals die from heat.
The white hand-glass cucumbers shew fruit.

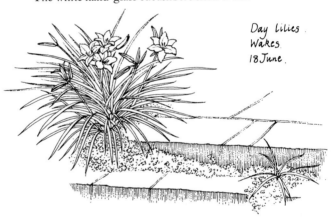

Day Lilies
Wakes
18 June.

Wednesday 29.
29 5/10; 65½; NE, E,
NE; 11.
Bright, fine shower, hot
sun, soft & still.

Distant thunder. The storm arose in the S: & parted; so that we
had only the skirts.
Distant thunder. Showers about.
Upland grass carried by some men.
When thunder arises in the S: we hardly ever receive the storm
over us, because the clouds part to the right, & left before they
reach us, influenced, I suppose, by the hills that lie to that
quarter.
Several nests of house-martins are flown this morning.

Thursday 30.
29 6/10; 67, 73; NE.

Mossed the white cucumber-bed.

Sun, hot sun, sultry,
sweet even:

Showers on all sides, with thunder.
Grass-walks burn brown.
Rain in June .. 1 inch 39 h:
The walnut-trees throw-out shoots two or three feet below the
extremities of the boughs: all above is dead.

JULY 1785

Friday 1.
29 4/10; 65; E, S, W.
Cloudless, scorching
heat,* dark clouds with
gale, shower.

Timothy Turner cuts the Sᵗ foin on Baker's hill: this is the 18:
crop; & not a bad one, the severity of the drought considered.
Showers about.
Grapes swell, & are forward from the great heat. Kidney-beans
thrive, & run-up their sticks.
Wheat blows finely.
My balsams are fine tall plants, & well variegated, except a few,
which blow white.

Saturday 2.
29 3/10, 5/10; 66; W.
Wind & clouds, strong
gales, gales.

*The heat at noon yesterday was so great that it scorched the white
cucumbers under the hand-glasses, & injured them much.
Annuals die with the heat.
Took away the moss from the white cucumbers, because it seemed
to scald them.
White cucumbers much injured by the heat.

Sunday 3.
29 7/10; 67½; W.
Sun, brisk gales, sun.

The boys brought me a wasps nest full of maggots.
Lime-trees blow, & shew their fine golden tassels.
No wood-strawberries.

Monday 4.
29 6/10; 67; W, SW.
Sun, dark & heavy,
bright gleam.

Gathered several pounds of cherries to preserve: they are very
fine.
Annuals die for want of moisture.
Began to cut the meadow-grass: it is very scanty, not half a crop.

Tuesday 5.
29 7/10; 64; W, NW;
11.
Shower, sun, & gale,
clouds.

Young *cocci* abound again on the vines.
Cocked part of the hay.
Men sow turnips; but the seeds lie in the ground without
vegetating. Those that sprout are soon eaten by the fly.
Hops look well, & throw-out side-shoots; & some plants show
rudiments of bloom.

Wednesday 6.
29 7/10; 62½; NE, E.
Sun, grey, dark &

Ground burnt to a powder.
Hay makes slowly.

chilly.

Some young Swifts seem to be out: they settle on, & cling to the walls of houses, & seem to be at a loss where to go: are perhaps looking for their nest.

Thursday 7.
29 8/10½; 67; N, NE; 8.
Blue mist, grey, sun, showers,* fine afternoon, cloudy.

Cocci abound: they are very small, just hatched from the egg, & occasion much trouble in picking off & killing.

*In some places the showers were heavy.

Friday 8.
29 9/10; 70; N, E, N.
Grey, dark, & still, dark & hot.

Ricked my Hay, which makes but a very small cob. All the produce of the great mead was carryed at two loads: & all that grew on the slip was brought up by the woman & boy at their backs. My quantity this year seems to be about one third of a good crop. In a plentiful year I get about seven good Jobbs.

Saturday 9.
29 8/10; 75¾; NW, W.
Bright, hot sun, clouds, & gale, red even:

Thatched the rick. Watered many things in the garden, which is much burnt.
Kidney-beans flourish, & do not give-out yet.
Ants swarm on the stairs: their male-flies leave them, & fill the windows: their females do not yet appear.
Swifts seem to increase in number.
Grapes swell. A good shower would bring some Rasp-berries.
Boys bring a second wasps-nest. Boys bring a third wasps nest.
Everlasting pea, & white lilies blow.
The China-pinks, that stood the winter, make a fine appearance: some are double.

Sunday 10.
29 7/10; 70; NE, E.
Grey, sun, & clouds, soft even:

My cherries are excellent.
Preserved cherries, & currans; & made curran-jelly.
Large clouds about.
Rasps begin to turn. Not one mess of wood-straw-berries brought this Year.

The spring in Kimber's mead is dry; & also that in Conduit-wood, from whence in old times the Priory was supplyed with water by means of leaden pipes. The pond on the common is also empty. All the while Well-head is not much abated, nor the spring at the bottom of the church-litten closes, where you pass over the foot-bridge to the Lithe.

Monday 11.
29 6/10½; 65; S, SW.
Grey, sun, hot, bright & cool.

My well is very low. We water much every day.
The down is so burnt, that it looks dismally.
Cleared the cherry-trees, & took-in the nets.
Saved seeds of columbines, & polyanths: the sorts are fine.

Tuesday 12.
29 5/10½; 62; N, SE.
Bright, hot sun, red
even:

BRAMSHOT-PLACE
My vines are nicely trimmed: not a superfluous shoot left.
Great honey-dew.
Several young swallows are out.
The pair of Fly-catchers in the vine are preparing for a second
brood, & have got one egg. This is the first instance that I
remember of their breeding twice.
M[r] Richardson's garden was not so much burnt-up as might be
expected. There was plenty of pease, & kidney-beans; & much
fruit, such as currans, goose berries, & melons, & cherries.

Wednesday 13.
E.
Bright, cloudless, gale.

Thursday 14.
SE, E; 9.
Shower, sultry, hot
night, clouds.

The wheat at Bramshot looks well; but the spring-crops are
injured by the drought.
Turnips come-up pretty well.
Vast shower in the evening towards Odiham.
Wheat reaped near Godalming.

Friday 15.
29 5/10; 64; S, W,
NW; 9.
Shower, clouds,
showers, cool.

SELBORNE
Boys brought the fourth wasp's-nest.
My garden abounds with currans, & goose-berries.
The grass of my walks seems to be killed.
Wheat on the strong lands looks finely. The crop in the Ewel
looked so thin, as if there would be nothing all the spring: but
now there is fine even wheat.

Fine rain at London.

Saturday 16.
29 6/10; 64; S, W.
Sun, dark & louring,
cool gale.

Trenched-out five long rows of Celeri.
Made Raspberry jam.
Began to hack pease.
Grapes swell, & are very forward.
The China-pinks that stood the winter blow beautifully. Scarlet
martagons blossom.

Sunday 17.
29 6/10¼, 6/10; 69;
W; 40.
Grey, sun, showers,
showers, showers.

Honey-dew.
Fine refreshing rains. Vivid rain-bow.

Newton great pond is almost dry: only two or three dirty puddles
remain, which afford miserable water for the village.
    My nephew Edm[d] White of Newton turns his sheep into five
acres of barley, which is spoiled by the drought. M[r] Pink of
Faringdon does the same by a field of oats.

Newton Valence Pond.

Monday 18.
29 4/10¾; 65, 69; W, S.
Sprinklings & hot gleams, sprinkling, rain, fog.

Savoys & artichokes over-run with aphides.
Hops thrive.
Few swifts are seen.
The Fly-catcher in the vine sits on her eggs, & the cock feeds her. She has four eggs.

Tuesday 19.
29 2/10; 65; SW; 62, 21.
Shower, hot sun, thunder-showers, showers.

Planted out more endive.
Loud thunder, & a heavy storm to the N:W.
6 swifts.

Wednesday 20.
29 2/10; 60; SW.

Much distant thunder.

Sun, showers, showers.

One pair of swifts.
Great part of men's hay lying in a bad state.

Thursday 21.
29; 62; 59, 34.
Heavy showers, showers, showers.

Planted-out savoys, cabbages, & borecole.
Much distant thunder.
Seven or eight swifts. Ponds fill.
Ferruginous foxglove blows.

Friday 22.
29 5/10; 59; NW, E, SW; 31.
Sun, showers, showers.
Full moon.

Some swifts.
Thunder about.
Boys bring the fifth wasp's nest.
Made black curran-jelly, & rasp: jam.

Saturday 23.
29 7/10½; W.
Sun & clouds, great dew.

Some swifts.
Men rick their damaged hay.
Some water in the pond on the down.
Mr Edmd White's tank has four feet of water.

Sunday 24.
29 8/10; 69; SW.
Wet fog, sun, small showers, mild & still.

My Nep: Edmd White sends me some fine wall-nuts for pickling: The trees at Newton were not at all touched by the severity of last winter; while mine were so damaged that all the bearing twigs were destroyed. My wall-nut trees have this summer pushed out shoots thro' the old bark, several feet from the extremities of the boughs.

Monday 25.
29 7/10; 69; SW.
Grey, sun, sun & clouds, red even: vast dew.

Boys bring in the sixth & seventh wasps nest.
Soft growing weather.
Sowed turnip-radishes, & Coss-lettuces.
While the hen fly-catcher sits, the cock feeds her all day long: he also pays attention to the former brood, which he feeds at times.

Tuesday 26.
29 4/10; 67, 72; SE.
Hot night, sun, sultry,
dark, sprinkling, dew,
gleams.

Thunder, & rain about.
Young martins begin to congregate.
Several swifts. By frequent picking we have much reduced the
Cocci on the vines.

Vast storm of thunder, & rain at Thursley, which damaged the
crops. Thursley is in Surrey, to the NE: of us.

Wednesday 27.
29 3/10½; 67; SW;
18.
Hot night, sun, sultry,
clouds, yellow even:

Thunder & rain in the night.
Grass grows at a great rate. Annuals & cucumbers thrive.
Gathered a few scarlet-kidney-beans. Many swifts.

Thursday 28.
29 5 10½; 62½, 65;
SW.
Sun, hot, showers, fine
even:

Pea-harvest is become general.
Showers about. My few apricots ripen.
The fly-catchers hatch their second brood.

Friday 29.
29 4/10¾; 64; SW;
41, 37.
Rain, rain, sun &
clouds, rain.

Cucumbers bear.
Distant lightening.

Saturday 30.
29 6/10; 64; SW.
Sun, hot sun, red even:

The wheat is not at all lodged.
Heavy clouds in the horizon.
Few swifts.
Boys bring the 8th & 9th wasps nest.
Pyramidal campanula blows.

Sunday 31.
29 6/10; 60; W.
Sun, sun & clouds,
sweet even:

Hops begin to form on their poles: but the gardens in general fall
off, & look lousy, since the rains.
Boys bring the 10th wasp's nest.
Rain in July . . . 3 in: 80 h.

AUGUST 1785

Monday 1.
29 6/10; 61; NW, NE,
S.
Great dew, bright, fine
even:

MEON-STOKE
The fly-catchers hover over their young, to preserve them from
the heat of the sun. All the way as we drove along, we saw wheat
harvest beginning. The ponds at Privet, where they have been
much distressed for water, are nearly full.

Sowed a crop of winter spinage, & some lettuces to stand the
winter under the fruit-wall. This has proved a fine crop.

Tuesday 2.
NE.
Heavy dew, grey, dark
& blowing.

The down-wheat about Meon-stoke a poor crop.
Many turnips fail.

Wednesday 3.
NE; Selb: 120.
Rain, rain, rain, rain.

Great tempest of thunder & lightening for many hours in the
night with heavy rains, & strong gusts of wind.
Harvest-bugs are troublesome.
Fly-catchers in Mr Mulso's garden, that seem to have a nest of
Young.
Tremella nostock abounds in Mr Mulso's grass-walks.

Thursday 4.
SE; 21.
Grey, sun, sultry, dark
& louring, shower.

Friday 5.
S.
Louring, gales, sun &
clouds, warm, rain,
rain.

Saturday 6.
29 5/10; 65; SW; 34,
9. Dark, hot gleams,
heavy showers, vivid
rain-bow.

SELBORNE
My young fly-catchers fledge.
Boys bring the 13th wasp's nest.

Swift seen at Selborne: this proved to be the last.

Sunday 7.
29 5/10½; 62; NW,
SW.
Grey, gleams, heavy
shower, vast clouds
about.

Hops seem to improve since the late great rains.
Little wheat is cut round Selborne.
Wasps begin on the goose-berries.
My Nephew Edmd: White's tank at Newton runs over.
Boys bring the 14th wasps nest.
Wheat begins to grow under hedges.
Agaricus pratensis, Champignion, comes up in the fairey-ring on
my grass-plot.

Monday 8.
29 3/10¼; 61½; SW,
W.
Shower, sun & clouds,
dark & moist.

Pease lie in a sad state, & shatter-out.
Some pease are housed.
Gleaning begins: wheat is heavy.

Tuesday 9.
29 5/10; 62; W, NW;
19.

Wheat-harvest becomes general.
Fly-catchers, second brood, forsake their nest.

Grey, dark, shower,   Mushrooms come-in.
fine gleams.

Wednesday 10.
29 7/10; 57; NW, W.   Endives, & celeri thrive.
Dark, still & mild.   Men bind their wheat as fast as they reap it.
                                 Wheat is heavy. Men house pease.
                                 Hops look black.

Thursday 11.
29 6/10; 59; W, S.   Wasps encrease.
No dew, sun, mild, &   Fine harvest weather.
still, odd clouds in
streaks.

Friday 12.
29 2/10; 60½; S, SW.   Boys bring the 15th wasps nest.
Grey, sun, showers &   Men house wheat.
wind, heavy clouds.   Boys bring the 16th wasps nest.
                                 Black-caps¶ eat the berries of the honey-suckle, now ripe.

Saturday 13.
29 2/10½; 59; W.   Boys bring the 17th wasps nest.
Dark, wet, & blowing.   Some wheat housed.
                                 Pheasant-cocks crow.

On the first of Aug:st about half hour after three in the afternoon the
people of Selborne were surprized by a shower of Aphides, which
fell in these parts. I was not at home; but those that were walking
the street at that juncture found themselves covered with these
insects, which settled also on the trees, & gardens, & blackened all
the vegetables where they alighted. My annuals were covered with
them; & some onions were quite coated over with them when I
returned home Aug: 6th. These armies, no doubt, were then in a
state of emigration, & shifting their quarters; & might come, as far
as we know, from the great hop-plantations of Kent or Sussex, the
wind being that day at E. They were observed at the same time at
Farnham, & all along the vale to Alton.
   On the conveyance of Insects from place to place, see Derham's
Physico-theology: p: 367.

Sunday 14.
29 4/10; 57½, 60; W,   The fallows about the neighbourhood are in fine order.
NW.   Boys bring in the 18th, & 19!th wasp's nest.
Cold, wet & blowing.

Monday 15.
29 6/10; 58½; W.   The harvest-scenes are very beautiful!
Sun, pleasant, chilly.   Farmer Spencer makes a wheat-rick. Wheat very fine & heavy.
                                 Sam, & Charles¶ come from Fyfield.

Tuesday 16.
29 4/10; SW.
Grey, sun, pleasant,
long shower.

My goose-berries are still very fine, but are much eaten by the dogs.¶
Boys bring the 20th wasp's nest.

Wednesday 17.
29 3/10½; 58, 60; W;
51.
Sun, & clouds, showers
about, showers, cold &
chill.

Few mushrooms to be found.
Sowed second crop of white turnip-radishes.
Abram Loe came the second time.

Thursday 18.
29 6/⅓; 56; NW.
Dark & cold, showers,
& gleams of sun.

Harvest much interrupted by the wet.
Rain-bows.
Colchicum, autumnal crocus, emerges, & blows.

Friday 19.
29 6/10; 61; NW, SW,
W.
Fog, sun & clouds,
pleasant, sprinkling.
Full moon.

Many house-martins have second broods newly hatched.
Gleaners get much wheat.
Sam & Charles leave us.

Saturday 20.
29 5/10; 58; NW; 19.
Grey, heavy clouds,
showers, vast clouds.

Men house, & rick wheat in cold, damp condition.

Sunday 21.
29 5/10½; 58; NW.
Dark, cold, & moist.

Hops improve.
Bad weather for the wheat, most of which is down.
Boys bring the 21 wasps nest.

Monday 22.
29 6/10⅓; 57, 59½;
NW, SW.
Dark, still, & warm,
red even: bright.

Men house much wheat.
Tyed up the first endive.
China-asters begin to open.
Turnip radishes.

Tuesday 23.
29 5/10½; 56½; NW.
White dew, sun, sweet
day, cloudy.

Grapes just begin to turn colour. Orleans plums ripen but have little flavour.
Martins, & swallows congregate by hundreds on the church, & tower. These birds never cluster in this manner, but on sunny days. They are chiefly the first broods, rejected by their dams, who are busyed with a second family.

Wednesday 24.
29 2/10½; 61; S, SW.
Grey, rain, rain, rain.

My crop of grapes is good.
Hops improve, & grow.

Thursday 25.
29 3/10½; 61; E, N;
29.
Sun, soft & sunny,
rain, rain.

Hop-picking begins in the great garden at Hartley.
Much wheat abroad in a bad state.
Roads very wet.
The dripping season has, this day, lasted six weeks: it has done some harm to the wheat, & retarded wheat-harvest; but has been of infinite service to the grass, & turnips, &c.

Friday 26.
29 7/10; 58; N; 19.
Sun, & air, sweet day,
red even:

Men house wheat.

Saturday 27.
29 8/10; 55; N, SW.
Sun & clouds, dark &
still, red even.

Much wheat housed.
Oats & barley are mown.

Sunday 28.
29 8/10; 55; S, SE.
Sun, dew, bright day,
fine even.

Boys bring the 22nd, 23rd & 24th wasps nest.
Many wasps at the plum-trees.

Monday 29.
29 5/10½; 57; S.
Shower, still & warm,
rain.

Several China-asters blow-out.
John Hale, & Farmer Spencer begin to pick hops.
Endive comes in.

Tuesday 30.
29 3/10½; 63, 65; S,
W.
Small showers all day,
red even:

The kings field is open to the down.
The hop-pickers have very uncomfortable weather.
No mushrooms to be found with us: the case was the same last year.

Wednesday 31.
29 4/10½; 64; W,
SW.
Sun & clouds, pleasant,
dull even.

Mich: daisies begin to open.
Planted out more endives. Tyed up many endives.
Many hops picked. Many wasps at my plums.
My well is very low: the water sometimes foul.
Rain in August . . . 3 inch 21 hund:

SEPTEMBER 1785

Thursday 1.
29 3/10½; 61; S, W;

Hop-picking much interrupted by heavy showers.

34.
Shower, rain, rain, sun,
pleasant.

Hops do not dry kindly.
Dogs eat the goose-berries when they became ripe; & now they
devour the plums as they fall: last year they tore the apricots off
the trees.

Friday 2.
29 4/10; 61, 62½;
SW.
Sun, showers, pleasant.

Plums fall very fast.
Many hops picked: they now dry well.

Saturday 3.
29 5/10; 60; SW.
Sun, heavy showers,
dark & moist.

Killed many wasps.
Distant thunder.
No mushrooms.

Sunday 4.
29 1/10; 60, 63; SW.
Shower, dark, sun &
clouds, rain.

Boys bring the 25th wasp's nest.
Strong gusts.

Monday 5.
29; 61; SW; 35.
Sun, grey & mild,
moist, heavy rain,
storm.

Destroyed numbers of wasps.
Plums fall much.

Tuesday 6.
28 8/10½, 29 3/10;
62½; SW; 93.
Storm, & rain, sudden
gusts, strong gales.

My grapes much retarded by the shady, wet weather. Peaches &
nectarines bad.

Stormy wind, which broke-down great part of my Orleans plum-
tree, & blew-down Molly White's horse-chestnut, & did vast
damage to the hop-gardens, which are torn, & shattered in a sad
manner! This storm was very extensive, being very violent at the
same time at Lyndon in Rutland. Much mischief was done at
London, & at Portsmouth, & in Kent, at Brighthelmstone also: &
in Devonshire.

Wednesday 7.
29 5/10; 62½; SW.
Sun & clouds, blowing,
fine & calm.

Wasps begin on the grapes. Killed many wasps.
Plums all blown down; all the few apples; & most of the pears.

Thursday 8.
29 5/10; 61; SE, E,
SE.
Hot & close, sun,
pleasant.

My crop of spinage is very fine, & not too thick.
Some leaves of the Virginia-creeper begin to turn red. Killed
many wasps.
Mr S: Barker came.
Planted a *Parnassia*,¶ which he brought out of Rutland in full
bloom, in a bog at the bottom of Sparrow's hanger.

Friday 9.
29 4/10; 60; SE, E,
SE.
Fog, sun, pleasant.

Tops of beeches begin to be tinged.
Killed many wasps. Wasps gnaw the grapes.
Mens second crops of clover cut, & spoiled by the rains. A bad prospect with respect to winter fodder! Farmer Spencer sows some wheat-stubbles with rye for spring-feed.

Saturday 10.
29 4/10; 62; SE.
Grey, sun, rain, rain,
soft, & moist, rain.

Gathered two bunches of grapes, but they were not ripe.
Killed many wasps.
Boys bring the 26.th wasp's nest.

Sunday 11.
29 4/10; 62; SW.
Heavy showers,
showers, gleams of sun,
rain.

Monday 12.
29 7/10; 60½; W; 54.
Showers, showers, sun,
pleasant.

Many broods of martins still in their nests: these are second broods.
Wasps much subdued.

Tuesday 13.
29 7/10; 65; S.
Wet, sun, warm, &
pleasant.

Killed a few wasps.
The leaves of the Virginia creeper begin to turn red.
The China-asters make a fine show.

Wednesday 14.
29 4/10½; 64, 65; SE,
S.
Sun, soft & pleasant,
sweet moonshine.

Few wasps.
Some oats housed.
Beautiful clouds.
Turned the horses into the great meadow: there is vast after-grass, more than when the meadow was mowed in the summer.

Thursday 15.
29 4/10½; 61½; W.
Rain, sun, soft, &
pleasant.

Oats housed. Wasps damage the grapes.
The dripping weather has lasted this day nine weeks, all thro' haying, & harvest: much hay is also spoiled of the second cutting; so that men, having lost both crops, will in many parts be very short of fodder, especially as turnips have missed in many places.

Friday 16.
29 4/10½; 62; SW.
Shower, louring, rain,
rain.

Oats carried. Sad harvest-weather.

Saturday 17.
29 6/10½; 60; W,

SW; 42.
Sun, hot gleams,
showers, moon-shine.

Sunday 18.
29 7/10; 62; SW.   A ring-ouzel shot on Hindhead.
Grey & mild, sun,
clouds, moonshine.
Full moon.

Monday 19.
29 7/10¼; 62; SW.   Fly-catchers seem to have withdrawn themselves for some time.
Grey & mild, gleams,   Some h: martins still in their nests.
& soft, dark.   Multitudes of martins this year.

Tuesday 20.
29 3/10½; 63; S; 115.   Much mown clover rots in the fields.
Vast rain in the night,   But few wasps.
grey, dark, & moist,   No mushrooms: plenty in Rutland.
rain.

Wednesday 21.
29 2/10; 63; S; 32.   Bro.ͬ Henry came.
Dark & hot, showers
about.

Thursday 22.
29 4/10; 61; S, SE.   Grapes good, but not delicate.
Rain, grey & hot, dark   Charles & Bessy White came.
& still, rain, rain.

Friday 23.
29 2/10½; S; 33.
Rain, wind, rain, rain.

Saturday 24.
61; SW; 36.   Some martins still in their nests.
Showers, sun, dry, &   Bro.ͬ Henry left us.
gale.

Sunday 25.
28 6/10; 60, 59; SW,   Violent current in the street.
W; 120.
Dark, rain, vast rain,
gale.

Monday 26.
29 6/10! 55; NW.   Few hirundines to be seen.
Grey, sun, pleasant, &   Men house some miserable barley.

cool.

Began to light fires in the parlor.

On Monday the 26th our flock of house-martins, many hundred in number, seemed to withdraw: & on that day also M[r] Barker saw vast numbers of Hirundines clustering on the great sand-rock just in the front of Waverly-house.

Tuesday 27.
29 8/10¾; 47½; NW.
White frost, sun,
pleasant, clouds, sharp.

Swallows; but few martins.
Men house barley in good order. Men turn hay.
My well, notwithstanding the rains is very low still, so that we let out all the rope to draw a bucket of water.

Wednesday 28.
29 9/10¾, 30; 49½,
53; N, SW.
Dew, sun, pleasant,
grey.

Men house barley: & hay cut many weeks since.
Several ring-ouzels on Nore hill.
Halo round the sun.
Many swallows, & some martins.
Farmer Tull mows mill-mead, a second crop, which it is expected will produce near 3 tuns on an acre. Men mow also clover, hoping to get some hay at last.

Thursday 29.
29 8/10½; 52; E.
White frost, sun,
pleasant, dark & still.

Tyed up more endive.
Men mow grass, & clover.

Timothy the tortoise spends all the summer in the quarters of the kitchen-garden among the asparagus, &c: but as soon as the first frosty mornings begin, he comes forth to the laurel-hedge, by the side of which he spends the day, & retires under it at night; 'till urged by the encreasing cold he buries himself in Nov[r] amidst the laurel-hedge.

Friday 30.
29 7/10½; 53; E.
Dark, still, & mild.

Will Tanner thinks he saw in the high wood marks where a wood-cock had been boring.
M[r] Barker, who rode this day to Rake, Rogate, & Furley-hill, saw much grass, & clover cut, & cutting. Some barley out.
Rain in Septem[r] . . 5 inch 94 hund:

OCTOBER 1785

Saturday 1.
29 8/10¼; N, NW.
Fog, cloudless, sweet
day, red even.

Ten hay-makers at work in Norton-mead.
Well-made clover in the N: field.

Sunday 2.
29 7/10; 49, 52; E,
SE.

No hirundines seen.

Dark & cool, grey &
blowing, misty.

Monday 3.
29 4/10; 51½; S, SW;
34.
Rain, rain, gleams,
starlight.

Several martins under the hanger.

Tuesday 4.
29 5/10; S, W, S.
Dark & mild, rain,
rain, rain.

Several martins.
Bro.ʳ Henry comes. *Aurora.*

Wednesday 5.
29 5/10½; 55; S; 76.
Grey, vast showers,
sun, starlight.

Grapes good.
Aurora.

Thursday 6.

29 5/10; 52½; S.
Sun, clouds, showers.

Several martings under
the hanger.
Gathered in the swans-
egg pears, a bushel:
more to be gathered.
Aurora.

Friday 7.
29 3/10; 53, 56; SW.
Dark & louring, rain,
rain, rain.

There are some few apples.
Much grass lies rotting in the meadows, & clover-fields.

Saturday 8.
29 2/10; 59; SW; 65.
Sun, small showers,
star-light.

Brother Henry, Bet, & Charles¶ left us.
Several swallows, & martins.
Finished turning the mould in the mead.
Received from M.ʳ Ed.ᵈ Woods 5 gallons, & 1 pint of French
brandy.

Sunday 9.
29 2/10; 56; S.
Dark & heavy, rain &
wind.

The beeches in the hanger are beautifully tinged.

Monday 10.
29 4/10; 54; SW, W;
32.
Sun, clouds, heavy
showers.

M.ʳ S: Barker left us.

Tuesday 11.
29 4/10; 52; S; 19.   Some swallows.

Sun, rain, rain.   Wet & blowing.
                                   The grass cut the last week in Sept.ʳ all lies rotting.

Wednesday 12.
29 2/10; 58; SW; 82,   Several showers.
3.   Several martins under the hanger.
Vast showers, sun &   Strong gales, with loud thunder, lightening, & hail!
clouds, rain.   My well begins to rise. It has been so low¶ all this autumn as not
                                   to afford water sufficient for the occasions of the family. Had it
                                   not been for the frequent rains, we should have been at a loss,
                                   when we wanted to wash or brew.

Thursday 13.   ALTON
55; SW; 72, 10.   Barley abroad at Faringdon.
Dark & windy.

Friday 14.   READING
Grey & mild.

Saturday 15.   OXFORD
Dark & mild.   Hay lies about in Berkshire, & Oxfordshire.

Sunday 16.
60; W.   Summer-like.
Sun, sweet day, low   Much gossamer about.
mist.

Monday 17.
N.   Timothy Turner finished the mowing of Baker's hill. Many
Deep fog. Full moon.   house-martins at Selborne.
                                   Red-wings appear.

Tuesday 18.
30 ½; NE.
Sun, cool air.

Wednesday 19.
30 ½; N.
Dark & still.

Thursday 20.   ALTON
30; N.   Much hay making all the way. Hay housing at Alton.
Dark & still.

Friday 21.   SELBORNE
30; N.   Timothy the tortoise lies in the laurel-hedge, but is not buried.
Dark, & still.   Some martins at the end of the brew-house.

Saturday 22.
30, 29 9/10; 45; SW.
Dark, & mild.

My well is risen six or seven Yards.

Sunday 23.
29 7/10; 50; E, SE, S.
Grey, grey & mild,
dark & louring.

The hay in Baker's hill smells well; but for want of turning is not half made.

Two young swallows seen at Fyfield.

Monday 24.
29 4/10; 50; SW.
Grey, sun, sweet noon,
dark & blowing, rain.

The water in the well rises.
Dug up my potatoes, a poor crop: many of them are rotten.

Tuesday 25.
29 3/10; 49; SW, W;
25.
Showers, showers,
blowing, & cold.

Wednesday 26.
29 5/10; 40½–10;
NW.
Frost, ice, sun, hail,
snow, frost.

People turn the hay in Baker's hill.

Thursday 27.
29 7/10; 41; NW.
Hard frost, thick ice,
sun, warm sun, bright.

Grapes delicate.
Water in the well very deep.

Swallow at Fyfield.

Friday 28.
29 4/10; 39½; SW.
White frost, grey,
pleasant, dark, wet.

Timothy the tortoise comes out.
Part of the hay in Baker's hill was cocked & housed: it smells well, & is not so much damaged as might have been expected.
Saw seven ring-ouzels on the old haw-thorns at Clay's barn.

Saturday 29.
29 4/10½; 45; NW,
W; 61.
Rain, snow, sun,
pleasant, bright.

Snow covers the ground.
Snow lies on the hay-cocks in Baker's hill!

Sunday 30.
29 6/10; 44; W; SE.
Grey, sun, showers,
showers.

The beechen-woods look very dark and rusty, & the maples very yellow. Leaves fall very fast.

Monday 31
29 3/10; 48; S, W; 42.
Rain, rain, dark.

21 cocks of hay lying still in Baker's hill.
Rain in October . . . 5 inc: 21 hund:

NOVEMBER 1785

Tuesday 1.
29; 54½; S.
Rain & wind, rain,
rain.

Bro.^r Tho: M^r & Mrs Ben White, & Nep: Thos Holt White came
from Fyfield.

Wednesday 2.
29 1/¼; 52; SW; 58.
Shower, sun &
showers.

Timothy comes out.

Thursday 3.
29 5/10; 50; S; 35.
Sun, soft & pleasant.

Great fieldfares appear.

Friday 4.
29 6/10¾; 54; SW.
Grey, sun, still, mild &
grey.

Grapes in vast abundance: are dead ripe & tending to decay.

Saturday 5.
29 1/10; 54; 57; S.
Grey, sun, & gale,
pleasant.

Wild wood-pigeons appear in a large flock in the coppice above
Combwood pond.
Timothy Turner housed the remainder of the hay in Baker's hill.
Dame Loe came.

Sunday 6.
29 3/10; 50; S; 29.
Sun, & blowing.

Rain in the night.
Leaves much fallen; hanger almost naked.

Monday 7.
29 8/10; 44; N.
Sun, cool & pleasant.

Timothy the tortoise does not appear.
The stone-curlew clamors.

Tuesday 8.
29 9/10½; 44; N.
Grey, sun, sweet day,
grey, still.

Many wood-pigeons, & many ring-doves appear in the vale
above Combwood pond.

Wednesday 9.
30 ½/10; 45; NE.
Frost, grey & mild,
sun, sweet weather.

The great holly at Burhant-house is now beginning to blow.
Farmer Lasham finishes hay-making!!

Thursday 10.
29 9/10; 29 abroad;
SE, W.
Frost, fog, sun, sweet
day.

Leaves much fallen.
Timothy seems to be withdrawn under the laurel-hedge.

Friday 11.
29 7/10; 44; SW, S.
Grey, mild, & still.

Began to use celeri: it is very large, & somewhat piped.¶ Tied-up more endive.
Ring-ousel on the common.

A Gent: writes word from St Mary's Scilly, that in the night between the 10th & 11th of this month, the wind being W: there fell such a flight of Woodcocks within the walls of the Garrison, that he himself shot, & carryed home 26 couple, besides 3 couple which he wounded, but did not give himself the trouble to retrieve. On the following day, the 12th, the wind continuing W: he found but few.

    This person farther observes, that easterly, & Northerly winds only have usually been remarked as propitious in bringing wood cocks to those islands, viz: Scilly. So that he is totally at a loss to account for this western flight, unless they came from Ireland. As they took their departure in the night between the 11th & 12th the wind still continuing W: he supposes they were gone to make a visit to the Counties of Cornwall, & Devonshire.

    From circumstances in the letter it appears, that the ground within the lines of the Garrison abounds with furze. Some wood-cocks settled in the street of St Mary's, & ran in to the houses, & out-houses.

Saturday 12.
29 6/10½; 49; W.
Rain, grey & warm.

The ring-ouzel is killed by a hawk.

Sunday 13.
29 9/10½; N, NE.
Fog, sun, sweet day,
fog.

Mr Ben White¶ left us, & went to London.
Summer-like.

Monday 14.
30; 42½; NE, E.
Fog, frost, sun, sweet
day.

Mowed the grass-plots for the last time, & walks.
Men finish their wheat-season.

Tuesday 15.
30 1/10; 31 abroad;
NE.
Hard frost, sun, sweet
afternoon.

We find several pheasants in our walks.
The hills thro' the fog appeared like vast mountains.

Wednesday 16.
30; 42½; NE.
Grey, mild, & misty.
Full moon.

Found some rasp-bushes on the down among the furze; & some low yew-trees, gnawn down by the sheep, among the bushes.

Thursday 17.
29 8/10; 42½; NE.
Deep fog, sun,
pleasant.

Found the feathers of a ring-ouzel on the down that had been killed by a hawk.
Mrs Ben White¶ left us, & went to London.

Friday 18.
29 3/10; 39½; SE, S.
Deep fog, sun,
pleasant.

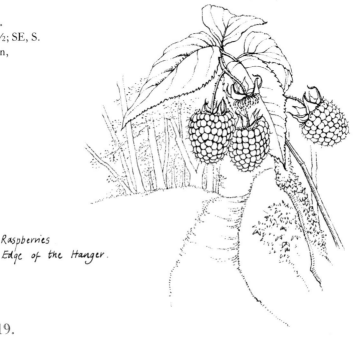

Raspberries
Edge of the Hanger.

Saturday 19.
28 6/10; 43; S.
Rain, clouds & wind,
blowing.

Harry Holt White left us, & went to Fyfield.

Sunday 20.
29 1/10; 44; S, W; 35.
Rain, rain, harsh.

Stormy in the night.

Monday 21.
29 6/10; 39½; W.
Some snow, sharp, sun,
pleasant.

Grapes delicate still.
Partridges associate in vast coveys.

Tuesday 22.
29 9/10; 39; NW, N.
Grey, frost, sun,
pleasant.

Thomas begins to dress the vines: the young wood appears to be well ripened.

Wednesday 23.
29 9/10¼; 41; N.
Grey, wet, sun &
clouds.

Flocks of great fieldfares.

Thursday 24.
29 8/10; 38; N, S.
White frost, sun, sweet
day, frost.

Friday 25.
29 5/10; 40 ½/10; S.
Dark, still & moist.

Mosses begin to grow, & look vivid; & will begin to blow in a
few weeks.

Saturday 26.
28 8/10; 50; SW.
Rain, rain, rain.

Sunday 27.
28 7/10; 46; S, NW;
30.
Grey, sun, pleasant.

Monday 28.
28 6/10½; 44; W; 22.
Rain, sun & clouds,
bright.

We have had this week in Hartley-wood, & those parts a
considerable flight of wood-cocks: while in the upland coverts few
or none were found.

Tuesday 29.
28 8/10; 42; SW.
Wh: frost, ice, sun,
sharp wind, bright.

There was about this time, as the newspapers say, a vast flight of
wood-cocks in Cornwall.
Horses begin to lie within.

Wednesday 30.
29; 38; W, N; 18.
Hard frost, sun,
pleasant, rain.

Grapes are at an end.
Rain in Novemᴿ . . . 2 inch 27 hund:

DECEMBER 1785

Thursday 1.
29 6/10; 36; W, SE.
Hard frost, sun,
pleasant, bright.

Friday 2.
29; SW.
Rain, rain, sun,

Mem: to send Thomas on this day to Mʳ Collis collector of the
excise.

shower.

Saturday 3.
29; 42; 42.
Shower, strong, cold
wind, shower.

Sunday 4.
29 1/10½; 43; W,
NW.
Wet, grey, sun,
pleasant.

Monday 5.
29 5/10½; 43; SW.
Hard frost, sun,
pleasant.

Tuesday 6.
29 1/10¾; 46; SE; 89.
Rain, rain, windy &
wet.

Wednesday 7.
29 5/10; 46; SW; 14.
Rain, grey, sun,
pleasant, cool air,
bright.

Thursday 8.
29 2/10; 40½; S.
White frost, ice, sun,
pleasant, dark, wet,
heavy rain.

Friday 9.
29 2/10; 46; S, SE;
107.
Much rain, rain, rain,
rain.

Saturday 10.
29 5/10½; 45; NE; 28.
Dark & moist.

Sunday 11.
29 2/10½; E.
Dark & sharp.

Much distant thunder.
Broʳ Thomas White, & Tho: Holt White left us.
Mʳˢ & Miss Etty came home.

Worms come-out on the grass-walks.

Some sportsmen beat the bogs of Wolmer-forest carefully: saw
but three brace of snipes.

Much rain in the night.

Several pheasants about.
Several large coveys of partridges left.

Some few flights of wild fowl come to Wolmer-pond; but do not
stay.

Swans-egg pears continue good.

Monday 12.
29 1/10; 40; E.
Dark & still, & sharp.

Young crickets now of all sizes in my kitchen-chimney.

Tuesday 13.
29 2/10; 46; S; 23.
Rain, grey, blowing &
mild, sharp showers.

Wednesday 14.
29 6/10½; 46; S, W;
54.
Grey & mild, sun,
mild.

Vast halo round the moon.

moss
Brachythecium   rutabulum
Long Lythe .

Thursday 15.
29 7/10½; 45; SE, E;
23.
Wet, showers, foggy,
& mild.
Full moon.

Friday 16.
29 7/10; 46; E, NE.
Deep fog, dark, moist
& still.

Helleborus foetidus blows. Crocus's, & snow-drops shoot.

Saturday 17.
29 8/10; 44; NE.
Dark & mild.

Antirrhinum cymbalaria thrives still, & is in full bloom, & will
continue 'till severe frosts take place.
Planted several firs from S: Lambeth: & several seedlings of the
Helleborus foetidus.

Sunday 18.
29 9/10; 41; NW.
Dark, still, & mild.

Sweet weather.

Monday 19.
29 7/10½; 40; SE.
Dark, mild & still.

Cut down the artichokes, & covered them; first with earth, &
then with long dung.
Covered the asparagus with long dung.

Tuesday 20.
29 7/10; 40; SE, S.
Some snow, rain, grey
& moist, small frost.

Dug up carrots, second crop.

Wednesday 21.
29 8/10; 40; SW, W,
NW; 22.

Planted 20 Scotch-firs round Benham's orchard.

Rain, small rain, sun &
stars.

Thursday 22.
29 8/10; 40; N, NE.   Dug-up the second crop of carrots.
Dark & mild.   Farmer Lassam's Dorsetshire ewes begin to lamb.

Friday 23.
29 6/10½; 38½; N.   Some frost.
Grey & sharp.   Mʳ Churton came from Oxford.

Saturday 24.
29 3/10½; 36½; N.   Some sleet falls.
Dark, frosty & sharp.

Sunday 25.
29 2/10½; 28 abroad;   Snow covers the ground.
NE.
Snow, snow, hard frost.

Monday 26.
29 4/10½; 24; NE.   Many wild-fowls, ducks & widgeons, at Wolmer-pond 'till the
Fierce frost, snow,   hard weather came: since which they have disappeared.
dark, & cold.

Tuesday 27.
29 6/10; 25; NE.   Tapped my new rick of hay this day, which, tho' made without
Strong frost, dark, &   rain, is vapid, & without much scent, & consists more of weeds
cold.   than grass. The summer was so dry, that little good grass grew,
                             'till after the first crop was cut. The rick also is very small.

Wednesday 28.
29 5/10; 32; NE.   Snow covers the ground.
Frost, grey & sharp.

Thursday 29.
29 3/10; 25; NE.
Sharp frost, sun,
bright, sharp, &
cloudy.

Friday 30.
29 3/10; 22; NE.
Sharp frost, sun, frost.

Saturday 31.
29 3/10; 21; NE.   Snow covers the ground.
Fierce frost, sun.   Rain in Decemʳ . . . 4 inch 2 hund.

Rain	at Lyndon in 1785 . . .	20 inch	206 h:
. .	at South Lambeth . . .	19 .	82
. .	at Fyfield . . . 24	.	55
. .	at Selborne . . . 31	.	55

JANUARY

— 1786 —

Sunday 1.
29 3/10½; 17, 18, 17;
N.
Fierce frost, bright.

Monday 2.
29 4/10; 17; SE, S, W.
Fierce frost, sun, deep
snow.

Tuesday 3.
29 7/10; 11, 18; NE,
S, SW.
Fierce frost, bright,
frosty, severe frost.

Snow on the ground six inches deep at an average.

Jan: 3rd On this day at 8 o'clock in the evening Captain Lindsey's hands were frozen, as he & Mr Powlett were returning from Captain Dumery to Rotherfield. The Gent: suffered great pain all night, & found his nails turned black in the morning. When he got to Rotherfield he bathed his hands in cold water.

Wednesday 4.
29 4/10½; 29; S.
Fierce, drifting wind
with much snow.

One of the most severe days that I ever remember with a S: wind. Snow deep, & much drifted.

Thursday 5.
29 4/10; 33; S.
Thaw, sleet, swift thaw
with rain.

The fierce drifting of wednesday proved very injurious to houses, forcing the snow into the roofs, & flooding the ceilings.
The roads also are so blocked up with drifted snow that the coaches cannot pass. The Winton coach was overturned yesterday near Alresford.

Friday 6.
29 4/10½; 48; S.
Wet, & thaw, rain.

Saturday 7.
28 9/10; 49; S; 100.
wet, rain, swift thaw.

The snow on wednesday proved fatal to two or three people, who were frozen to death on the open downs about Salisbury. Much damage happened at Sea about that time. In particular the *Halsewell* outer-bound India-man was wrecked, & lost on the shore of Purbeck.

Sunday 8.
29 1/10½; 47; S.
Mild, sun, pleasant,
fog.

Winter-aconites begin to bloom.

Monday 9.
28 7/10; 49; SW; 157.
Wet & mild, rain.

Much rain in the night.
Mr Churton left us.¶
Vast condensations on walls, & wainscot.

Tuesday 10.
28 6/10; 49; SW; 35.
Rain, moist, & mild.

Rain in the night. The ground drench'd with wet.

Wednesday 11.
28 4/10½; 46½; S.
Blowing & wet, rain,
rain.

Thursday 12.
28 9/10; 45; SW; 31.
Sun, clouds, &
showers.

Rain-bows.

Friday 13.
29 2/10; 45; W; 22.
Grey, sun, & clouds.

Saturday 14.
29 1/10; 33; E.
White frost, snow,
snow, snow.
Full moon.

Sowed 36 bushels of peat-ashes on part of my farthest field, which
has never been ashed since it was laid down in grass.
Qu: if it †it be right to sow ashes amidst so much rain & snow? So
much moisture must probably dilute the ashes too much, &
render them of no effect. Much snow on the ground. These ashes
did no manner of good.

Sunday 15.
28 7/10½; 38; NW,
W.
Swift thaw, rain, rain,
rain.

Much snow on the ground.

Monday 16.
28 8/10; 38; N; 147.
Deep fog with thaw.

Snow on the ground.

Tuesday 17.
29 2/10¼; 24½; NW.
Frost, bright sun, frost.

Snow in the night: snow covers the ground.

---

†GW's error – a rare occurrence.

Wednesday 18.
29 4/10; 25; W, SW.
Hard frost, sun,
pleasant.

Snow covers the Ground.
Covered the spinage beds with straw: celeri & winter-lettuces are
also covered.

Thursday 19.
29 6/10½; 18, 29; E,
SE. Severe frost, sun,
dark, frost.

Snow covers the ground.

Friday 20.
29 6/10; 28; S.
Grey, dark, thaw.

Snow on the ground.

Saturday 21.
29 8/10; 47; S.
Thaw, dark, & wet,
fog.

Snow gone.

Sunday 22.
29 8/10¼; 49; SW.
Rain, rain, rain.

Snow-drops blow. Soft & warm.

Monday 23.
29 5/10; SW; 51, 11.
Dark, rain, rain, dark,
& mild.

Tuesday 24.
29 4/10½; 46½; S.
Dark & mild, rain,
rain.

Wednesday 25.
29 6/10¼; 48; SW.
Dark, mild & wet.

Thursday 26.
29.6/10½; 48½; SW;
35.
Dark, wet, & blowing.

Friday 27.
29 8/10; 50; W; 52.
Rain, sun, pleasant.

The male-bloom of the hazel begins to open.

Saturday 28.
29 9/10; 49½; S.
Dark & wet, dark.

Mr Richardson, & son William came.

Sunday 29.
30; 50; SW.
Dark, warm & wet.

Peter Wells's well at Gracious street runs over.

Monday 30.
30 ½/10; 49; W.
Dark, still, & warm,
bright.

Some Crocus's in warm aspects begin to open.
Spinage very fine. Worms engender.

Tuesday 31.
30 ½/10; 46½; W.
Sun, dark & mild.

Mr Richardson left us.
Rain in Jan: – 6 inch: 91 hun:

FEBRUARY 1786

Wednesday 1.
29 7/10; 47½; W,
NW.
Dark & much wind in
the night, blowing,
showers, windy.

The hazels are finely illuminated with male bloom. Female
bloom of hazels appears, & the male-bloom sheds it's farina.

Thursday 2.
29 7/10½; 40; N; 11.
Frost, sun, sprinklings,
sleet.

Strong, sharp wind.

Friday 3.
29 8/10; 38; N.
Hard frost, sun,
pleasant.

The marsh-titmouse begins his two harsh, sharp notes.

Saturday 4.
29 8/10; 38; W.
Shower, sun, sharp but
pleasant.

Sowed a good coat of ashes, on Baker's hill & also on the great
meadow. Bought 40 bushels of ashes of Mrs Etty, & 36 bushels
of sundry others. Sowed my own also.

Sunday 5.
29 7/10; 40; SW.
Grey, dark & wet.

Crocus's open.

Monday 6.
29 4/10½; 37; SW.
Rain, rain, bright.

Tuesday 7.
29 1/10½; W.
Driving rain, sun,
wind, & clouds.

Strong flaws, & gusts, with rain, hail & thunder. Hail & gusts.

Wednesday 8.
29 2/10½; 37; W; 42.
Hail, & showers,
strong gales, blowing &
cold.

Thursday 9.
29 6/10; 37; NW.   Hepatica's blow.
Flight of snow, sun &
sharp wind, still, &
grey.

Friday 10.
29 2/10½; 40; W; 11.
Rain, strong gales with
showers.

Saturday 11.
29 5/10; 45; SW.   Finished trimming, & tacking the fruit-trees.
Rain, sun, wet.   There will be bloom.

Sunday 12.
29 7/10; 44; W.   Strong gales all day.
Sun & clouds.

Monday 13.
30 1/10½; 41; N, SW.   *Papilio rhamni*, brimstone butter-fly, appears.
Small frost, sun, sweet   Bees gather on Snow-drops, & crocus's.
day, fog.   Flies come out.

Tuesday 14.
30 1/10; 47; SW.   Many winter-aconites are out of bloom.
Fog, sun, grey & mild.   Bullfinches eat the buds of honey-suckles.
                          Made seedling cucumber-bed with two loads of dung.

Wednesday 15.
30 ½/10; 45; SE, E.   The air is full of Gossamer. Insects swarm.
Vast, white dew, ice,   Flies come out on buds. Bees gather on crocus's.
sun, cloudless, sweet
day.

Thursday 16.
29 8/10½; 45; E.   Mezereon blows.
Fog, fog, sun, pleasant.

Friday 17.
29 6/10; 43; SW.   Sowed cucumber-seeds in the hot-bed.
Fog, fog, wet fog.

Entrance
to Priory Lane.

Saturday 18.
29 7/10½; 49; SW.
Dark, soft & still.

Pleasant season: paths dry. Men plough, & sow.
Large titmouse sings his three notes.

Sunday 19.
29 8/10½; 48; SW, S.
Fog, rain, dark &
mild.

Monday 20.
29 6/10½; 48; SE; 22.
Deep fog, wet fog.

Yellow-hammer, song, & missle-thrush sing.
Bro.ʳ Henry, & his son Gil: came.
Bat out.

Tuesday 21.
29 7/10; E. Dark,
strong, sharp wind.

Dug up some garden-ground.

Wednesday 22.
29 7/10; 28; 30, 28;
NE.
Hard frost, cloudless,
hard frost.

Sowed a crop of radishes, under the melon-screen: & a crop of
onions.

Thursday 23.
29 6/10½; 24, 28; E.
Severe frost, sun, sharp
wind, hard frost.

Friday 24.
29 6/10; 22; E.
Severe frost, sun, sharp
frost, cutting wind.

Ploughs are stopped by the frost; & men cannot dig in the hop-
gardens.

Saturday 25.
29 5/10; 28; NE.
Severe frost, sun:
cutting wind! dark.

Bro.ʳ Henry & Son left us.
Ground as hard as iron. Thick ice.
Some flakes of snow.

Sunday 26.
29 2/10¼; 28, 30;
NE.
Small snow, cutting
wind, driving snow.

Snow covers the ground.

Monday 27.
29 2/10¼; 29; E, NE.
Snow, snow, snow,
snow.

Snow all night. Snow shoe-deep.
Wrote to Dʳ Chandler at Nismes.

Tuesday 28.
29 3/10½; 35; NE; 58.
Deep snow, sun, grey
& frosty.

The snow is at an average about seven inches deep. As it fell without any wind, it is lodged much on the trees, so that the prospects are very grotesque, & picturesque.
Rain in Feb: . . . 1 inch 42 h:

MARCH 1786

Wednesday 1.
29 3/10½; 29, 25;
NE.
Hard frost, dark &
sharp, frost, dark.

Snow not at all melted. Trees covered with snow.

Thursday 2.
29 3/10; 27, 32, 25; N.
Dark & very sharp,
small snow, gleam,
dark.

My cucumber-plants look poorly.
Snow not melted.
Bull-finches injure the fruit-trees by eating the buds.

Friday 3.
29 4/10; 26, 22; NE.
Dark, small snow, sun,
bright, sharp frost.

Netted the wall-cherry-trees, to preserve the buds from the finches.
Snow little abated.
Sowed more cucumbers.

Saturday 4.
29 7/10; 19, 13!; N,
NW.
Grey, severe, small
snow, sun, bright &
keen!

The netting keeps off the birds.
Snow little abated.
Sowed more cucumber-seeds: most of the plants seem to be spoiled.

Sunday 5.
29 4/10½; 8; NE, E.
Fierce frost! Cloudless,
sharp air.

The sun melts the snow on the roofs of houses. Vast Icicles on eaves.
Snow deep on the ground.

Monday 6.
29 ½/10; 15; NE.
Fierce frost! Sun, sharp
cutting wind.

The birds are so distressed,¶ that ring-doves resort to my garden to crop the leaves of the bore-cole! black birds come down to the scullery-door. Snow little abated. Snow is drifted by the wind.

Tuesday 7.
29 4/10½; 19; N.
Severe frost, sun, small
snow, red even, frost.

Snow drifted over hedges & gates! Ring-doves, driven by hunger, come into John Hale's garden, which is surrounded by houses!

Wednesday 8.
29 8/10; 10, 24; N,
NW.
Severe frost, sun, still,
cloudless, red even,
frost.

Black-birds, & thrushes die. A starving wigeon settled yesterday in the village, & was taken. Mention is made in the newspapers of several people that have perished in the snow. As Mr Ventris came from Faringdon the drifted snow, being hard frozen, bore his weight up almost to the tops of the stiles. The net hung over the cherry trees is curiously coated over with ice.

Thursday 9.
29 8/10½; 15, 21;
NW, SE, NE.
Severe frost, sun, warm
sun, red, bright, frost.

Snow not much abated.
The sunny sides of roofs clear of snow.

Friday 10.
29 8/10; 12, 34; S, W.
Hard frost, sun, thaw,
warm, flisky clouds,
frost, halo round the
moon.

Snow wastes. Paths dirty.

Saturday 11.
29 6/10½; 36; S, W.
Grey, gleams, mild,
swift thaw.

Snow wastes very fast. Roofs clear of snow.
The ground appears.

About this time my niece Brown was brought to bed of her fifth child, a girl, who encreases the number of my living nephews & nieces to 43.

Sunday 12.
29 4/10½; 39; W.
Grey, sun, mild.

The snow wastes very fast.
Crocus's blow: bees gather on them.

Monday 13.
29 3/10½; 44; NE.
Smart frost, sun, mild,
& pleasant.

Little snow left.
Crocus's make a fine show.

Tuesday 14.
29 3/10; 32, 36; NE,
E.
Hard frost, haze, dark
& cold.
Full moon.

Took away the netting from the wall-cherries.
Carted-in 6 loads of dung for the cucumber-beds.
Snow lies deep under hedges.

Wednesday 15.
28 9/10½; 32; SE, S;
81.
Snow, sleet, rain, rain,
rain.

Thursday 16.
29; 40; SW.
Sun, & clouds,
pleasant.

Friday 17.
29 1/10; W, S.
White frost, sun, grey
& still.

Turned the dung for the Cucumber-bed.
Made an hand-glass-bed for celeri: sowed celeri.
Cucumber-plants thrive.

Saturday 18.
29; 45; S; 21.
Showers, sun, soft &
moist.

Some snow on the hanger & under hedges.
Dog's violets begin to bloom. Walls sweat.
Much snow in some hollow lanes.
Crocus's make a fine appearance.

Sunday 19.
29 3/10; 47; SW.
Grey, sun, sweet
afternoon.

The small uncrested wren, chif-chaf, seen.
Bees gather on Crocus's.
Apricot-bloom begins to open.
Flies come forth in windows.
Strong *Aurora*.

Monday 20.
29 3/10; 35; SE, SW.
Frost, ice, sun, big
clouds, sweet afternoon.

Sowed six rows of garden-beans in the meadow; & two in the
garden.
Chif-chaf is heard: his notes are loud, & piercing.
Aurora.

Tuesday 21.
29 2/10½; 39; S.
Grey, shower, sun, &
clouds, sweet weather,
soft & still.

Ground digs, & rakes.

Wednesday 22.
29 3/10½; 47; S.
White frost, sun,
clouds, wet.

Turned the dung: it's still very hot.
Some patches of snow still on the hanger: much snow in Newton
hollow lane, below the cross.
Men sow pease.

Thursday 23.
29 1/10; 49; S, SW;
42.
Rain, rain, dark &
moist.

Snow under hedges, & deep in some lanes.

Friday 24.
29 1/10½; 49; SW.

Grey, sun, warm &
pleasant.

Saturday 25.
29 2/10; 46; W.   Some hail.
Grey, cold showers,
bright.

Sunday 26.
29 4/10; 42; NW.   Viper comes out.
Cold air, sun, sharp   Apricots blow: peaches, & nectarines begin to blow.
wind, snow showers,
bright & cold.

Monday 27.
29 5/10; 29; NE.   Made the bearing cucumber-bed with six cart-loads of dung, that
Severe frost, sun, &   had been well turned.
cutting wind.   Cucumbers thrive well, & show rudiments of fruit.

Tuesday 28.
29 8/10½; 28; N.   On this day the streets of Lyons were covered with snow.
Severe frost, sun,   March 26th Two swallows were seen at Nismes in Langedoc: &
cutting wind, snow   on the 28th even tho' the air was sharp, & some flakes of snow fell.
storms, bright & sharp.

Wednesday 29.
29 9/10; 28; N.
Severe frost, sun, sharp
air, dark & cold.

Thursday 30.
29 7/10½; 32; NE, E.   M[r] Taylor & his Bride¶ came to Selborne.
Frost, dark & harsh,
sleet, rain.

Friday 31.
29 7/10¼; 36; NE, E;   Hot-bed steams, & reeks much.
18.   Rain in March . . . 1 inch 62 hund:
Deep fog, wet, gleams
of sun.

APRIL 1786

Saturday 1.
29 5/10½; E, SE.
Deep fog, dark, sun,
sweet afternoon.

Sunday 2.
29 4/10; 49; SE.
Small frost, sun, sweet
afternoon.

Monday 3.
29 2/10; 49; E.
Fog, sun, sweet
summer weather.

Earthed the cucumber-bed: plastered some fresh cow dung under
the hills. Sowed two ounces of carrot-seed in the garden-plot in
the meadow.

Tuesday 4.
29 ½/10; NE.
Mist, sun, blue mist,
dark & warm.

Planted 1 doz: of white currans, & six goose-berry-trees, with
many rasp-plants on the orchard side of the bank. Turned out the
cucumber-plants into the hills of the bearing-bed; they are large
& strong, & began to be too big for the pots. Sowed onions, &

Wednesday 5.
29 1/10½; NE, N.
Dark, still ,wet.

parsnips: the ground is dusty, & works well. 10 pots of
Cucumber-plants remain.
Sowed radishes, & lettuce. Planted one Roman, & one
Newington Nectarine-tree against the fruit-wall.

Thursday 6.
29 1/10½; 45; NE, N.
Shower, dark, & moist.

Swallow appears near the forest.
Some cucumber-plants have fruit in bloom.

Friday 7.
29 2/10½; 50; E.
Shower, dark, & moist,
fog, rain.

Cucumbers blow, & thrive.
Sowed the slip with peat ashes.
Grass begins to grow.

Saturday 8.
29; 47; E, NE; 56, 41.
Rain, rain, rain.

A very wet day.

Sunday 9.
29 3/10½; 38; NE.
Dark & harsh, sleet,
sun & clouds, moon-
shine, frost.

Monday 10.
29 6/10; 29; NE, E.
Hard frost, thick ice,
icicles, sun, red even:

Planted 12 goose-berry trees, & three monthly roses, & three
Provence roses.
M^r & Mrs Taylor left Selborne.

Tuesday 11.
29 7/10½; 30; N,
NW, E.
Hard frost, sun,
pleasant, red even:

Curlew clamours.

Wednesday 12.
29 9/10; 30; E, S.
Sharp frost, sun, dark.

Thursday 13.
29 8/10¼; 50; S, S.
Grey, mild, sun,
pleasant, yellow sunset.
Full moon.

Daws are building in the church.
Nightingale sings in French-mere.
Lined the back of the cucumber bed.

Friday 14.
29 8/10½; 50; S.
Grey, mild, sun,
pleasant, wet fog.

Timothy heaves up the mould, & comes out of his hibernacula
under the wallnut-tree.
Caltha palustris blows.
House martin at Bramshot.

Saturday 15.
29 8/10¾; 50, 59;
NE, N.
Fog, sun, sweet
summer weather!!

Timothy out at seven in the morning.
Air swarms with insects.
Nightingale sings at Bradshot.
Cucumbers begin to set.
Three swallows at Rood. Three swallows at Candovers.

Timothy the tortoise, after a fast of more than five months, weighs
6 pd 12 oz 11 dr:

Sunday 16.
29 9/10½; 46, 58; N,
NE.
Sun, sweet summer, red
even:

Some snow in the Shalden lanes.
Crown Imperial blows.

Monday 17.
30, 30; 47; N.
Sun, brisk gale, bright
& cool.

Sowed an other hand-glass with celeri.
Sowed a box with polyanth-seeds, our own saving.

Tuesday 18.
29 7/10; 41; N.
Sun, sharp wind, sun,
red even:

Sowed Savoy & borecole seed.
Cuckow at Bradshot.
Wheat improves, & looks thriving. Men sow clover in their
wheat. Roads dry very fast. Women hoe the wheat.

Wednesday 19.
29 4/10½; 44; NE, E.
Grey, warm, brisk
gales, dark, blowing,
rain.

Sowed hollyhocks, columbines, & sweet Williams.

Thursday 20.
29 3/10¾; 51; E; 26.
Wet, dark, mild &
pleasant.

Slipped-out & planted many doz: of good polyanths.
Wall cherries blow. Several swallows, & some h: martins.
Men pole hops. Grass grows. Bats out.

Young Geo: Tanner shot a water-ouzel,¶ *merula aquatica*, near
Jm: Knight's ponds. This is the first bird of the sort that was ever
observed in this parish. This bird, being only pinioned, was caught
alive, & put into a cage; to which it soon became reconciled; & is
fed with woodlice, & small snails. W: ouzels are very common in
the mountainous parts of the N: of England, & in N. Wales. They
haunt rocky streams, & water-falls; & tho' not web-footed often
dive into currents in pursuit of insects.

Friday 21.
29 4/10½; 54; E, S.
Dark & warm, still,
hot, dark & moist.

The voice of the cuckow is heard in the hanger.
Several martins appear. Pulled down their old nests, which are
foul & full of vermin.
Nightingale sings in my out-let.

Saturday 22.
29 6/10½; 54; SE.
Sun, warm, summer
weather.

Crown Imperials, & Fritillaria's make a show.
Wheat improves much. Double hyacinths blow.
Pronged the asparagus beds.
Two nightingales in my outlet.

Sunday 23.
29 8/10; 57; E, SE; 29.
Dark, gleams,
thundrous clouds,
shower, fine.

Grass-lamb.¶
Some beeches in the hanger are coming into leaf.
Bombylius medius much about.
Timothy, if you offer him some poppy leaves, will eat a little: but
does not seek for food.

Monday 24.
29 7/10¼; 55; @.
Sun, warm, broken
clouds, showers.

Growing weather. Some few shell-snails.
Blackthorn blows.

Tuesday 25.
29 6/10; N; 11.
Dark & still, heavy
clouds, gleams of sun.

Began mowing the grass-walks.
Early tulips, & polyanth-narcissus blow.
Two Swifts appear. Growing weather.

Wednesday 26.
29 5/10; 55; N.
Dark & mild, moist,
moist, & still.

My hay is out.
Many cock-pheasants are heard to crow on Wick-hill farm. We
have a large stock of partridges left to breed round the parish.

Thursday 27.
29 6/10½; 41; N.
Dark & harsh.

Farmer Knight brought me ½ a ton of good meadow-hay; price –
45s.

Ashes blow. Vine-buds open.
Sowed seeds of Nasturtium, & sweet pease.
Black snails.

Friday 28.
29 6/10½; 39; N.
Dark, & harsh.

Black-thorn winter: Swifts not seen.
Some few apricots are set: the great tree much injured, & has not one fruit.

Saturday 29.
29 3/10; 39; NE, SE.
Dark & harsh, sun,
cloudless, chill air.

Scarlet straw-berries begin to blow.
Cucumbers swell. Roads much dryed.
Red-breasts have Young.

Sunday 30.
29 5/10; 41; NE; 18.
Dark, wet, sun, sharp
air.

Rain in the night.
Rain in April . . . 1 inch: 81 hund:

MAY 1786

Monday 1.
29 6/10½; 32; NE,
SW.
Hard frost, thick ice!
Sun, & clouds, sharp
air.

The flowers all hung their heads, & bent to the ground. Few hirundines to be seen.
Bombylius minor appears.
Cut the first *cucumber*, a fine fruit: lined the cucumber bed in front.

Tuesday 2.
29 6/10; 34; SW.
White frost, sun, cold
air.

ALTON
Cut a fine cucumber.
No swifts.

Wednesday 3.
29 1/10¼; SW.
Heavy showers, sun,
showers, sun, cold air.

SELBORNE
Made the annual-bed for a large three-light frame with 3 loads of dung.
Thunder about.

Thursday 4.
29 1/10; 44; SW; 49,
24.
Grey, hail, showers,
showers.

Cut two fine cucumbers; & began to eat the brown lettuces under the fruit-wall, where they stood the winter.
Lettuce well-loaved, & very fine.
No swifts.

Friday 5.
29 3/10; 40; SW.
Grey, showers,
showers, showers.

Pulled radishes.
Vivid rain-bow. Two swifts. Young geese.

Saturday 6.
29 2/10½; 40; NE,
SE, E; 34, 24.
Dark, shower, hail,
gleams of sun, showers.

Great showers, & hail all round. Showers of hail at a distance
look of a silvery colour.
Rain-bow.
Four swifts.
The hanger is bursting into leaf every hour.
A progress in the foliage may be discerned every morning, &
again every evening.

Sunday 7.
29 2/10½; 45; NE.
Grey, bright sun, sweet
afternoon.

Vast clouds in the horizon to the NE: & N:W.

The fossil-wood buried in the bogs of Wolmer forest is not yet all
exhausted: for the peat-cutters now & then stumble upon a log. I
have just seen a piece which was sent by a labourer who lives at
Oakhanger to a carpenter of this village: this was the but-end of a
small oak, about five feet long, & about five inches in diameter. It
had apparently been severed from the ground by an axe, was very
ponderous, & as black as ebony. Upon asking the carpenter for
what purpose he had procured it; he told me it was to be sent to his
brother a joiner at Farnham, who was to make use of it in cabinet-
work by inlaying it along with whiter woods.

Monday 8.
29 1/10½; 45; NE, E;
11.
Sun, dark & cold, rain,
sun & clouds.

Cut two fine cucumbers.
Polyanths make a fine show. Pastures yellow with bloom of
dandelion, & with cowslips.

Tuesday 9.
28 8/10¾; 46; E, S;
41.
Rain, rain, rain.

Cut 3 fine cucumbers.
Timothy, contrary to his usual practice, lies out all day in the
rain.
Cadilliac-pear blows. The Meris, or wild cherry, blows.

Looking south from Nore Hill.

Wednesday 10.
29 ½/10; 50; E, SW;
18.
Sun, showers, wind,
wet & wintry.

My grass is long enough to wave before the wind.
Wheat turns some what yellow.

Thursday 11.
29 4/10; 52; SW.
Sun, blowing, blowing,
sweet afternoon.

Sowed a variety of annuals in the large annual frame; & an hand-glass with large white cucumbers.
Four pairs of swifts.
Fern-owl chatters in the hanger.

Those that are much abroad on evenings after it is dark in the spring & summer, frequently hear a nocturnal bird passing by on the wing, & repeating often a short, quick note. This bird I have taken notice of but could never make out 'till lately. I find now that it is the Stone-curlew. Some of them pass over or near my house almost every evening after it is dark from the uplands of the common & N: field away down towards Dorton; where among the meadows & streams they may find a greater plenty of food. Birds that fly by night are obliged to be noisy: their notes are signals or watch-words to keep them together, that they may not stray, & lose each other in the dark.

Friday 12.
29 2/10¼; SW; 39.
Heavy showers, sun, &
wind, bright sun,
shower.

Some flesh-flies, & *Musca meridiana*, appear.
The water-ouzel is living, & recovered of its wound.
16, or 18 swifts.

Saturday 13.
29 7/10; SW.
Grey, sun, strong wind,
bright sun, & wind, &
clouds, sweet red even:

The wind beats the buds off the trees, & blows the cabbages out of the ground.
The planet Venus appears.
Began to cut asparagus.
House-martins begin to build, where we pulled down the old nests.

On this day my niece Clement was brought to bed of her fifth child, a boy, who makes my 44th nephew, & niece, all now living.

Sunday 14.
29 9/10; 56; SW, SE.
Dark, & louring, sun,
sweet evening.

Fly-catcher returns. This is the last summer-bird that appears.
Much bloom on some pear-trees.

Monday 15.
29 7/10¼; S, SE.
Sun, sweet summer
weather.

Cut two brace, & half of fine cucumbers.
Timothy began to march about at 5 in the morning.
Some chafers about. Horses begin to lie out.
Fern-owl chatters.

Tuesday 16.
29 6/10½; 58; S, SE.
Sun, summer, dark &
louring.

Sowed three rows of scarlet kidney-beans.
Tulips make a fine show.
Two nightingales are singing in my outlet.

Wednesday 17.
29 6/10¾; W, N.
Soft showers, showers,
sun, sweet, red even:

Planted three rows of potatoes.
My apple-trees show much bloom.

Timothy Turner's Bantham sow¶ brings 20 pigs, some of which
she trod-on, & over-laid, so that they were soon reduced to 13.
She has but 12 teats. Before she farrowed, her belly swept on the
ground.

Thursday 18.
29 7/10; 53, 53; N.
Sun, sun & clouds,
grey, & cold air.

Dandelions are going out of bloom; & now the pastures look
yellow with the *Ranunculus bulbosus*, butter-cups.
Many Swifts.

Friday 19.
29 8/10; 45; N.
Sun, cool airs, sweet
even: much dew.

Cut two brace of cucumbers.
Mʳˢ Yalden came.

Many pairs of daws build in the church: but they have placed their
nests so high up between the shingles, & the ceiling, that yᵉ boys
cannot come at them. These birds go forth to feed at ½ hour after
four in the morning.

Saturday 20.
29 7/10½; NW.
Grey & cool, dark &
wet.

Women tie hops to their poles.
Swallows wash. Swallows & house-martins much employed in
building.

Sunday 21.
29 7/10; W.
Dark, brisk gale, dark
& mild.

Radishes are good.

Monday 22.
29 7/10; 55; W.
Shower, sun, & gale,
summer, red even:

Hawthorn blows.
Sowed more scarlet kidney-beans.

Tuesday 23.
8/10, 29 8/10; 52; W.
Sun, clouds, & brisk
air.

Cut a fine cucumber.
Slipped-out artichokes, & earthed them up.
Mʳˢ Yalden left us.

Wednesday 24.
29 8/10½; 54; W.
Grey & cool, gales,
clouds, red even:

Annuals thrive in their frames. Sowed larkspurs, & other hardy
annuals. Vine-shoots very short, & backward; yet show much
rudiments for bloom.

Thursday 25.
9/10, 29 9/10; 67; W,
E.

The prospect from my great parlor-windows to the hanger now
beautiful; the apple-trees in bloom add to the richness of the

Sun, summer weather,
red even:

scenery!

The grass-hopper lark whispers in my hedges. That bird, the fern-owl, & the nightingale of an evening may be heard at the same time: & often the wood-lark, hovering & taking circuits round in the air at a vast distance from the ground.

 While high in air, & pois'd upon it's wings,
 Unseen the soft, enamour'd wood-lark sings.
 Wood-larks in summer sing all night in the air.

Friday 26.
29 8/10¼; 50, 72; S,
SE, NE.
Vast dew, cloudless,
hot, red even.

Much gossamer. Cut six cucumbers.
The air is full of floating cotton from the willows. Men bring much peat from the forest.
Dames violets begin to blow.
Polyanths, which have been beautiful, are going-off: some tulips fade.
There are young lapwings in the forest.
Vine-shoots grow.

Saturday 27.
29 9/10; 65; N.
Vast dew, hot, summer,
red even:

My kidney-bean seed proves bad.
Chafers increase.
Apis longicornis bores holes in the walks.
Mr Richardson came.
Several beeches in the high wood, & hanger show much bloom.

Female wasps about: they rasp particles of wood from sound posts & rails, which being mixed-up with a glutinous matter form their nests. Hornets collect touch-wood.

Sunday 28.
30, 30; 62; NE.
Sun, hot sun, red even:

Fly-catcher begins to build in the vines.

Monday 29.
29 9/¾; 65; NW, W.
Vast dew, sun, gale, red
even:

Tuesday 30.
29 8/¾; 74; NW, SW.
Dew, sun, cloudless,
gale, red even:

Honey-suckles begin to blow. Columbines very fine.
Mr Richardson left us.

Wednesday 31.
29 8/10½; 60; N, NE.
Sun, sultry, blue mist,
red even.

Tulips are gone off.
Chafers abound: they are quite a pest this year at, & about Fyfield. Grass-walks burn.
Brisk evening gale. Swifts are very gay, & alert.
Rain in May – 2 inch: 40 hund.

JUNE 1786

Thursday 1.
29 9/10; 70; NE, SW.
Bright, sultry, fresh
gale.

S[t] foin begins to blow. Sowed several rows of white kidney-beans.
Potted nine tall balsams, & put the potts in a sunk bed.
Dragon-flies have been out some days.

The oaks in many places are infested with the caterpillars of the
Phalaena quercus¶ to such a degree as to be quite naked of leaves.
These palmer-worms hang down from the trees by long threads.
The apple-trees at Faringdon are annoyed by an other set of
caterpillars that strip them of all their foliage. My hedges are also
damaged by caterpillars.

Friday 2.
29 9/10¼; 60; N.
No dew, sun, sultry,
red even:

Columbines in high beauty. Wheat shows some ears.
Planted several hand-glasses with large white cucumbers.
Lathraea squammaria in seed. *Serapias latifolia* in bloom.

Saturday 3.
29 9/10½; 56, 67;
NE.
Some dew, cloudless,
gale, red even:

Daws from the church take the chafers on my trees, & hedges.
Thomas picks the caterpillars that damage the foliage of the
apricot-trees & roll up their leaves.
Cut six fine cucumbers.

Sunday 4.
29 9/10; 70; SE, S,
NE.
Cloudless, sultry,
cloudless, red even:

Monday 5.
30; 75; NE, @.
Sun, sultry, broken
clouds, turbid sun-set.

Dames violets make a fine show.
Began to cut loaf-cabbage.
Sultry.

Tuesday 6.
29 9/10; NE, SW.
Sun, sultry, dark &
hot.

Began to tack the vines; they are again infested with the cotton-
like appearance which surrounds the eggs of the *Coccus vitis
vinifera*. For some account of this Insect, see my Journal for
summer last 1785.
My vines show for a good crop of grapes.

Wednesday 7.
29 8/10; 60, 65; NE;
30.
Dark, moist, sun &
clouds.

Rain in the night, with distant thunder.
Vegetation much refreshed, & the air cool & pleasant.

Thursday 8.   ALTON

NE.
Dark & cool.

Cut five fine cucumbers.

Friday 9.
29 3/10¾; 62; E, SE.
White dew, cloudless,
sweet even: red.

SELBORNE
House martins begin to hatch, & throw-out their egg-shells.
Captain Dumaresque cuts his S^t foin.

Saturday 10.
29 4/10; 50; NE, E.
Vast dew, cloudless,
turbid sunset.

Men have a fine season for their turnip-fields, which work very
well, & are well pulverized.

Sunday 11.
29 5/10; E, NE.
Sun, brisk air, red
even: cool.
Full moon.

Fraxinellas, pinks, corn-flags blow. The gardens want rain.
Spring-sown Coss-lettuces come in.

In Richd Butler's garden there is a Fly-catcher's nest built in a very
peculiar manner, being placed on a shelf that is fixed against the
wall of an out-house, not five feet from the ground; & behind the
head of an old rake lying on the shelf. On the same spot a pair of
the same birds built last year: but as soon as there were young the
nest was torn down by a cat.

Monday 12.
29 5/10¼; 64; E.
Grey, sultry, grey.

Put the sticks to the kidney-beans: the rows are but thin.
Cucumbers set very fast. Watered the hot-beds, & annuals well.

Tuesday 13.
29 4/10¼; 54; E.
Grey, sprinkling,
gleams with gales.

Cut 12 cucumbers. Ground much parched.
Wavy, curdled clouds, like the remains of thunder.

Wednesday 14.
29 11; 69; E.
Dark & cool, hot
gleams, sultry, dark.

SOUTH LAMBETH
About Newton men were cutting their S^t foin: & all the way
towards London their upland meadows, many of which,
notwithstanding the drought, produce decent crops.
We had a dusty, fatiguing journey. Bro: Thos has made his hay:

Thursday 15.
29 13; 75; NE.
Sun, sultry, dark,
distant lightening.

& his fields are much burnt-up.
Alder blows. Roses bloom.
Some strawberries, but dryed-up, & without flavour.

Friday 16.
29 12; 73; NE.
Sun, showers about,
dark, rain.

Distant thunder.
Rain in the night.

Saturday 17.
29 13; 70; N; 20, 81.

Cystus ledon blows.

Sun, dark, rain, rain.   Distant thunder.

Sunday 18.
29 11; 73; E.   Beans come in.
Dark & hazey, brisk   *Hemerocallis* blow.
gale, rain, rain.   Rain at Selborne: . . . 35 hund:
                               . . . . 10.

Monday 19.
29 12; 69; 53.   My brother's gardeners plant out annuals.
Rain, rain, dark &   The ground is well moistened. They prick out young cabbages,
warm.   celeri, &c.
                               Sultry night.

Tuesday 20.
70; NW.   Very growing weather. Cucumbers abound: Coss-lettuces turn-
Dark & warm.   in, & are in high order.
                               Fly-catchers have young.

                               On this day Miss Anne Blunt, by being married to Mr Edmd White,
                               encreased the number of my Nephews & nieces to forty & five.

Wednesday 21.
29 12½; 72; NW, S;   Bror Thomas's melons set, & swell.
12.   Red kidney-beans blow. Cucumbers are turned-out from under
Dark, still, & warm,   the hand-glasses.
rain.   Cauliflowers are large & fine: pease abound.

Thursday 22.   LONDON
29 12; SW.   Jasmine in warm aspects begins to blow.
Clouds & sun.

Jasmine on a cottage wall.
Selborne village.

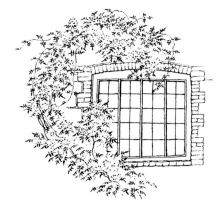

Friday 23.
29 13; 74; S.
Bright & hot.

Saturday 24.
29 14; 75; W; 14.   Nights miserably hot & sultry.
Clouds, & sun, shower.   Wheat is in bloom, & has had a fine still, dry, warm season for
                              blowing.

Sunday 25.
29 17; 77; W.
Sun, & clouds, sultry,
heavy clouds to the W.

S. LAMBETH
Vines begin to blow.
Grass-fields become verdurous.
Strawberries not finely flavoured: the season has been too dry.
Cherries begin to come in: artichokes for supper.
Cauliflowers, Coss-lettuce, marrow-fat pease, carrots, summer-
cabbage, & small beans in great profusion, & perfection.
Cucumbers abound; melons thrive & set.

Monday 26.
29 15; 77; SW.
Sun & clouds, strong
gales, sprinklings.

Rain at Selborne . . . 28
Roses make a lovely appearance.

Bro: Ben's outlet swarms with the *Scarabaeus solstitialis*, which
appears at Midsum:
   My two brothers gardens abound with all sorts of kitchen-crops.

Tuesday 27.
29 13; 68; W; 11.
Rain, clouds, sun.

Young fly-catchers have left their nest.
Many of Bro: Thomas's young fowls pine, & die; & so they did
last summer.
Celeri is trenched-out at once from the seedling bed.

Wednesday 28.
29 16; 75; NW.
Sun, dew, cooler air,
gleams.

Bro: Thomas's gardener stops his vines, & tacks them. Bro: Ben's
vines (those that came from Selborne) have very weak, scanty
shoots. Bro: Tho: vines have good wood, & show for much fruit.

Thursday 29.
SW; 10.
Sun, dark clouds, cool,
rain.

LONDON
Selborne rain . . . 17.

Friday 30.
29 15; 72; NW.
Clouds, & sun.

Bro: Ben: cuts his Lucern a second time: the second crop is very
tall.
Rain at Selborne in June . . 1 inch 20 hund.

JULY 1786

Saturday 1.
29 16; 74; NW.
Sun, gale, gleams.

S: LAMBETH
Sun sets in a vast bank.

Sunday 2.
29 16; 73; SW.
Sun, louring, heavy
clouds.

Limes in bloom. The leaves of the purple-juiced vines begin to
be tinged.
Showers about.

Monday 3.
29 17; W.
Sun, clouds, & gale.

Tuesday 4.
29 17; 71, 69; NW.
Dark, & louring, gales.

The fruit of D.ʳ Uvesdale's great S.ᵗ Germain pear swells, & grows large. Dwarf kidney-beans begin to pod. Brother Ben's Selborne vines have much bloom: some grapes are set. Cherries begin to be ripe. Many wall-nuts.
Black-caps, & titlarks sing.
Rasps begin to ripen.
Some apple-trees bear well. Kidney-beans in, & are well-flavoured.
A cloud of Swifts over Clapham: they probably have brought out their young.

Wednesday 5.
30 ½/10; 67; E, N.
Sun, grey, sun.

The roads are very dusty.

Thursday 6.
29 19; 67; NW.
Sun, clouds, gleams.

On this day Thomas got up all my hay in good order, & finished my rick, which contains eight good jobbs or loads; at least six tuns. Two jobbs of the hay were from Baker's hill, the other six from the meadow, & slip. Baker's hill cut the 19.ᵗʰ year: the Saint foin is got very thin, but other grasses prevail.

Friday 7.
N.
Dark, showers, gleams.

ALTON
Many swifts near Kingston.
Dust laid in many places. Swallows feed their young at Marelands, as they flie.
Thatched & secured my hay-rick.

Saturday 8.
29 4/10; 57; NW.
Sun, showers, gleams.

SELBORNE
Wheat looks well. Hops are healthy round Alton, & Selborne.
Hops throw out side-shoots.
Vast rain at Bagshot.
The pond at Faringdon is dry: my well is very low, having been much exhausted by long waterings.
The rick sweats, & fumes, & is in fine order.
Received five gallons, & a pint of brandy from M.ʳ Edm.ᵈ Woods.

Sunday 9.
29 3/10½; 60; N.
Fog, cold dew, sun, clouds.

Cool morning.
Showers abound. M.ʳ White's tank at Newton measures three feet in water.
Roses, sweet-williams, pinks, white & orange lilies make a gaudy show in my garden.
Annuals are much stunted for want of rain.
Rasps begin to turn. Apples very few.
The hand-glass cucumbers look but poorly, & have but scanty shoots.
Many broods of fly-catchers about the out-let.

Monday 10.

29 4/10; 59; E, @; 74, 75.
Heavy shower, gleams, heavy showers, thunder.

Finished planting out the annuals: they are small, & backward.
Housed the cucumbers, & annual frames.
The crop of wood-strawberries this year has been very great: children continue to bring them still.
Some hail.
Some young martins flown.

Tuesday 11.

29 7/10½; 61; NE, S, NE.
Shower, dark, & louring, shower, gleams of sun.
Full moon.

The wheat is lodged in several fields.
The ground is well soaked.
Much hay lies unmade.
Some wheat lodged by the late showers.
Planted out several basons of late cucumbers.
Put out Savoys, & borecole.
Gathered the wall-cherries, & preserved them with sugar: they are large, & fine.

Wednesday 12.

29 9/10; 61; NE, NW; 7.
Sun, sun & brisk air, red even:

Some hay ricked.
Trenched the first row of Celeri.
Planted out all the annuals.
Swallows feed their young flying.

Thursday 13.

30, 30 ½/10; 57; NW; N.
Sun, dark & louring, shower, sun.

Wheat begins to turn colour: it is very large, & tall, & will have a great burden of straw.
Much hay ricked.
Began to cut my tall hedges, which in many places were much injured by the late severe winters. Their foliage is not good, being much hurt by the caterpillars of *phalaenae*.

Friday 14.

30 1/10; 64; NE, S.
Sun, dew, sun & clouds, sweet even:

Currans come in.
Trenched out more Celeri.

Saturday 15.

29 9/10; 61; N, NW.
Sun, sweet day, red even:

Made jellies, & jams of red currans.
Gathered broad beans.
Much hay made.
Mushrooms begin to come in Mr Edmᵈ White's avenue, under the Scotch firs.
The cat gets upon the roof of the house, & catches young bats as they come forth from behind the sheet of lead at the bottom of the chimney.

Sunday 16.

29 8/10; 70½; N, SW.

Nasturtions blow.

Sun, hot, & bright, fresh gale.

Rye, & pea-harvest begins.

Monday 17.
29 9/10¼; 61; N, NW. Sun, grey, sun, red even:

Hollyhock blows. Much hay ricked.
Several nightingales appear all day long in the broad walk of Baker's hill.

Tuesday 18.
29 9/10¾; 64; N, S. Cloudless, dew, sun & clouds, sweet even:

Rasps ripen. Gathered & preserved some Rasps.
Finished cutting my tall hedges.
Planted-out the fourth row of Celeri.

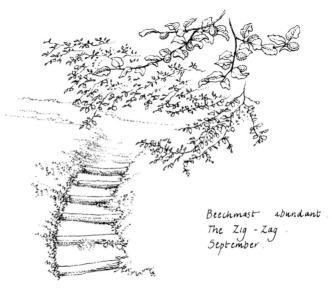

Beechmast abundant.
The Zig - Zag.
September.

Wednesday 19.
29 8/10; 69½; SW. Grey, & blowing, sultry, gale.

Began to trim, & tack the wall-trees.
Finished six rows of celeri.
Wheat turns very fast. My garden is dryed-up.

Oaks put-out their midsummer shoots, some of which are red, & some yellow; & those oaks that were stripped by caterpillars begin to be cloathed with verdure. Many beeches are loaded with mast, so that their boughs become very pendulous, & look brown. I see no acorns.

Thursday 20.
29 6/10; 63; NW, N. Dark with a brisk gale, sprinkling, heavy clouds.

Made black curran-jelly, & Rasp jam.
Grapes swell, & are forward.
Cut the first white cucumber. Watered cucum.rs

Friday 21.
29 7/10; 63; N, NE.

Ferruginous foxglove blows.

Dark & cold, gale, sun, bright even:

Hay & clover ricked.

Selborne down is very rusty: the pond still is one part in three in water.

Saturday 22.
29 6/10½; 64; SW.
Grey, gale, dark & spitting.

Sunday 23.
29 5/10½; SW.
Dark & soft, sprinklings, dark & warm.

Garden much dryed up.
Showers about.

Monday 24.
29 5/10½; 65; S, SW.
Wet mist, gleams, sultry, red even:

BRAMSHOT PLACE
Mr Hale reaps a small field of wheat. A large field of wheat is cut near Petersfield.
Made rasp jam.

Tuesday 25.
SW.
Bright, sultry.

Pease are hacked: rye is reaping: turnips thrive, & are hoing.

Mr Richardson's garden abounds with all sorts of crops, & with many sorts of fruits. His sandy soil produces an abundance of everything; & does not burn in droughts like the clays, which now are bound up so as to injure the growth of all garden matters. The watered meadows at Bramshot flourish & look green, the upland grass is much scorched. M^r R: has a pretty good show of Nectarines.

Wednesday 26.
SW.
Dark & hot, sun, grey & still.

Grass-hopper-lark whispers.
Two swifts at Bramshot church.

Thursday 27.
29 5/10½; 68; S, SW.
Deep fog, gale, sun, sprinklings, yellow even:

SELBORNE
Saw a nightingale. Stifling dust.
Two swifts at Selborne.

Friday 28.
29 4/10; 68; SW.
Sun, vast dew, brisk gale, cloudless, blowing, cloudy.

Hops thrive & are in bloom. The grass in my meadows burns.
Watered the gaden much.
Annuals do not thrive, for want of moisture.

Saturday 29.
2/10½; 29 4/10; 61;

Plums fail in all gardens.

W, NW; 16.
Shower, sun, with
heavy gales, showers,
gales.

The sharp wind soon dried the surface of the ground. The wind damages the flowers, & blows down the apples, & pears. Two swifts.

Sunday 30.
29 6/10½; 59½; NW.
Shower, dark, & cool,
sun, cool.

Some hop-gardens are injured by the wind of yesterday. Artichokes so dryed up that they do not head well.

Monday 31.
29 4/10; 57½; SW,
NW; 19, 8.
Showers, showers, &
gales.

Several men begin to reap.
Planted out some polyanths.
Rain in July . . . 1 inch 99 hund:

Good King Henry growing with chives and chicory in the herb garden. Wakes.

AUGUST 1786

Tuesday 1.
29 4/10; 60; W.
Dark & still,
sprinkling, cool.

The poor begin to glean wheat.
Gathered the first kidney-beans, scarlet.
The country looks very rich, being finely diversified with crops of corn of various sorts, & colours.

Wednesday 2.
29 6/10½; 57; NW,
NW. Sun, fine summer
weather, sprinkling.

Wheat-harvest becomes general. Pease housing.
Planted-out two rows of endive.
Planted more trenches of celeri, in all eight.
Smart shower to the NE.

Thursday 3.
29 7/10; NW, N, SE.
Sun, sweet harvest
weather.

The fallows of good husbandmen are in a fine crumbling state, & very clean.
Turnips thrive.

Sowed a crop of prickly-seeded spinage to stand the winter: the ground was very hard, & cloddy, & would not rake; so we levelled it down as well as we could with a garden-roller, & sprinkled it over with fine dusty mould to cover the seeds.

Nightingales appear in the walks: fly-catchers not seen: no swifts for some days.

Friday 4.
29 4/10½; 61½; W, SE.
Sun, cool air, dark & mild.

After-grass is very scanty: the pastures & meadows are very bare. Men bind wheat, & house pease. One swift.
Planted out more endive in the orchard.

Saturday 5.
29 2/10, 4/10; 65; SW, W, 21, 29.
Showers, sun & showers, fine even:

Planted-out more endive; & some rows of seedling polyanths: a fine refreshing rain.
Saw now 13 swifts!
The first broods of swallows, & martins congregate, & play about in great numbers.

Sunday 6.
29 6/10; 61; SW, W; 34.
Shower, louring, showers, fine even:

Mrs Ben White, by being delivered of a boy this morning, has encreased my nephews, & nieces to the number of 46.

Monday 7.
29 7/10½; 60; SW, W.
Sun, heavy clouds, fine afternoon.

Fallows stir well, & fall to pieces.
Much wheat reaped: men bind what was reaped last week.

Tuesday 8.
29 8/10; 61; @, @.
Sun & clouds, sultry, sweet even:

Planted some broccoli, & more endive.
Pease housed: much wheat bound.
Young swallows, & swifts congregate on the tower.

Wednesday 9.
29 7/10½; 63; S, SE.
Great dew, sweet harvest weather.
Full moon.

Planted a row of sweet Williams in the garden; & many polyanths in the orchard & field.
Large wheat-ricks are making.
Fern-owl chatters: white-throats still seen.
Fly-catcher, & nightingale still appear.

Thursday 10.
29 7/10; 68, 71; SW.
Sun, sultry, fresh breeze.

The leaves of my black-cluster vine begin to be tinged.
Much wheat housed. Reapers complain of heat.
Gathered two large apricots, my whole crop.

Friday 11.
29 7/10; 68½; W, S.
Bright & hot, louring,
sprinkling.

ALTON
Much wheat housed. Ponds in vales are dry.
Sultry. Showers about.
No wasps appear: earwigs abound every where.

Saturday 12.
29 2/10; 66; S, S; 22.
Deep fog, rain, rain.

SELBORNE
Wheat housed.

Sunday 13.
29 3/10; 63; SW, W;
24.
Cloudy, & blowing.

Rain in the night.
Showers about.
The crop of spinage comes-up well.

Monday 14.
29 1/10½; 59; SW;
55.
Sun, clouds, showers.

Kidney-beans abound, & cucumbers bear well.
Vast showers about with thunder, & hail.
Sowed lettuces to stand the winter; & planted-out more endives,
& sweet williams.

Tuesday 15.
29 2/10; 60; W, NW,
N; 57.
Showers, showers,
heavy showers.

Planted cuttings of dames violets, & slips of pinks under hand-
glasses: planted also more sweet williams, & polyanths.

Wednesday 16.
29 6/10; 64; N, NW,
N; 45.
Shower, dark clouds, &
showers.

Rain in the night.
Planted-out more sweet williams, & polyanths.
Some wheat a little grown under hedges.

Tremella nostoc abounds on the grass-walks.
Colchicum blows:
Say what retards, amidst the summer's blaze,
Th' autumnal bulb, 'till pale declining days?

Thursday 17.
29 8/10; 62; N, E.
Dark & still, gleams.

Much wheat bound: much gleaning brought home.
House-martins have young, second broods.

Friday 18.
29 6/10; 61; S.
Grey & still, dark &
wet.

Wheat housed, but not in fine order.

Saturday 19.
29 3/10; 64; S, SW;
50.
Rain, rain, heavy
clouds.

Mushrooms come in Mr White's avenue at Newton.

Sunday 20.
29 3/10½; 62; SW;
33.
Showers, showers,
showers.

Much wheat abroad.

Monday 21.
29 5/10¼; 60; SW.
Showers, cloudy, &
mild, small shower.

Kidney-beans bear by heaps: & cucumbers abound.
Coveys of partridges are said to be very large.
Butchers meat keeps badly.
Mushrooms are brought me from Hartley.

Tuesday 22.
29 6/10½; 57; W,
SW.
Grey, dark & warm,
sun, grey.

Men house, & rick wheat.
Young fern-owls are found, a second brood.
I do not meet with one wasp.
Fly-catchers are still seen.

Wednesday 23.
29 7/10½; 59; @; 24.
Sun, sultry, thunder,
shower, & hail, bright.

Vast clouds about.
Much wheat housed. Great showers about. We had only the
skirts of a thunder-shower.
One hornet.
Farmer Spencer finishes wheat-harvest.

We kept a young fern-owl for some days in a cage, & fed it with
bread, & milk. It was moping, & mute by day; but, being a night
bird, began to be alert as soon as it was dusk, often repeating a
little piping note. Sent it back to the brakes among which it was
first found.

Thursday 24.
29 9/10; 59½; NW.
Shower, heavy clouds,
shower, bright gleam.

Much wheat housed.

Friday 25.
29 9/10; 57; N.
Fog, vast dew, louring,
soft & still.

Some wheat housed. Most men have finished wheat harvest.
Hop-picking begins in the Hartley gardens.
Nightingales still appear in my walks.
Mushrooms are brought in great plenty.

Earwig on plums
Selborne .

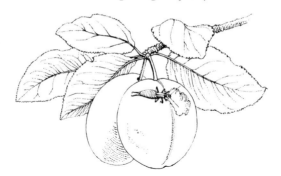

Saturday 26.
29 7/10; 61; SW, W;
24.
Rain, rain, fine even:

Earwigs damage the wall-fruit before it gets ripe.
Warm & moist. Mich: daiseys begin to blow.
Young fowls die at Newton.
Removed, & planted afresh the fiery, & orange-lilies, &
martagons.

Sunday 27.
29 6/10; 64; W; 16.
Dark, still, & wet.

Young swallows: a second brood. Second broods of martins, &
swallows come out daily.

Mr White of Newton brought down his three swivel-guns,¶ to try
them in Baker's hill with their muzzles towards the hanger,
expecting the report would have been very loud: but it did not
answer his expectation. He then removed them to the alcove; when
the sound rushing along the Lythe, & Combwood was very grand.
But it was at the hermitage that the repercussions & echoes
delighted the hearers; not only filling the Lythe with the roar, as if
all the beeches were tearing-up by the roots; but turning to the left
they pervaded the vale above Combwood-ponds; & after a pause
seemed to take-up the crash again, & to extend round Hartley-
hangers; & to die away at last among the coppices, & coverts of
Wardle-ham.

Monday 28.
29 6/10; 60, 64; W.
Sun, fine day.

The air is full of thistle-down blown from the top of the hanger.
Made five bottles, & a pint of catsup.

Tuesday 29.
29 6/10; 61; W.
Fog, sun, fine day.

Tyed-up the unmoved endives.
Men house oats, & barley.
Farmer Spencer & J: Hale began to pick their hops. The crop is
very great.
Grapes begin to turn colour.
Earthed-up the celeri.

Wednesday 30.
29 6/10½; 61; NW.
Sun & brisk wind, cool
even:

Hop-picking becomes general. The women earn good wages this
year; some of them pick 24 bush: in a day, at 3 half pence pr
bushel.

Thursday 31.
29 6/10; 58; W.
Sun & clouds, strong
wind.

Showers about.
The wind injures the hops.
Rain in Augst: . . . 4 inch: 34 hund:
Fly-catchers abound.
My well is very low.

SEPTEMBER 1786

Friday 1.
29 6/10; 63; W, SW.
Sun, strong gale, dark
& mild.

Sowed more lettuce-seed to stand the winter. The first sown did not come-up well.

Saturday 2.
29 6/10; 62, 65; W.
Rain, sun & wind, red
even:

Finished the transplanting the lilies, & martagons.

Sunday 3.
29 ½/10; 58; S, W;
85.
Bright, grey, rain,
rain.

Much rain with heavy gusts.

Monday 4.
29 6/10; 54; W.
Sun, clouds, shower,
cool.

Cut my new rick: the hay is good.

Tuesday 5.
29 7/10½; 52½; NW.
Sun, clouds, shower,
hail, cool.

Black-caps still appear. Frost.
Showers about.

Wednesday 6.
29 8/10; 51½; NE, S.
White frost, sweet day,
great dew.

China asters begin to blow.
Peaches, & Nectarines are good, but are eaten up by earwigs.
Hirundines cluster on Hartley-house, & on the thatch of the Grange barn.

Thursday 7.
29 6/10; 59½; S.
Grey, louring, wet,
still.

Planted out some Dames violets raised from cuttings.
Some young martins still in nests.
Grapes were once forward; but from the coolness of the season do not come on.

Friday 8.
29 3/10; 56, 60; S; 15.
Sun, clouds, rain, rain.

Rain in the night.
Made a pint of catsup.
Heavy rain.
Transplanted Fraxinella's, & ragged Robins.

Saturday 9.
29 1/10½; 58; SW,
W; 82.

Rain-bow.
Lighted a fire in the parlor.

Blowing, & showery.   The flight of swallows, & martins now is very great.

Sunday 10.
29 5/10½; 56; NW,   Many annuals are very backward.
SW; 14.   Saw one wasp.
Sun, gale, pleasant.

Monday 11.
29 7/10; 56; NW.   The hops unpicked turn brown very fast.
Sun, pleasant.   The foliage of the Virginia creeper turns red.

Tuesday 12.
29 4/10; 58; SW.   Hop-gathering ended.
Blowing & wet, heavy
shower.

Wednesday 13.
29 2/10½; 59; SW;   The tops of the beeches begin to be tinged.
65.   Nectarines very good.
Dark, blowing, & wet.

Thursday 14.
28 8/10; 60; SW; 70.   Much rain & wind in the night.
Strong wind, wind.   The flowers are much injured: apples are blown down: & the
                          hedges are torn.
                          Few hirundines are seen.
                          Fly-catcher still appears.

Friday 15.
29 1/10½; 57; W.   Virginian creeper much shattered by the wind.
Strong gales, sun &   Golden-crowned wren, & the creeper, *certhia*, seen in my fields.
clouds, gales.   Some few hirundines.

Saturday 16.
29 3/10½; 51, 55; W,   Hirundines appear again under the hanger: during the strong
S.   winds they were not seen.
Sun, pleasant day.   Endive blanched comes in. Tyed up more endive.

                          The vines were very forward in June: but now the grapes are quite
backward, having made no progress in ripening for some weeks,
on account of the blowing, black, wet weather. The bunches are of
a good size, & the grapes large, & much want hot sunshine to
bring them to perfection.
     My potted balsoms, which stand within, are still in beauty, tho'
they have been blowing now more than three months. One in
particular is more showy now than ever, & has such double flowers
that they produce no seed. The blossoms are as large as a crown-
piece.

Sunday 17.
29 6/10; 60; SW.
Grey, sun & wind, wet.

Wind & rain in the night.
Much damage has been done at sea & land by the late strong winds; in particular about London.

Monday 18.
29 8/10; 61; SW; 32, 11.
Soft, misty rain, sun, warm & pleasant.

Tuesday 19.
30 1/3/10; 57; N, NE.
Vast dew, grey, sun, sweet day.

Much gossamer on the grass, & floating in the air.
Marvel of Peru blows. Bright N: *aurora*.
Swallows cluster on a barn at Newton parsonage.

Wednesday 20.
30; 56; NE.
Deep fog, sun, sweet day.

Some hirundines.
Nectarines over.

Thursday 21.
29 7/10; 54; NE, E, SE.
White dew, cloudless, sweet day, red even:

Gathered the first grapes.
Some few swallows. Endive finely blanched.
Men bag their hops.
The fallows are in good order, & harrow very fine.

Friday 22.
29 8/10½; 52; N.
Great dew, cold air, cloudless.

ALTON
Celeri grows very fast.

Saturday 23.
29 8/10½; 61; N.
Sun, pleasant & cool.

SELBORNE
Gathered berberies.
Bro: Thomas & sons came.

Sunday 24.
29 9/10; 50; N.
Dark, still & cool.

Dame Loe came.

Monday 25.
29 5/10½; 50; N, SW.
Sun, grey, pleasant, dark, rain & wind.

Niece Betsey¶ came from Fyfield.

Tuesday 26.
29 3/10½; 54; SW; 41.
Sun, cold, showers.

Began to turn the horses in to the great meadow.
Grapes improve a little.

Saw a nest full of young swallows, nearly fledged, in their nest under Captain Dumaresq' gate-way at Pilham-place. Saw the same day many martins over Selborne village. I have often seen young house-martins in their nests in the Mich: week; but never swallows before.

Wednesday 27.
29 3/10; 50; W.
Sun, showers, showers.

Glow-worms shine faintly.

Thursday 28.
29 1/10¼; 50; NW.
Dark & blowing.

Friday 29.
29 2/10; NW; 61.
Rain, blowing, & cold.

Stormy weather in the night, that blew-down many of my apples, & pears, & tore my annuals.
Aurora.

Saturday 30.
29 6/10; 50; NW; 3.
Showers, sun, bright.

Rain in Septemᵣ . . . 4 inch: 79 hund:

OCTOBER 1786

Sunday 1.
29 8/10; NW.
Sun, grey, & still.

Many hirundines.

"About Octobrᵣ 1ˢᵗ the weather was cold & wet at Vevey in Switserland; when the Hirundines flew so near the ground as to be a prey to cats which watched for them; & some entred mens windows so tame & hungry as to sit on a finger, & take flies when offered, or which they saw on the glass, & walls."

Monday 2.
29 7/10¾; 52; W, S.
Grey, sun, sprinkling.

Many martins, & some swallows feeding along the hanger.
Began to gather the keeping apples.
Soft & mild.

Tuesday 3.
29 3/10½; 58; SW, S, SE.
Grey & mild, curdled clouds, mild, rain.

Saw no Hirundines.
Gathered in the apples called dearlings, which keep well & are valuable kitchen apples. My only tree of the sort stands in the meadow, & produced ten bushels of fruit. Apples this year have sold at 8s: per bushel: so had the price continued the produce would be worth four pounds. Next Year probably there will be no crop; because I do not remember to have seen this tree bear two years following.

Wednesday 4.
29 1/10; 54; SE, E,

Gathered in the Royal russets, & knobbed russets: the former are

NE; 30.
Sun, mild, dark, rain,
vast rain.

fine shewy apples.
There is a good crop of each sort.
Some hirundines about.

On this day an woodcock was seen in a coppice at Froyle.

Thursday 5.
29 4/10; 53; W; 100.
Sun, brisk gale, bright.

Friday 6.
29 ½/10; S.
Rain, rain, rain, wind.

Swallow.
Strong gales.

Saturday 7.
28 9/10½; 52; W, S;
70.
Sun, showers,
drowning rain.

Gossamer floats.
Hirundines feeding along the hanger.
The great rains do not influence our wells in the least.
Niece Betsey returned to Fyfield.

On this day Miss Mary Haggitt of Rushton, Northamptonshire, by being married to my Nephew Sam Barker, encreased the number of my nephews & nieces to 47.

Sunday 8.
29; 55; S; 205.
Rain, rain, vast rain.

Rain in the night.

"We saw a great †number on the wing at Rolle: & about that time their departure seems to have been general."

Monday 9.
29 3/10½; 53; S, SE;
20.
Sun, soft, & pleasant,
louring, rain.

The rocky lanes are much torn by the rains.
Swallows.
Nep: Tom, & Harry White went to Fyfield.

Tuesday 10.
29 3/10; 57; S.
Sun & clouds, soft, &
pleasant, rain.

My grapes rot very fast, & do not ripen.
Several swallows at Bentley.

Wednesday 11.
29; 55; S; 31.
Dark, & mild, rain,
rain.

The news papers mention vast floods about the country; & that much damage has been done by high tides, & tempestuous winds.

Thursday 12.
29 4/10; 55; NW, W;
48.
Rain, gleams, mild,
showers.

---

†Presumably of hirundines, mentioned on October 7th.

Friday 13.
29 7/10½; 46; NW.
Sun, sun & clouds,
heavy clouds.

Men sow wheat. Earthed up celeri.
Red *Aurora*.

Saturday 14.
29 9/10½; 45; NW.
White frost, ice, sun,
sweet day.

Men sow wheat in good order at Temple, & Wick-hill.
The hop-planters of this parish returned from Wey-hill fair with
chearful faces, & full purses; having sold a large crop of hops for
a good price. The hops of Kent were blown away by the storms,
after the crop of this country was gathered in.
Nasturtions, & potatoes greens cut-down by the frost.

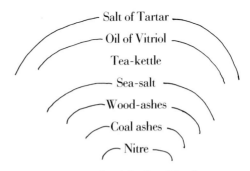

With the above-mentioned articles Bro.ʳ Tho.ˢ has attempted to
make a fairey-ring, circle within circle: & we are to take notice in
the spring which circle, & whether any, wil produce grass of a
deeper green than before. The tea-kettle which has occasioned the
dots was set-out, time after time, full of boiling water. The circles
made with oil of vitriol, with sea-salt, & with salt petre, have
discoloured the grass: those with Sal. Tartar, wood & coal ashes
have no visible effect at present. The grass seems killed where the
tea-kettle stood.

Sunday 15.
29 9/10; 30; NW.
Frost, ice, sun,
pleasant, dark.

Prodigious damage appears to be done by the late tempests, all
over the kingdom; & in many places abroad.

Monday 16.
29 8/10; 45; W, NE.
Dark & still, grey,
dark & cold.

Celeri comes in.
Bro.ʳ & Sister Benj.ⁿ came.

Tuesday 17.
29 8/10; 47; N.
Grey, still & pleasant.

Ground in fine order for sowing with wheat.
Deep red *aurora*.

Wednesday 18.
29 9/10; NE.

Gossamer fills the air, & covers the ground.

Deep fog, sun, sweet
day.

Thursday 19.
30 ¼/10; 45; NE.
Frost, ice, sun,
pleasant.

The well rises very fast.
Men pull up turnips, & stack them.

Friday 20.
30 ½/10; 45; NE.
Dark & still, fog.

Grapes improve.
The fields, & paths are very dry, & the roads much mended.
My balsoms in pots, that have been in bloom four months, now
begin to fade.
Men sow wheat in fine order.
Rover springs several pheasants in Harteley-wood.

Saturday 21.
29 9/10; NE.
Grey & mild.

Sweet autumnal weather.
We find many large coveys of partridges.

Sunday 22.
29 9/10; NE.
Grey & pleasant,
spitting fog.

Bro.r & Sister Benj.n left us.

My tall hedges, & the hanging woods do not shew their usual
beautiful tints, & colours: the reason is because the foliage was so
much torn & shattered by the rains & tempests.

Monday 23.
29 9/10; NE.
Deep wet fog.

The paths are wet, & slippery.
A flock of Red-wings are seen in the high wood.

Red-wings are late this autumn. Perhaps the vintage was late this
year in Germany: so that these birds were detained by the grapes,
which they did not wish to exchange for our hips, & haws. Red-
wings do much damage in vineyards, when the grapes are ripe.

Tuesday 24.
29 9/10¼; 52; E.
Fog, sun, sweet day.

Field-fares are seen.
A few mushrooms on Nore hill.

Wednesday 25.
30; 29; E.
White frost, sun, sweet
day.

Men draw their turnips, & stack them.
Insects in the air, & on the bloom of late asters.

Thursday 26.
31; 29, 52; E.
Very white frost, sun,
sweet day, red even:

Grapes good.
Flocks of lapwings come to the uplands.
Several wet, floated fields are now sown that must have missed
their wheat-crop, & have lain 'till spring, had not this fine dry
season drained them, & rendered them fit for sowing.

Friday 27.
30; E.
Frost, fog, grey & cool.

Men draw turnips.
Planted two rows & an half of lettuces under the fruit-wall to stand the winter.

Saturday 28.
29 9/10½; E, NE.
Grey, sun, sharp wind, red even.

Bro.ʳ Tho.ˢ left us, & went to Fyfield.

Sunday 29.
29 8/10½; 29; NE.
Frost, sun, sharp wind.

Monday 30.
29 7/10; N, NE.
Sun & clouds, sharp wind.

The paths are very dry, & the horse roads very much mended.

Tuesday 31.
29 6/10; 39; NE.

Planted more lettuces under the fruit-wall, in all three rows; & an 100 of cabbages to stand the winter. The ground was well dunged.
Rover springs several pheasants, & some coveys of partridges.
Rain in Octobᵣ . . . 5 inch: 4 hund:

NOVEMBER 1786

Wednesday 1.
29 6/10; 39; N; 7.
Dark, some small snow, cold & moist.

Thursday 2.
29 5/10½; NE.
Small rain, grey & cold.

Ground wet.

Friday 3.
29 6/10½; 32; N.
Hard frost, sun, grey.

Paths greasey from the frost.
The oaks in Comb-wood, & below Temple are in full leaf, & many of them in good verdure.

Saturday 4.
29 7/10; N.
Fog, grey, sun, pleasant.

The beeches in general have lost their foliage.

Sunday 5.
29 7/10; 45; N.
Grey, small rain in the
night, sun, cloudless,
sharp wind.

March-like winds.
Here & there a wood-cock is found.
Sweet moon shine.

The evening manouvers of the rooks at this season of the Year is
curious. Just before dusk they return in long strings from the
foraging of the day, & rendezvous by thousands over Selborne
down, where they wheel round in the air, & sport & dive in a
playful manner; all the while exerting their voices, & making a
loud cawing, which being blended & softened by the distance that
we are from them becomes a confused noise, or chiding, or rather a
pleasing murmur very engaging to the Imagination, & not unlike
the cry of a pack of hounds in hollow woods, or the rushing of the
wind in tall trees, or the tide tumbling on the pebbly shore. When
the ceremony is over, with the last gleam of day they retire for the
night to the deep beechen woods of Tisted, & Ropley.

Monday 6.
29 7/10½; 30; N.
Hard frost, sun, cutting
wind.
Full moon.

Gathered-in all the grapes, a vast crop, many of which are not
ripened.
The limes opposite have cast all their leaves.

The beautiful planets Jupiter, & Venus appear now of an evening
soon after sunset almost opposite, the former in the N:E: & the
latter in the S:W:

Tuesday 7.
29 8/10; 29; NE.
Hard frost, sun, cutting
wind.

Timothy the tortoise has withdrawn himself for some time, & is
retired under the dead laurel-hedge.
March winds.

Wednesday 8.
29 7/10½; 28; NE.
Frost, grey, still &
cold.

Covered the asparagus beds with long dung.
Mrs Etty returned to Selborne.

Thursday 9.
29 7/10; 35; NE.
Small rain, sun &
clouds, pleasant.

This day compleats the 28th of this dry fit, which has done infinite
service to the low districts, that were floated with water by the
heavy rains in the beginning of last month.

Friday 10.
29 7/10½; 34; NE.
Dark & still, dark &
cold.

Began to trim the vines: they produce some good wood; but much
is not well ripened.

Saturday 11.
29 7/10¾; 35; NE.
Grey, sun, pleasant, red
even:

Some Insects, *tipulae* I believe, fly about in my fields.
N. *Aurora.*

Sunday 12.
29 8/10½; 33; NE.
Hazey, sun, cold &
pleasant, frost.

The hogs have been turned for some weeks into the high-wood,
& hanger, where they have availed themselves much of the large
crop of beech-mast. The hogs find, no doubt, many trufles in the
high-wood, where they are said to abound.

Last week Wolmer-pond was sewed,¶ & fished after an interval of
more than 20 years. And yet there was no quantity of fish: for the
carps did not amount to one hundred; nor was there any young
stock: tench there were none; many perch; a few large, lank pikes;
& a few large eels. It is said that the pond is to lie a sew all next
summer. The pond, being an area of more that[n] 60 acres, was
several days in running dry. If this pond continues dry next spring,
more Roman coins may be found, in windy weather, on the
surface of the sand. Many hundreds were found when it last lay
dry, about the year 1741.

Monday 13.
29 6/10¾; 25; E.
Severe frost, sun, sharp
wind.

Cut down the artichokes, & covered them well with straw:
covered also the lettuces under the fruit-wall.
Some loads of peat were carted from the forest.
The water in my well continues to rise all thro' this dry weather.

Tuesday 14.
29 5/10; 22; E.
Severe frost! Cloudless,
pleasant.

Boys slide on the Ice! Flocks of hen-chaffinches are seen.
The paths, & roads quite dry.
Swept up the leaves in the walks, & burnt them.
Large coveys of partridges about.

Wednesday 15.
29 ½/10; 29; E.
Dark & cold, sleet,
sleet.

Covered the rows of celeri with straw.
This day compleats the 34 of the dry weather.
Horses begin to lie within.

Thursday 16.
28 7/10; 35; E, NE.
Deep fog, small rain,
wet.

I have often observed many titmice in beechen woods: by a heap of
beech-mast now lying in my orchard I see that t: mice feed on the
kernels of the fruit of that tree, & that marsh-tit-mice are
employed all day in carrying them away.

Friday 17.
28 8/10; 42; E; 24.
Rain, rain, mild, &
wet.

Dew appears on the outsides of windows.
Condensations on walls, & painted wainscot.

Saturday 18.
29 2/10; 39; N, NE.
Dark & moist, grey,
dark.

Hogs frequent the hanger, & high wood, & batten on the beech-
mast.

Sunday 19.
28 6/10; 44; NE, SE,
SW. Rain, rain, rain.

Much rain.
Worms lie out.

Monday 20.
28 8/10½; SW; 214.
Grey, & warm, rain,
rain.

Vast rain in the night.
Many insects in the air.
Much rain.

Tuesday 21.
29 5/10; 39; NE; 41.
Grey, still, & mild.

Bought 61 bushels of peat-ashes, & laid them up in the ash-
house.
Farmer Lassam's Dorset: ewes begin to lamb.

Wednesday 22.
29 6/10; 38; NE.
Grey & still, moist.

I sent a woman up the hill with a peck of beech-mast, which she
tells me she has scattered all round the down amidst the bushes &
brakes, where there were no beeches before. I also ordered
Thomas to sow beech-mast in the hedges all round Baker's hill.

Thursday 23.
29 6/10; 38; E. Grey
& cold, sun, sharp.

The pound-field is sowing with wheat after turnips, which were
drawn, & stacked.

Friday 24.
29 5/10; 37; E.
Dark & harsh.

Saturday 25.
29 4/10; 37; E.
Grey, & cold.

Paths dry.

Sunday 26.
29 3/10½; 41; SE.
Rain, rain, grey,
bright.

Soft air, with dew on the outside of the windows.

Mr Cane saw in one flock some hundreds of whistling plovers on
the downs.

Monday 27.
44; SE.
Dark & moist.

FYFIELD
Grey crows on the downs.

Tuesday 28.
29 4/10; 51; S; 60.
Rain, rain, rain.

Mr Talbot turned-out a stag which after wounding some hounds,
& an horse, was taken alive.

Wednesday 29.
29 1/10; 42; S; 92.
Rain, rain, rain.

Thursday 30.
29 5/10; 35; N.
Sun, bright.

Rain in Novemr . . . 4 inch: 38 hund:

DECEMBER 1786

Friday 1.
36; E.
Rain, rain, wet.

WINTON
The downs are very heavy.

Saturday 2.
29 5/10; 39; S; 11.
Sun, sweet day.

SELBORNE
The roads are very wet.
Several white gulls, as usual, wading about in the stream beyond Alresford.

Sunday 3.
29 2/10½; 46; S, SW;
72.
Rain, rain, rain.

Strong wind.
Walls sweat.

Monday 4.
28 8/10½; 42; SW.
Sun, showers, thunder.

Tuesday 5.
28 7/10½; 40; SW,
W; 89.
Sun, sun, soft air.
Full moon.

Rain all night.

Wednesday 6.
28 7/10; 48; SW; 34.
Rain, rain, rain.

Thursday 7.
29 1/10½; 44; SW;
63.
Showers, showers.

Hail in the night.
Polyanths blow. *Antirrhinum Cymbalaria* in bloom.

Friday 8.
29 3/10¾; 39; SE; 17.
Dark & mild.

Saturday 9.
29 3/10; 45; SW; 69.
Sun, soft & pleasant.

Much rain in the night.

Sunday 10.
29 1/10; 41; SE; 11.
Sun, gusts, wet &
stormy.

Showers in the night.

Monday 11.
29 1/10¼; 43; SW;
71.
Grey & mild, showers.

Much rain in the night. Distant thunder; some hail. Worms lie out.

Tuesday 12.
28 9/10; 45; SW; 69.
Rain, rain, rain.

Wednesday 13.
29 1/10; 45; SW.
Hail, sun, shower, stormy.

Peter Well's well is 36 feet deep, my own 63.

Thursday 14.
29 3/10; 45; W; 8.
Sun, sun, blowing, bright.

Peter Well's well runs over; when this is the case, the springs are very high. This overflowing lasted only two or three days.

Friday 15.
29 3/10¼; 35; W.
White frost, sun, pleasant.

A cellar in the back-street Faringdon is full of water.

Saturday 16.
29 1/10; 35; W.
White frost, sun.

Rain in the night.
The walks in my fields are strewed with the berries of Missletoe, blown from the hedges.

Sunday 17.
29 1/10½; 31; NW;
N.
Frost, sun, dark, & cold.

Still.

Monday 18.
29 1/10¼; 30; E.
Frost, dark, sun, pleasant, snow.

Still.

Tuesday 19.
29 2/10½; 29; 30; NE.
Dark, & sharp.

Snow covers the ground.
The beeches in the hanger are beautifully powdered.

Wednesday 20.
29 4/10; 28; NE.
Dark, & frosty, sun, dark & cold.

Snow on the ground.

Thursday 21.
29 6/10½; 23; N.
Hard frost, sun, sharp
air.

Snow on the ground.
Therm! Newton . . . 30.

Friday 22.
29 8/10; 22, 26; NW.
Severe frost, sun,
pleasant, dark & still.

Ice in my chamber.
Therm! Newton: . . 28.

Saturday 23.
29 4/10; 30, 34; SW,
W.
Dark, snow, snow,
thaw.

Snow all day.

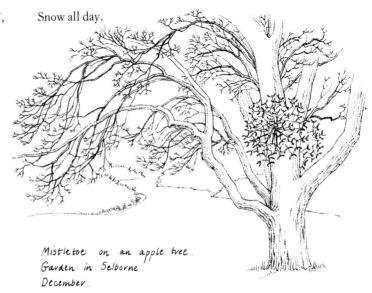

Mistletoe on an apple tree.
Garden in Selborne.
December.

Sunday 24.
29 6/10½; 29, 28; E.
Hard frost, sun, sharp
wind.

Therm: Newton 28.

Monday 25.
29 4/10; 23; NE.
Hard frost, still,
cloudless, sharp.

[Therm: Newton] 23.
Snow covers the ground.

Tuesday 26.
29 4/10; 18, 26; S, @.
Severe frost, sun,
pleasant.

[Therm: Newton] 29.
Mʳ Churton came.

Wednesday 27.
29 1/10½; 35, 44; S,
S.

[Therm: Newton] 27.

Dark, thaw, fog, rain,
swift thaw.

Thursday 28.
29 7/10; 35½; W; 31.   [Therm: Newton] 38.
White frost, sun, still,
pleasant.

Friday 29.
29 6/10; W; 17.
Rain, sun, showers,
bright.

Saturday 30.
30 2/10; 36; W.
White frost, sun,
pleasant.

Sunday 31.
30 2/10; 36; S.
Deep fog, grey, &
mild, & moist.

Dr.	Rev.ᵈ Mʳ Randolph			Cʳ.			
1783¶		£ s d		1783		£ s d	
To pᵈ Beagley, bricklayer,				By bank-bill sent			
at Faringdon	2: 5: 2			by post.........	10: 0: 0		
To pᵈ I. Finden, carpenter							
at Dᵒ	4: 2: 0						
To pᵈ Shawyer, brick-							
burner....................	1: 6: 9						
	7:13:11						
Xmas: 1783							
To pᵈ to sundry poor....	2: 2: 0						
	9:15:11						
1784							
To balance received							
Septʳ 13.................	0: 4: 1						
	10: 0: 0						

Herb! Randolph

```
17:  7:  2
 2:  6:  3
 1:16:  1
_____
21:  9:  6
15:  5:  0
_____
 6:  4:  6
```

JANUARY   — 1787 —

Monday 1.
30 1/10; 36; S.
Dark, mild & moist.

SELBORNE
Slept at Newton.

Tuesday 2.
30; 38; E.
Dark, moist, & soft.

Helleborus foetidus, polyanths, & double daiseys blow.

Wednesday 3.
30 1/10; 34; NW.
Deep fog, grey, & mild.

On this evening there was a total eclipse of the moon: but the sky was so cloudy, that we saw nothing of the progress of it.

Thursday 4.
30 2/10; 34; NW.
Dark, still, & mild.

Winter aconites blow: snow-drops bud, & crocus's sprout.

Friday 5.
30 1/10; 41; NW.
Soft, & spring-like.

Saturday 6.
30 1/10¾; 41; NW.
Dark & mild, wet.

Paths dry: boys play at taw on the Plestor.

Sunday 7.
30 2/10½; 31, 28; E.
Frost, bright, frost.

Hepatica's blow.

Monday 8.
30 3/10; 22; N, S, N.
Hard frost, bright, grey.

Wheeled dung into the garden, & to the basons in Baker's hill. Mr Churton left us.

Tuesday 9.
30 1/10½; 33; E.

Wheeled dung down to the dug ground in the meadow.

Deep fog, thaw, wet
fog.

Wednesday 10.
29 9/10½; 33; E.
Deep, wet fog.

Thursday 11.
29 6/10; 33; E, SE.
Grey, sun, soft, &
pleasant.

This afternoon I saw at the house of my neighbour Mr Burbey,
54 young girls, which he entertained with tea, & cakes: they
were, except a few, natives of this village.

Friday 12.
29 2/10; 33; E.
Very hoar frost, sun,
cloudless, pleasant.

Saturday 13.
29 4/10; 40; SE, E.
Dark & mild, wet.

Carted from my dung-hill two loads of hot dung, & made a
seedling cucumber-bed.

Sunday 14.
29 6/10½; 34; E.
Frost, sun, pleasant.

Monday 15.
29 6/10½; 29; NE, E.
Frost, very white,
cloudless, pleasant,
deep fog.

Tuesday 16.
29 6/10; 32; SE, S.
Deep fog, sun, dark &
mild.

Wednesday 17.
29 9/10; 33; N.
Deep fog, sun,
pleasant, frost.

Strong *aurora*.

Thursday 18.
29 8/10¼; 29; SW,
NW.
White frost, sun,
shower, bright.

Friday 19.
29 9/10; 33; NW, SW;

Sowed cucumber-seeds in the hot-bed.

13.
Frost, white, sun, thaw,
wet, & dark.

Saturday 20.
29 8/10½; 43; NW,   Walls sweat: dew on the outsides of windows.
N.
Dark & mild, wet mist.

Sunday 21.
29 8/10; 43, 44; NW.   Snow-drops, winter-aconites, & hepaticas make a pleasing show.
Dark, & mild, bright
gleams, dark & mild.

Monday 22.
29 8/10; 42; NE.
Dark, soft, & still.

Tuesday 23.
29 7/10½; 40; SW,
W.
Dark, still, & moist,
mild.

Wednesday 24.
29 8/10; 39; NE, E.   Sowed radishes under the melon-screen.
Dark & still, wet mist,
dark & mild.

Thursday 25.
29 8/10¼; 31, 27; E.   Trenched some quarters in the Garden.
Frost, sharp wind, sun,   Short *Aurora*.
frost.

Friday 26.
29 5/10¾; 25; NE.   Potted some Cucumber-plants.
Hard frost, sun, sharp
wind, flakes of snow.

Saturday 27.
29 5/10; 26; NE.   Snow on the ground.
Snow falls, sun, bright,
frost.

Sunday 28.
29 5/10; 26, 39; SE, S,   Snow covers the ground.
SW.
Snow, snow, bright,
frost.

Monday 29.
29 2/10, 7/10; 40, 48;
S.
Rain, rain, dark &
mild.

Snow all melted.

Tuesday 30.
30; 45; S; 75.
Grey, & mild, sun,
pleasant.

Wednesday 31.
30 ¼/10; 40; SE.
Small frost, sun, still,
& pleasant.

Rain in January: . . 0 inch: 88 hund:
Beautiful dappled sky.

FEBRUARY 1787

Thursday 1.
29 9/10; 40; W.
Sun, fog, sun, deep
fog.

Friday 2.
29 9/10; 45; SW.
Wet & warm, gleams,
wet.
Full moon.

Storm-cock sings.
Brown wood-owls come down from the hanger in the dusk of the
evening, & sit hooting all night on my wall-nut trees. Their note
is like a fine *vox humana*, & very tuneable.

Saturday 3.
29 8/10½; 45; SW,
W; 20.
Rain, showers, & sun.

Some Crocus's begin to blow.
The owls probably watch for mice about the buildings. White
owls haunt my barn, but do not seem to perch often on trees.

Sunday 4.
29 8/10; 32; W, SE.
Frost, sun, pleasant.

Monday 5.
29 6/10; 33; E.
Grey, sun.

Tuesday 6.
29 4/10; 42; S.
Grey & mild, deep fog.

Wednesday 7.
29 5/10; 47; SW; 21.

Rain, rain, blowing,
bright.

Thursday 8.
29 2/10; 37; SW.   Crocus's blow.
Sun, pleasant.

Friday 9.
29 2/10; 45; S.
Grey, & mild, rain,
rain.

Saturday 10.
29; 42; S, SW; 42.   Took Mrs Etty's ashes, 28 bushels, paid her.
Dark & mild, rain,
rain.

Sunday 11.
28 6/10; 41; S.   Very wet day.
Rain, rain, rain.

Monday 12.
28 3/10½; 40; S; 115.   Carted in dung for the cucumber-bed.
Rain, rain.   Several claps of loud thunder.

Tuesday 13.
29; 39; W; 82.   Much rain in the night.
Rain, sun, & brisk
wind.

Wednesday 14.
29 6/10; 35; SW.   Carted-in dung for the bearing cucumber-bed.
White frost, sun,
pleasant.

Thursday 15.
29 6/10¼; 37; S, SW.
Wet, & windy, rain,
rain.

Friday 16.
29 6/10; 45; SW; 62.
Wind & rain, rain,
rain.

Saturday 17.
30; 36; SW, W; 4.   Crocus's make a fine show: bees gather on the crocus's.
Bright, sun, pleasant.   Cucumber-plants thrive, & are pinched to make them throw-out
                           side shoots.

Sunday 18.
29 9/10¾; 42; W.
No sun, grey, & mild.

Monday 19.
29 9/10¾; 38; NW.
White frost, sun, sweet
day, red evening.

Sowed Baker's hill, & the great mead with ashes.
Crocus's make a glorious show: bees much out. The air full in
insects, & gossamer.
Bat appears. Butterfly.

Tuesday 20.
29 8/10¾; 40; N.
Deep fog, gleams, dark
& mild.

Turned the dung for the cucumber-bed.
Radishes come up.

Wednesday 21.
29 8/10; 42; N.
Sun, pleasant, red even:

Male yew-trees shed/send forth clouds of farina.

Thursday 22.
29 7/10; 42; NE, E.
Sun, pleasant, red even:

Planted five rows of long-pod beans in the meadow-garden.
The air some what sharp.

Friday 23.
29 7/10; 26; E, S.
Hard frost, very white,
sun, mackarel sky.

Rooks build at Faringdon parsonage.

On Feb: 23: & 24 the cuckow was heard at Rolle in Switserland.¶

Saturday 24.
29 7/10; 32; W, NE,
SE.
Frost, sun, pleasant.

Turned the dung.
The blossom-buds of the apricot swell, & are just ready to open.
Cucumbers thrive, & show side shoots.

Sunday 25.
29 6/10½; 36; W,
NW.
Grey, sun, sweet
weather.

Monday 26.
29 7/10; 42; SW.
Dark, & still, sun,
sweet weather.

Insects, & gossamer float in the air.
Made the bearing cucumber-bed for four lights.

Tuesday 27.
29 4/10½; 42; S.
Grey, clouds, rain,
rain.

On this day my Niece Edm^d White was delivered of a daughter,
who encreases my Nephews, & nieces to the number of 48.

Wednesday 28.
29 6/10½; 44; W,
SW; 21.
Grey & mild, sun,
dark, shower.

Apricot-blossoms begin to open.
Rain in February . . 3 in: 67 hun:

MARCH 1787

Thursday 1.
29 2/10; 47; S, SW;
19.
Wet & blowing,
driving rain, & strong
wind.

Cucumber-bed very hot.

Friday 2.
29 3/10; 45; SW, W.
Blowing, & showery,
moon-shine.

Slugs out in damp weather.
Hanger.

Saturday 3.
28 6/10¼; 42; S, SW;
62.
Blowing with driving
rain.

Sunday 4.
29 4/10½; 40; NW,
N.
Louring, sun & clouds.

Showers in the night.
Cucumber-plants very strong, & flourishing.

Monday 5.
29 1/10½; 36; SE, S,
SW; 20.
Frost, ice, blowing with
much rain.

Tuesday 6.
28 7/10; 42; SE, SW;
122.
Rain, rain, rain.

The earth is very full of water.

Wednesday 7.
29 4/10; 40; W, NW.
Sun, pleasant.

Thursday 8.
29 4/10½; 34; W, S.

Earthed the Cucumber-bed.

Frost, sun, pleasant,
spring-like.

Pile-wort blows.

Friday 9.
29 ½/10; 39; S.
Red morning, rain,
rain.

Saturday 10.
29 1/10; 42; S, W; 59.
Rain, stormy, & wet.

Sunday 11.
29 7/10; 38; SW, NW;
9.
Frost, sun, shower,
hail, sun, pleasant.

Peach-trees begin to blow.

Monday 12.
30, 30 ¾/10; 36; NW,
SW.
White frost, sun,
pleasant, grey.

Turned-out the cucumber plants into the hills of their bearing
beds: they are very stout, & fine.
Dogs-toothed violets begin to blow.

Tuesday 13.
30 1/10; 42; W, SW,
W.
Sun, dark, grey, mild,
& still.

Daffodils blow.
Bat out.

Wednesday 14.
30 1/10; 42½; NE, E,
NE.
Dark, still, & mild,
warm.

Planted more roses from South Lambeth.
The male-bloom of the cucumbers opens: the bed is warm, & the
plants thrive.

Thursday 15.
30, 30; 41; NE, SW,
NE.
White frost, sun, sweet
weather, dark, bright.

Sowed a box of polyanth-seed, saved from my own flowers. Fine
bloom on the fruit-wall.

Friday 16.
29 9/10; 38; NW, W.
White frost, sun, dark,
still, & mild.

Hot bed warm. Watered cucumbers well.
The cats brought-in a dead house-martin from the stable. I was in
hopes at first sight that it might have been in a torpid state;¶ but it
was decayed, & dry.

Saturday 17.
29 9/10; 43; N, NE.

Polyanths blow. Jet-ants appear.

Grey, dark, warm, &
still.

Sowed cucumber-seeds in the great bed.
Cucumbers show rudiments of fruit.
Ground is mellow, & digs well.

Sunday 18.
30 1/10, 1/10; 38; NE,
N.
White frost, ice, sun,
spring-like.

Timothy the tortoise heaves up the earth: he lies under the wall-
nut tree.

Monday 19.
29 9/10; 31; E, S.
Wh: frost, ice, sun,
sweet day.

Women hoe wheat.
Gossamer abounds.
Sowed a bed of Celeri under a hand-glass.

Tuesday 20.
29 7/10½; 32; SE.
White frost, sun,
pleasant.

Some Apricots begin to set.
Sent me from South Lambeth, two Nectarine-trees; several sorts
of curious pinks; some mulberry-rasps; some scarlet lichnis's: a
root of Monk's rhubarb. ¶

Wednesday 21.
29 6 10½; 35; SE, E.
White frost, sun, sweet
day.

Thursday 22.
29 6/10; 35; NW, W,
S.
Wh: frost, ice, sun,
gale.

The tortoise comes forth from his hole.
Men open their hop-hills,
& cut their hops.

Friday 23.
29 1/10; 45; SW; 36.
Rain, rain, sun,
showers, hail.

Timothy hides his head under the earth.

Saturday 24.
29 4/10; 35; NW, W,
S.
Frost, ice, sun,
pleasant.

Sowed onions, parsnips, parsley,
& lettuce-seed.

Crown Imperial.
Wakes.
April.

Sunday 25.
29 2/10; 42; S, SE.
Dark & louring, rain,
rain, rain.

Driving rain.

Monday 26.
29 3/10¼; 44; S, W;

Transplanted some of the best, blowing seedling polyanths from

31.
Dark, shower, sun,
pleasant.

the orchard to the bank in the garden.
Planted some scorpion-senna's from S. Lambeth.

Tuesday 27.
29 4/10; 43; W.
Sun, brisk gale, sun, &
clouds.

Sowed a large bed of carrots, with radishes, & lettuces. Planted
three rows of broad beans.

Swallows were first seen this year at Messina in Sicily.

Wednesday 28.
29 1/10½; 45; SW.
Driving rain, sun, dark
& moist.

Timothy continues to lie very close.
Several cucumbers are beginning to blow; set some of them.

Thursday 29.
28 9/10½; 43; SW.
Driving rain, rain,
dark & wet.

Honey-suckles are in full leaf; roses, goose-berries, & currans,
shoot much: grass grows, turnips shoot.

Friday 30.
29/10; 44; SW; 61.
Rain, rain, sun,
showers, soft, &
bright.

Chaffinches pull-off the blossoms of the polyanths, which are
beautifully variegated.

On March 29.th Some swallows were seen over the lake of Geneva,
& at Rolle.
    On March 30 several were seen at the same place.

Saturday 31.
29 3/10¼; 40; SW; 9.
White dew, rock-
clouds, showers, bright
& mild.

Tanner shoots the chaffinches.
Mackarels come.
Bantam-hen lays. Black & grey snails without shells.
Rain in March . . 4 inch. 28 hund.

APRIL 1787

Sunday 1.
29 7/10; 40; NE.
Fog, sun, & clouds,
cold air.

SELBORNE
Three Swallows appear.
Crown imperials, double hyacinths, cherries against walls, blow.

Monday 2.
29 5/10; 39; NE.
Dark & harsh, dark &
moist.

Lined the back of the Cucumber bed with hot dung.
Fritillaria blows.

Tuesday 3.
29 3/10; 42; NE.
Dark, & hazy, dark &
wet.

Polyanths make a fine show.
Cowslips blow under hedges.

Wednesday 4.
29 4/10½; 42; NE; 10.
Grey, sun, sweet day,
summer.

Tortoise comes out.
Black caps, & Chif-chafs appear.

Thursday 5.
29 4/10⅓; 42½; NE.
Dark, & harsh, dark,
rain.

Lined the front of the cucumber-bed.
Birds still pick-off the polyanth blossoms.

Friday 6.
29 3/10½; 46; NE; 11.
Dark & moist, grey,
wet, rain.

Stone-curlews pass along over my house of an evening with a
short quick note after dark.
Wry-neck pipes in the orchard.

April 6. Nightingale sings at Citraro in the nearer Calabria.

Saturday 7.
29 6/10; 42; NE; 15.
Sun & clouds, sharp
wind.

Some cucumbers set.
40 or 50 swallows were seen skimming over a pond between
Godalming & Guildford.

Sunday 8.
29 8/10⅓; 40; NE, N.
Dark & harsh, sharp
wind, bright gleam.

Birds still pull-off the polyanth blossoms.
Mrs Clement's daughter, born this day, makes my nephews &
nieces 49.

Monday 9.
29 8/10¾; 38; NE.
Sun, sharp wind.

ALTON

Tuesday 10.
29 7/10; 56.
Cloudless, red even.

READING
Goslings.
No swallows.

Wednesday 11.
29 7/10; 47; SE.
Shower, sun, & clouds,
warm.

OXFORD
Nightingale heard near Temple.

Thursday 12.
29 5/10; 42; E.
Frost, bright, cold.

First radishes.

Friday 13.
29 4/10; 42; N.
Shower, dark, sun,
harsh.

Sam White elected fellow of Oriel College in Oxford.

Saturday 14.
29 5/10; 34; N.
Frost, ice.

Swallows.

Sunday 15.
29 8/10; 45; S.
Shower, sun.

Monday 16.
30 ½; 44; N.
Sun, clouds, pleasant.

CAVERSHAM
Men are busy in their barley season.

Tuesday 17.
29 8/10; NW.
Dark, & harsh.

ALTON
Pears, cherries, & plums in fine bloom along the road.
Made large annual bed.

On April 17. Some hundreds of martins were seen to pass over
Rolle towards Geneva; & two swifts: the day wet & cold.

Wednesday 18.
29 7/10; NW.
Dark, & harsh.

SELBORNE
Cut a brace of fine cucumbers.

Thursday 19.
29 8/10½; N.
Sun, sharp, harsh wind.

My polyanths make a beautiful show.
My wall-cherries are covered with bloom.
Men pole their hops.

Friday 20.
30 1/10; 40; N.
Sun, sharp wind, sun &
clouds.

Cucumbers set very fast. The bees are tempted into the beds by
honey.

Saturday 21.
30 1/10, 30½/10; 33;
N, W, SW.
Sharp frost, ice, sun,
dark, harsh.

Early tulips blow.
Made hot-bed for hand-glass cucumbers.
Mowed the grass-walks in part: they were crisp with hoar frost.
Swallow on a chimney.
Cut some grass in the orchard for the horses.

Sunday 22.
29 9/10; 42; W.
Dark & harsh, cutting
wind.

Polyanth-Narcissus blows. Honey-suckles show bloom. Dust
flies.
Finches still pull-off the blossoms of the polyanths. Vines shoot.

Monday 23.
29 8/10½; 45; W.
Cold wind, harsh.

Cut two brace, & half of Cucumbers.
Cuckow sings on the hill. Nightingale sings in my outlet.

Tuesday 24.
29 8/10; 48; W.
Grey, sun, pleasant,
rain, rain.

Earthed the annual bed.

Wednesday 25.
29 1/10½; 47; SW,
W; 32.
Sun, with gale.

Cut five brace, & half of fine Cucumbers.
Sowed cucumber-seed, white & green.
Sent 9 bantam's eggs to be put under a sitting hen at Newton.

Thursday 26.
29 4/10½; 45; NW.
Sun, small showers,
sun, pleasant.

Sowed the large three-light frame with annuals.
Young red-breasts.

Friday 27.
29 1/10; 45; NW, SW;
6.
Sun, dark & cold, rain,
stormy, hail, bright.

Cut two brace of Cucumbers.
Wheat on the ground looks poorly.
Swallows hardly appear in the village: no house-martins.

Saturday 28.
29 1/10; NW.
Rain, strong, cold
wind.

Set Gunnory the Bantam hen, on nine of her own eggs.
Cut two brace of fine Cucumbers.

Sunday 29.
29; 45; W.
Rain, rain, showers, &
hail.

Strong, sharp wind.

Monday 30.
29 4/10; 38; NW.
Showers, hail, & cold
winds.

Rain in April . . 0 inch: 74 hund:
Cut two brace & half of fine cucumbers.
Planted potatoes in the meadow-garden.

April 30. was cold & sharp at Rolle; when a number of Martins formed two thick clusters on a ledge projecting in the front of an house in one of the streets of that town. They descended gently as they arrived on one another.

MAY 1787

Tuesday 1.
29 6/10½; 33; N,
NW.
Hard frost, ice, sun &
sharp wind, still.

Cut one cucumber.
Young brown owls.

Wednesday 2.
29 6/10½; W, NW.
Thick air, grey, dark &
harsh.

The foliage of peach, & nectarine-trees scorched by the winds:
the leaves are shrivelled, & blotched.
Polyanths still make a fine show.

Thursday 3.
29 5/10½; 46; SW,
NW.
Fair, warm, dark &
louring, shower.

Cut five brace & half of Cucumbers.

Friday 4.
29 6/10½; 55; NW,
N.
Bright, gale, sun, sweet
evening.

Sowed a plot of red beet.
Cut two brace of cucumbers.
One Swift appears. Swallows at Dorton.

Saturday 5.
29 9/10; 43; N.
Bright, sharp wind,
bright & cold.

The hanger is green, but not in full leaf.
Tulips blow. Sowed ten weeks stocks, & radishes, & lettuces.
One swift.

Timothy, the tortoise, who has just begun to eat, weighs 6 pd:
12½ oz.

Sunday 6.
29 9/10; 42; N.
Frost, sun, sharp wind,
red even.

Agues are much about; at Hawkley, & Emshot, & Newton; & in
Selborne street.
Wheat looks badly.

Monday 7.
29 9/10; 45; NE.
Sun, cold, sharp wind.

The large white pippin-tree full of bloom.
Cut eight brace & half of fine cucumbers.
No house-martin seen yet!

Tuesday 8.
29 6/10½; 45; N.
White frost, sun, dark,
milder, red even.

Cut five brace & half of cucumbers.
Halo round the sun.
Men cart up much peat. Two swifts.
Peat is not quite dry.

Wednesday 9.
29 4/10; 49; N.
Grey, sun, hot sun, cold
wind.

No housemartin.
Cut three brace of cucumbers.

Thursday 10.
29 2/10; 45; N.
Dark & louring, rain,
rain.

Farmer Spencer's orchard in fine bloom.
No house-martin.

Friday 11.
29 3/10; SW; 66.
Grey, sun, pleasant.

Cut three brace of Cucumbers.
The ground is finely soaked.
Two pairs of swifts: no h: martins.

Saturday 12.
29 4/10; 41; SW, S,
SE.
White dew, sun, sweet
even:

House martin appears: only one.
3 brace, & half of swifts.

Tulipa sylvestris.
Bakers Hill.
Wakes.

Sunday 13.
29 4/10; 42; SE.
Frost, sun, summer-
like.

Ice at Nore-hill. Tulips make
a show. 14 swifts. 3 h: martins.
Showers about.

Monday 14.
29 4/10½; 52; SE.
Dew, bright, showers,
thunder, gleam of sun.

MARELANDS
Cut 5 brace & half of
cucumbers.

Tuesday 15.
E.
Fog, sun, pleasant.

SOUTH LAMBETH
The showers did not extend to the east beyond Cobham.

Wednesday 16.
61; E.
Sun, harsh wind.

Agues abound around S: Lambeth.
Cucumbers not plenty.

Thursday 17.
30; E.
Sun, harsh wind.

Dust very troublesome.
Two swifts.

Friday 18.
30; 62; E.
Sun, harsh wind.

Loaf-cabbages very fine.
Spinage good.

Saturday 19.
30; 65; E.
White frost, sun, cold
wind.

Fields & gardens burn.
Dust flies.

Sunday 20.
30½; 68; SE.
Bright, hot sun, brisk
gale.

The red-start sits, & sings on the fane in Bro: Ben's garden upon
the top of an high elm.
No house-martins. No fly-catcher.

Monday 21.
29 9/10½; 72; E, S.
Hot sun, gale, sultry,
dark clouds to W.

Mr Charles Etty returns from Canton. He left in March 1785,
& sailed first for Bombay.

Tuesday 22.
29 8/10; 71; W.
Sun, sultry, clouds.

White-thorn bloom fragrant.
Fields & gardens much exhausted for want of rain.
Medlars blow. Mushrooms in a bed under a shed in Brother
Thomas's garden.

Wednesday 23.
29 6/10; 60; SW; 62.
Rain, rain, rain 8.

Soft rain.
A pair of red-backed Butcher-birds, *lanius collurio*, have got a
nest in Bro: Tho: outlet. They have built in a quickset hedge. We
took one of the eggs out of the nest: it was white, but surrounded
at the big end by a circle of brown spots, *coronae instar*.

Thursday 24.
29 1/10½; 60; SW,
SW; 34.
Wind & rain, rain, rain
14.

Friday 25.
29 5/10; 60; NW, SW;
23.
Showers, showers, rain
12.

Bro: Ben cuts three rows of Lucern daily for his three horses: by
the time that he has gone thro' the plot the first rows are fit to be
cut again.

Saturday 26.
29 3/10½; 66; SW,
W.
Strong wind &
showers.

Many oaks show no signs of foliage.
A few h: martins. No fly-catcher. A pair of swifts.

Sunday 27.
29 6/10; 60; NW; 16.
Clouds, rain 9.

Fly-catcher, *stoparola*, appears.

In outlets about town, where mosses, lichens, & gossamer, &c, are
wanting, birds do not make nests so peculiar each to it's species.¶
Thus the nest of the chaffinch has not that elegant appearance nor

is it so beautifully studded with lichens as those in the country; & the wren is obliged to construct his nest with straws & dry grasses, that do not give it that roundness & compactness so remarkable in the edifices of that little architect.

Monday 28.
W.
Blowing, sprinklings,
sun & clouds.

Fierce, driving showers.

Tuesday 29.
58; NW.
Windy & cloudy.

Wednesday 30.
29 9/10½; 61; N, NE.
Sun, cool, red even:
Full moon.

Lactuca virosa spindles for bloom: the milky juice of this plant is very bitter, & acrid.

Thursday 31.
30 ½/10; 68; W, SW.
Summer weather, warm
even:

Rye-grass blows.
Rain in May . . 2 inch: 6 hund:
Elders begin to blow. At Selborne the bloom is solstitial.

JUNE 1787

Friday 1.
29 9/10; 74; W, NW.
Sun, grey & warm,
dark, wet.

Some fly-catchers: but they do not yet begin to build.
Carrots drawn.

Saturday 2.
29 8/10; 53; 49; N; 15.
Dark, & cool, cold
even:

Hay is making at Vaux-hall.

Rain	
May the 23:	62
May the 24:	34
May the 25:	23
May the 28:	16
June 2:	15
June 5:	14
June 14:	41
	2,05

Sunday 3.
29 7/10½; 62; NW.
White frost, pleasant.

Bro! Thomas cuts cauliflowers.
The foliage on the Lombardy poplars is very poor.

Monday 4.
29 6/10; 67; E, NW,
NE, @.
Fog, dark, pleasant,
sun, clouds.

Bro.ʳ cuts his hay.
Pease are cryed about at 1s: 6d per peck.
Kidney-beans & potatoes are injured by the frost of saturday
night.

Tuesday 5.
29 5/10; 65; W; 14.
Sun, clouds.

LONDON

Wednesday 6.
29 7/10; 49; NW.
Sun & small shower,
hail, rain 5.

The tortoise took his annual ramble, & could not be confined
within the limits of the garden. His pursuits, which seem to be of
the amorous kind, transport him beyond the bounds of his usual
gravity at this season. He was missing for some days, but found at
last near the upper malt-house.

Thursday 7.
29 8/10; 62; NE.
Ice, sun, cool.

Ice thick as a crown piece. Potatoes much injured, & whole rows
of kidney-beans killed: nasturtiums killed.

Friday 8.
29 9/10; 68; SW.
Sun, & brisk gale.

Saturday 9.
29 8/10; 70; SE.
Cloudless, sun, & brisk
air.

S: LAMBETH

Sunday 10.
29 9/10; 67; SE, E.
Cloudless, hot sun,
brisk gale, red even.

The gale rises, & falls with the sun.
Levant weather.
Some house-martins at Stockwell chappel.

Monday 11.
29 8/10; 74; SE.
Cloudless, brisk gale.

Straw-berries, scarlet, cryed about. Straw-berries dry, &
tasteless. Quail¶ calls in the field next to the garden.

Tuesday 12.
29 8/10½; 73, 76;
NE.
Fog, sun, hazey, sultry,
rusty sunshine.

A poor gardener in this parish, who had three acres of kidney-
beans, has lost them all by the frost of last week!
Hay finely made, & making. The rudiments of the vine-bloom
does not seem to be injured by the late frost.

Wednesday 13.
29 8/10; NE.
Fog, hazey, gale.

Pease & beans want rain: dust very great.
The late frost, I find, has done much damage in Hants.

Thursday 14.
29 7/10; 65; E, S, SW;

The dust is finely laid.

Selb. 41; rain 28.
Rain, clouds, strong
gale, showers about.

Friday 15.
S, W.
Sun, vast dew, sun &
clouds, hot evening.

ALTON
The dust finely laid.
Field-pease in fine bloom. Many swifts at Wansworth, Kingston,
Cobham, &c.

Saturday 16.
29 6/10; 66; SW.
Sun, & clouds, hot
gleams.

SELBORNE
Hay-making general about London: some meadow hay cut about
Farnham.

Sunday 17.
29 7/10; 60; W.
Sun, dark, cool gale,
dark & cool.

Not so many house-martins as usual.
The crop of goose-berries large: not many currans: wall-cherries
abound.
Some swifts. Nightingale is silent.
Apricots, some.

The number of swifts are few, because they are stopped-out from
the eaves of the church, which were repaired last autumn.

Monday 18.
29 6/10; 58; 60; SW.
Dark, showers, rain,
rain, rain.

Tuesday 19.
29 4/10¾; 58; NW,
W; 16.
Sun & clouds, cold
wind.

A pair of fly-catchers build in my vines.
The late frost did much damage at Fyfield, but little or none at
Selborne. My potatoes, kidney-beans, & nasturtiums are not
injured: some balsoms, that touched the glasses, were scorched.
Began to tack the vines: there is a good show for fruit.
Turn down the cucumbers from under the hand-glasses. Roses
begin to blow. Elders begin to blow.
Fiery lilies in full bloom.
Young nightingales appear in my walks.
Potted some of the balsoms, & brought them in.
The nest of a Flusher, or red-backed Butcher-bird was found
near Alton.

Wednesday 20.
29 4/10; 59; SW, S.
Dark & still, louring,
& warm.

Wheat in ear by honey-lane.
Swallows have young. Fly-catchers have young.
Pease, barley, & oats look well, especially the first, which show
fine bloom: wheat looks but poorly. Wheat at market rises.
Sheep are washed.

Thursday 21.
29 3/10½; 60; SE, 16.
Louring, wet, wet.

Men mow rye-grass.

Friday 22.
29 4/10½; 66; SW.
Sun, & clouds, bright,
& cool, wet.

Netted the wall-cherries.
Boys bring wood-straw-berries; not ripe.
Began to plant out annuals.

Saturday 23.
29 6/10⅓; 67½; SW.
Sun, brisk air,
summer, red even:

Brood of Nightingales frequents the walks.

Sunday 24.
29 4/10; 66; SW, S.
Sun, bright, clouds,
louring, rain about,
rain.

White cucumbers under the hand-glasses begin to set.
16 swifts about the church.

The squirrel, the field-mouse, & the bird called a nut-hatch, *Sitta Europaea*, live much on nuts, which they open each in a very different manner. The first splits the shell in two with his long fore-teeth, as a man does with his knife: the second drills a small round regular hole in the side of the nut: while the last picks a irregular hole with it's bill. This bird fixes the nut in some chink or crevice as it were in a vice before he attempts to open it. We have often put nuts in the crack of a gate-post, & have observed that the nut-hatch has soon pierced them. The space behind my alcove is covered with the shells of nuts which the bird had bored after he had fixed them in the corners of the cornice of that edifice. While it is penetrating/opening a nut, it makes a rapping noise with it's bill that may be heard at some distance.

Monday 25.
29 4/10; 64; W; 23.
Grey, clouds, rain.

Nep & niece Ben White brought little Ben.
Men sow turnips, & cut S^t foin. Wheat comes into ear.

Tuesday 26.
29 3/10½; 62; SW.
Dark, rain, rain, rain,
warm.

Put out more annuals.
Fly-catcher brings out Young.

Wednesday 27.
29 4/10; 64; SW; 25.
Rain, rain, sun, sweet
even:

Bees swarm. Wheat in bloom.
A brood of little partridges was seen in Baker's hill among the Sainfoin.

Thursday 28.
29 5/10½; 62; NE, N.
Dark & louring, sun,
summer, red even.

Planted out more annuals.
Gracious street pond dry, & cleaned-out.
Much water in the pond on the hill. The pond at Faringdon dry.
Many swifts.

Friday 29.
29 6/10; 64; SW.
Sun & clouds, summer.

Saturday 30.
29 7/10½; 64; SE.
Sun, dark, still, &
warm.
Full moon.

Gathered first cherries, almost ripe.
Vines begin to blossom.
Rain in June . . 1 in: 50 h:.

African Marigolds .
Wakes .

JULY 1787

Sunday 1.
29 9/10½; 66; NE, N,
S.
Sweet, summer
weather, red even.

The fly-catchers in my vine have left their nest.
Many swifts: have they not brought-out their young?

The pupils of the eyes of animals are diversified: in all the birds &
fishes that I have seen they are round, as in man: but those of
horses, & cows, & sheep & goats & I think, deer & camels, are
oblong from corner to corner of the eye. The pupils of the domestic
cat differ from those of all other quadrupeds; for they are long &
narrow, yet capable of great dilation, & standing near at right
angles with the opening of the eye-lids. The eyes of wasps are said
to be lunated, in shape of a crescent.

Monday 2.
30, 30; 69; W, S, N.
Sun, hot, vast clouds,
sweet even:

Began to cut my meadows. Wheat in full bloom: the ears are
small. The fallows seem in fine order.
Many swifts. Watered the annuals, & cucumbers.

Tuesday 3.
30; 72½; NE, N.
Great dew, cloudless,
sweet even, red.

The number of h: martins but few.
Hay makes very fast. Vines blow. Cherries are ripe: rasps begin
to turn: begin to cut cucumbers from the hand-glasses.

Wednesday 4.
29 9/10¾; 70; NE,
SE.
Bright, fog, sun, hot,
sweet even, red.

Timothy Turner cuts Baker's hill, the 20th crop: over ripe.
My hay makes well: half in great cock.
Took off the glasses from the bearing cucumber-bed: hand-
glasses show much fruit.

Thursday 5.
29 7/10; 72; E, SE, S.
Sun, hot, cloudless, air,
sweet even.

Hay in the great meadow made & cocked.
Hand-glass cucumbers come very fast.
Apricots drop.
Flowers hurried, & injured by the heat.
Curious pinks blow. Watered annuals & cucumbers.
Ricked my hay in beautiful order: there were seven loads.

Friday 6.
29 4/10; 71; S, W.
No dew, bright,
showers about, & near,
brisk gale.

Hops suffer much for want of rain; & are infested with honey-
dews, & aphids.

Saturday 7.
29 3/10½; 65; SW,
W.
Shower, heavy clouds,
showers.

Thatched the rick of hay.
Preserved some Duke cherries, very fine fruit.
Heavy showers & thunder at Harn dean.

Sunday 8.
29 5/10; 64; NW.
Sun & clouds, brisk
air, cool.

Rain blown-off.
Annuals die for want of moisture.

Hops are diecious plants:¶ hence perhaps it might be proper, tho'
not practiced, to leave purposely some male plants in every garden,
that their farina might impregnate the blossom. The female plants
without their male attendants are not in their natural state: hence
we may suppose the frequent failure of crop so incident to hops-
grounds. No other growth, cultivated by man, has such frequent &
general failures as hops.

Monday 9.
29 5/10½; SW, SE.
Sun, clouds, rain, rain.

Cucumbers bear well. Cucumbers stewed.
Cut first artichokes.

Tuesday 10.
29 6/10; 63½; W,
NW; 40.
Showers, sun, red
even., cool.

Fine rain.
Planted out annuals: sowed endive.
The borders will now rake, & dig.

Wednesday 11.
29 5/10¾; 59, 61; SE.
Sun, pleasant, wet,
rain.

Cherries, & wood-straw-berries very fine, & rasps & white
currans ripe.
Planted a line of kidney-beans.

Thursday 12.
29 3/10½; 61½; SW;
36.
Rain, sun, showers,
showers.

Planted-out most of the annuals.
Frequent distant thunder; & heavy rains.

Friday 13.
29 2/10½; 61½; SW.
Grey, sun, showers,
showers.

Hay down in a bad way.
Great showers about, & distant thunder.
The apricots drop-off in a surprizing manner.

Daniel Wheeler's boy found a young fledge-cuckow in the nest of
an hedge-sparrow. Under the nest lay an egg of the hedge-
sparrow, which looked as if it had been sucked. In the late hot
weather the cock bird has been crying much in the neighbourhood
of the nest, but not since last week.

Saturday 14.
29; 60, 62; N, NE, S,   Planted a bed of Savoys.
NW; 56.   Thunder. These showers will wash the hops.
Great shower, sun,   Twenty or thirty apricots fall-off in a day.
pleasant, heavy shower,
hail.

Sunday 15.
29 3/10; 60, 62; SE.   The lime-trees over the way are in full bloom, & hang in
Sun, pleasant, heavy   beautiful tassels.
shower, shower,   Thunder. Thunder.
showers.   Mr White of Newton finds mushrooms in his fir-avenue.
                                 Tremella abounds on my grass-walks.

Monday 16.
29 5/10; 59, 62; SW;   Young swallows come out. The hedge-sparrow feeds the young
108.   cuckow in it's cage.
Showers, sun & strong   Planted-out a bed of Savoys. Lime-trees are fragrant.
gales.

Tuesday 17.
29 4/10; 59½; SW,   Trenched-out seven rows of cerleri.
W; 38.   Rasps ripen slowly; cherries very fine.
Showers, showers, sun,   Rain & thunder to the N:W.
& wind, chilly air.

Wednesday 18.
29 6/10; 56, 59½;   Vast showers at Chawton & Alton. Great showers, & thunder to
SW.   the NW. Hail.
Sun, shower, vast
clouds, heavy shower,
chilly.

Thursday 19.
29 6/10½; 56; SW;   Only one pair of swifts for some days.
21.   Sowed turnip-radish seed.
Cold white dew, sun,   Cherries are still delicate.
showers, dark & chill.

Friday 20.
29 2/10; 55; SW; 8.   Planted-out African Marrigold's, & sun-flowers.
Showers, rain, rain,   Made a fire in the parlor.
rain.   Kept the horses within because of the cold & wet.

                                 Sam White entered on his year of probation at Oriel College¶ in
                                 Oxford.
Saturday 21.
29 1/10; 59; SW; 61,   No swifts appear.
6.   Thunder. Vast crop of goose-berries: white currans very fine.

Rain, rain, heavy
showers, chilly air.

Martins feed their young 'till after 8 in the evening.

Sunday 22.
29 2/10; 58, 62; SW.
Bright, clouds,
pleasant, clouds.

Mushrooms appear on the short Lythe.
Showers about.
Several swifts round the church.
Cherries still fine.

Monday 23.
29 2/10; 60, 64; SW,
S; 14.
Showers, sun, pleasant.

Hops throw-out side-shoots.
Young red-breasts, a second brood.
Notwithstanding the showery season the aphides encrease on the
hops.

Tuesday 24.
29 2/10; 62; SW; 57,
46.
Showers, vast showers
with loud thunder,
showers.

Many young martins flying along the side of the hanger, where
the dams feed them in the air.

Wednesday 25.
29 3/10; 60; SW; 23.
White dew, rain, rain,
sun & showers.

Nightingales appear in my walks.
Much hay is spoiled, & lies rotting on the ground. After-grass
grows.

Thursday 26.
29 5/10½; 58, 60;
SW, W.
White dew, sun, &
clouds, fine even.

The farmers talk much that wheat is blighted.
Kidney-beans do not thrive.
Showers about.

Friday 27.
29 6/10¾; 57, 62;
NW, S.
Sun & clouds, small
shower, red even.

Some young partridges in the N: field are flyers.
Rooks in vast flocks return to the deep woods at half past 8 o'clock
in the evening.

Saturday 28.
29 4/10; 60, 63; SE, S.
Blue mist, sun &
clouds, louring.

Men rick their damaged hay.
Planted-out a bed of green curled endive.

Sunday 29.
29 3/10¾; 63; SW.
Wet, grey, & warm,
rain, rain.
Full moon.

Saw four swifts.

Monday 30.
29 4/10½; 63, 66; W;
14.
Sun & clouds, pleasant,
fresh gales.

Saw two swifts.
Apricots begin to turn colour.
Wheat harvest will be backward.
Many young martins under the hanger.
Mr White's tank at Newton runs over but Captain Dumaresque's,
which is much larger, is not full.

Tuesday 31.
29 6/10; 63, 65; N, E,
W; 125.
Vast rain:* sun, &
clouds, clouds.

*an inch & quarter in 8 hours.
Nightingales appear in my walks.
Flycatchers.
Rain in July . . 6 inch. 53 hund.

AUGUST 1787

Wednesday 1.
29 6/10½; 64; SW, S.
Grey, sun, wet.

Men hack pease.
The rains have torn the hollow lanes.

Thursday 2.
30; 65½; W, NW.
Cold white dew,
cloudless, sweet day.

Finished cutting the tall hedges, & skimming the horse-fields.
Four swifts. Out-let very neat.
Several golden-crowned wrens appear in the tall fir-tree at the
upper end of Baker's hill: they were probably bred in that tree.

Friday 3.
30; 69; SE, S, E.
White dew, sun, sweet
day.

Sowed a crop of spinage to stand the winter, & trod it in, &
rolled it with the stone-roller.
Four swifts.

Saturday 4.
29 8/10½; 68; SE.
Great dew, sun, grey,
sun, dark & mild.

Apricots ripen.
Men rick their hay.
Many swifts round the church.

Sunday 5.
29 6/10; 65, 72; S,
SW.
Sun, sultry, golden
even.

Ripening weather.
Some swifts.

Monday 6.
29 7/10½; 66; NW,
NE.
Grey & warm, sun,
sultry, hot even.

Hay finely made. Pease harvest general.
Young swallows, & martins, a considerable flock congregate on
the tops of trees. Four swifts.

Rooks flying
over the Hanger.

Tuesday 7.
29 8/10¼; 67, 71; SE,
S.
Fine dew, grey, sun,
summer weather.

Apricots come very fast. Cucumbers abound.
Fine hay-making, & pea-harvest.
Some swifts.

Wednesday 8
29 7/10¾; 66, 71; SE.
Fine dew, sun, hot sun
with gale, golden even.

Wheat-harvest begins.
Some swifts. These seem to have been the last that were seen at
Selborne.

Thursday 9.
29 6/10; 65, 75; SE, S.
Fog, sun, fine dew,
sultry, louring clouds,
thunder.

Hot, ripening weather. Nightingales on the hill.
Short showers of heat-drops. Fine hay made.
Distant thunder in the night.

Friday 10.
29 7/10; 67, 70; SW.
Grey, no dew, sun,
louring clouds.

When the redbreasts have finished the currans, they begin with
the berries of the honey-suckles, of which they are very fond.

Saturday 11.
29 7/10; 65, 67; SW.
No dew, grey, brisk
gale, sun.

The children in straw-berry time found & destroyed several
pheasant's nests in Goleigh wood.
Nep & Niece Ben White came from London.
Nightingales in my walks.

Sunday 12.
29 6/10½; 63; W.
Rain, rain, sun,
shower, hail, chilly.

Bull-finches feed on the berries of honey-suckles.
Thunder. Spinage comes-up well. B. Hall came.

Monday 13.
29 8/10¾; 63; W; 23.
Dew, sun, pleasant,
cool.

Mr & Mrs Richardson & son came.
Men house pease.

Tuesday 14.
29 6/10¾; 59, 63;
SW.
Dark & blowing.

Gleaning begins.

Honeysuckle berries.
Wakes.

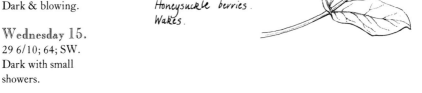

Wednesday 15.
29 6/10; 64; SW.
Dark with small
showers.

Thursday 16.
29 3/10¾; 64½; S.
Dark & moist, grey &
warm, rain.

M^r & M^{rs} R: left us.
Farmer Parsons houses wheat.
Gleaners carry home large loads.

Friday 17.
29 5/10; 61, 62; SW;
18.
Grey & blowing,
showers, sun &
showers, bright.

Rain-bow.

Saturday 18.
29 4/10; 59, 61; SW;
16.
Great dew, sun,
showers, showers.

Nightingales in my walks.

Several swifts seen at Fyfield round Mr White's brew house, under
the eaves of which they build, 'till the end of this week.

Sunday 19.
29 4/10; 62; SW, W.
Sun, sun, & heavy
clouds, soft.

Fly-catchers seen.
Showers about. Rain-bows. Vivid N: *Aurora*.

Monday 20.
29 7/10; 63; N.
Deep fog, sun &
clouds, soft & pleasant.

Pease & wheat housed.
Nep. T. H. Wh. came from Fyfield. *Aurora*.

Tuesday 21.
29 9/10; 59½; N, E.
Deep fog, sun &
clouds, sweet even.

Hops begin to appear on the poles, where there is likely to be any
crop. Most of the hops are shriveled, & look black.
Much wheat bound.

Wednesday 22.
29 7/10; 59; SW.
Cold dew, sun, & gale,
chilly air.

Much corn housed.
First kidney-beans.

Thursday 23.
29 6/10; 62; NW.
Grey, sun & clouds,
soft & cool.

Much wheat carried.
The Ewel, & Pound-field thrown open.
Cool autumnal feel.
Nightingales seen in Honey-lane: these were the last that I
observed.
Cut at one time 191 fine cucumbers.
Farmer Spencer finishes wheat-harvest.

Friday 24.
29 2/10½; 59; S, SW.
Dark & cool, rain,
dark, dark & cool.

Nep Ben White left us.
Much wheat still abroad.

Saturday 25.
29; 56, 55; SW; 26.
Shower, cold wind,
rain, blowing, & harsh.

Mich: daisey, & autumnal crocus blow.

Sunday 26.
29 4/10; 54½, 55;
SW.
Sun, sun & clouds,
louring.

Few hirundines seen.
The wind yesterday injured the few hops that men have.
Cold air.

Timothy the Tortoise, who has spent the two last months amidst the umbrageous forests of the asparagus-beds, begins now to be sensible of the chilly autumnal mornings; & therefore suns himself under the laurel-hedge, into which he retires at night. He is become sluggish, & does not seem to take any food.

Monday 27.
29 6/10½; 55, 59; N,
NW.
Cloudy, still, &
pleasant, showers.

Molly White & Nep Tom rode to Fyfield.
Wheat housed. Planted-out more endive.

Tuesday 28.
29 7/10¼; 55, 58; N,
NW.
Great dew, sun, shady
& cool.
Full moon.

Many fly-catchers.
Much wheat bound, & carried.

Wednesday 29.
29 7/10; 62; NW.
Grey, sun, hot sun,
louring, & soft.

Sweet harvest weather. Cut many cucumbers.
Some showers about. Shower.
Few bank-martins were to be seen this morning around the sand-pit at Short heath.

Thursday 30.
29 9/10¼; 60, 63; N.
Dark & louring, bright
red even.

Hops improve a little.

Friday 31.
30, 30¼; 60, 63; N.
Wet fog, grey, sun,
sweet even.

Young hirundines cluster on the dead boughs of my walnut-tree.
Wheat housed.
Not one wasp.
Rain in August . . . 0 inch. 83 hund.

SEPTEMBER 1787

Saturday 1.
30, 30; 60; N.
No dew, dark &
louring, cold wind,
small rain.

The shooters find many coveys, but not large ones.
Wheat-harvest finished in fine condition.

Sunday 2.
30, 30¼; 58½; N.
Dark & moist, louring,
cold wind.

China-asters begin to blow.
Young swallows come out.

Monday 3.
30½; 58½; N, NE.
Dark & hazey, cool.

Some beeches on the hanger begin to be tinged.
Bro.ʳ Tho.ˢ sons & daughter came for Fyfield.

Tuesday 4.
30; 59; E.
Dark & cool, gleams of
sun, dark & cool.

Vast numbers of partridges.
A young fern-owl shot at Newton.

Wednesday 5.
29 8/10¼; 66; NE.
Sun, bright, brisk gale,
sweet even.

Ladies Traces, *ophrys spiralis*, blows.
Hopping began at Chawton.
Stone-curlews pass over followed by their young, which make a
piping, wailing noise.

Thursday 6.
29 7/10; 62, 66; NE.
Sun, hot sun, sun &
clouds, sweet even.

Much barley housing. Gathered a vast heap of cucumbers.

Friday 7.
29 7/10; 62; E, NE.
No dew, sun, hot sun,
sweet even.

Berriman begins to pick his hops.
Some grapes begin to turn.
Watered annuals, which wither for want of moisture.

Saturday 8.
29 8/10; 60, 63; NE,
N.
Sun, dark, dark & cool,
sun, red even.

Much barley, & oats housed.
Many people finish harvest.

Mrs Brown brought to bed of a boy, who added to 49 before,
encreased my nephews & nieces to the round number of fifty.

Sunday 9.
29 8/10¼; 60, 61;
NE.
Grey & cool, sun, grey
& cool.

Fly-catchers seem to have withdrawn themselves for some days.
The down-farmers cannot sow their wheat for want of showers to
moisten their fallows, which are all dust. Farmers wish for rain.

Monday 10.
29 9/10; 57½; 60; NE,
E.
Grey & cool, sun,
chilly, red even.

Thistle-down floats.
Hop-picking becomes general. Hops so small that a notable
woman & her girl can pick but nine bushels in a day, where last
year they could pick 20.

Tuesday 11.
29 9/10; 61; NE, E.
Wet fog, sun, cool,
cool, red even.

Young martins in their nest over the stable-door.
Cow-grass housed. Gathered heaps of Cucumbers.
Several h: martins have young still in their nests.

Wednesday 12.
29 9/10; 56½; 59; NE.
Dark & cool, dark &
cool.

Lapwings leave the low grounds, & come to the uplands in
flocks.
A pair of honey-buzzards, & a pair of wind-hovers appear to
have young in the hanger. The honey-buzzard is a fine hawk, &
skims about in a majestic manner.

Thursday 13.
29 8/10; 58½; 59; NE.
Dark, still, & mild.

Gathered-in my early white pippins.
A white-throat is seen in my garden.

Friday 14.
29 6/10½; 58; NE, E.
Dark & still, sun, dark
& still.

Swallows & martins cluster on the tower.
Housed onions & carrots. Gathered cucumbers, & kidney-beans
for picklers.
Women make poor wages in their hop-picking.

Saturday 15.
29 4/10; 58, 60; SE.
Grey & mild, sun,
drops of rain, wet.

Housed all my potatoes, & tyed-up many endives. Celeri grows.
Several young martins in their nests.

Mr Charles Etty has brought home with him from Canton a dog &
a bitch of the Chinese breed,¶ such as are fatted in that country for
the purpose of being eaten. They are about the size of a moderate
spaniel; of a pale, yellow colour; with coarse bristling hairs on their
backs; sharp, upright ears, & peaked heads which give them a
very fox-like appearance. They carry their tails curved high over
their backs like hounds: their eyes are jet-black, small, & piercing,
the insides of their mouths & lips of the same colour, & their
tongues blue. The bitch has dew-claws on each leg behind, the dog
has none. When taken out into a field they seemed to show some
disposition for hunting, & dwelt on the scent of a covey of
partridges, 'till they sprung them. They might probably therefore
become springing spaniels; but have more the appearance of
vermin-hunters. They are dainty about food, & did not care at first
to touch carrion, nor even raw flesh, having been fed in their own
country with rice-meal, on which they are fattened for the table. In
the Islands of the Pacific Ocean, the dogs are bred-up on
vegetables, & would not eat flesh when offered them by our

circumnavigators. We believe that all dogs in a state of nature have sharp, upright, fox-like ears; & that hanging ears, which are esteemed so graceful, are the effect of choice breeding, & cultivation. In the travels of Ysbrandt Ides the dogs which draw the Tartars on snow-sledges near the river Oby are engraved with prick-ears, & curved tails like these from China. Moreover the Kamschatdales¶ make use of the same sort of sharp-eared, peaked-nosed dogs to draw their sledges, as may be seen in a fine print engraved for Captain Cook's last voyage.

Well-bred spaniels, which naturally hunt partridges with such vehemence, & alacrity, will not touch their bones, when offered them as food: nor will my mongrel dog, Rover, tho' he is remarkable for finding that sort of game. But when we came to tender the bones of partridges to Mr Ch: Etty's two Chinese dogs, they devoured them with the utmost greediness, & licked the platter clean.

No sporting dogs will hunt wood-cocks, 'till trained to the sport, & inured to the scent; nor will they meddle with their bones, but turn from them with abhorrence, even when they are hungry.

Mr Etty's Chinese dogs bark in a thick short manner like foxes. Mr E. says, that Quiloh is Chinese for a dog.

The hind legs of these two dogs are remarkably straight without any bend at the ham: they have also a bare place each on the outer side of their tails, that does not seem to be matter of accident, but some what singular.

Sunday 16.
29; 60, 62; SE, W; 48.
Rain, rain, wind, & sun.

The bed of spinage is very fine.
Gathered a vast heap of cucumbers.

Monday 17.
28 8/10; 61; SW.
Showers, sun & showers, sun & clouds.

Red-start still appears. Linnets flock.
Thunder. Grapes do not advance towards ripeness.

Tuesday 18.
29 2/10; 57, 60; NW, W.
Sun, sun, sweet, soft day.

Mr Churton came from Cheshire. N: *Aurora*.

Wednesday 19.
29 2/10; 56, 59; SW.
Sun, dark, showers, showers.

Nep Ben, & wife left us, & went to London.

Thursday 20.
29 4/10; 54, 58; SW, S.

Saw pheasants at long coppice.
My well sinks much, & is very low.

Sun, sweet morning,
rain, rain.

Friday 21.
29 4/10; 54, 61; S; 76.   Rain all night.
Showers, & wind.   Young martins in their nests.
                                Vast halo round the moon. Began fires.

Saturday 22.
29 4/10; 59, 61; S,SW;   Planted-out some endive-plants upon ridges, & sloping ground,
11.   to preserve them from wet.
Rain, rain, pleasant.   Guns are heard much from Portsmouth.

                                Five gallons, & one quart of French brandy.

Sunday 23.
29 6/10; 59; S.   Many hirundines under the hanger.
Wind, & clouds, sun &   Began to use the spinage sown the first week in August, very fine
clouds.   & abundant.

Monday 24.
29 6/10; 60½, 63; S,   Grapes hardly turn at all.
SE; 21.   Young martins in their nests.
Rain, rain, sun, soft &
pleasant.

Tuesday 25.
29 3/10½; 57½; SE.   Soft & warm.
Fine, rain, fog, sun,   Swallows wash much.
dark, thunder.
                                Many swallows, & some bank-martins at Oakhanger-ponds. A
                                multitude of swallows at Benes-pond; & some few house-martins,
                                which probably roost on the willows at the tail of that pond. The
                                swallows washed much, a sure sign that rain was at hand.

Wednesday 26.
29 4/10; 62; SE.   Distant thunder.
Grey, soft, sun, sweet   Many ravens on the hill, & a flight of starlings.
day.

Thursday 27.
29 5/10½; 61; N,   Blanched endive comes in.
NW.
Fog, dark, wet, light
clouds.
Full moon.

Friday 28.
29 7/10; 54; NE.
Vast dew, sun, sweet
day, grey, & mild.

Saturday 29.
29 6/10; 49½; 54; NE,
E.
White frost, sun,
pleasant, moon light.

Vast flock of ravens on the down.

Sunday 30.
29 3/10; 52, 56; E,
SE.
Grey, mild, sun,
pleasant, clouds.

No martins appear for two days; a few swallows.
Rain in Sept.ʳ . . 1 inch 56 h.

OCTOBER 1787

Monday 1.
29 2/10½; 56, 60; E,
SE.
Shower, grey, sun,
warm & pleasant.

Some martins. Wheat not so good as last Year: 50 sheaves do not
yield more than forty did this time twelve month.
Ivy begins to blossom. Gathered the first grapes: they were not
ripe, but eatable.

Tuesday 2.
29 4/10; 59; NE.
Dark & louring, sun,
pleasant, dark, & mild.

Some martins. Farmer Spencer gathers apples.

The quantity of potatoes planted in this parish was very great, &
the produce, on ground unused to that root, prodigious.¶ David
Long had two hundred bushels on half an acre. Red or hog-
potatoes are sold for six pence pʳ bushel.

Wednesday 3.
29 3/10; 58; N, NW.
Dark & louring, wet,
dark & heavy.

Men sow wheat; but wish for more rain to moisten their fallows.
Two swallows.
Mʳ Churton left us, & went to Waverly:
Nep: Tom & Harry left us, & went to Fyfield.

Thursday 4.
29 2/10½; 56½, 58;
SW.
Rain, rain, rain, clear,
& cool.

Several house martins, & some swallows.
Soft rain.

Friday 5.
29 5/10; 57; S; 63.
Rain, rain, showers,
sun, showers.

Many martins under the hanger. Bro.ʳ Ben & wife came.
Grapes mend in flavour. Bright *Aurora*.
Put my fine hyacinths into a bed, that were taken-up in the
summer. Put also some good tulips, & striped crocus's from Bro:
Tho.ˢˢ garden into beds.

Saturday 6.
29 7/10; 58; S; 31.

Several martins. Rain in the night.

Dark & louring, dark & still.

My well is very low; & the streams from Gracious street almost dry.

Wet & warm.

The trees, & hedges are not much tinged, but promise a late verdure.

Sunday 7.
29 8/10; 58; E, N; 42.
Hazey, & mild, grey, gleams of sun.

Some hirundines.

My tall, streight Beech at the E. corner of Sparrow's hanger, from a measurement taken by Rich: Becker & son, proves to be exactly 74 feet & ½ in height. The shaft is about 50 feet without a bough.

Monday 8.
29 8/10; 58; N, NE.
Deep fog, grey, still, & warm.

One waggon carries this year all the Selborne hops to Weyhill: last year there were many loads.

One or two martins. Vipers, & snakes still out.

Jack Burbey's brown owl washes often when a pan of water is set in it's way.

    Wood-cock killed at Bramshot.

Tuesday 9.
29 7/10; 57; E, S.
Fog, vast dew, sun, pleasant, dark & mild.

Wheat-lands in fine order for sowing.

Gathered in Chaumontelle, & Virgoleuse pears.

Timothy sets his shell an edge against the sun still.

Wednesday 10.
28 7/10½; 56½; S, SW.
Rain, rain, rain.

Strong gale.

The best Selborne hops were sold for 15 pounds, & 15 Guineas per hund:

Thursday 11.
28 8/10½; 50, 50; SW, SE; 78.
Vast dew, sun, grey & still, rain, still.

Began to gather apples.

Saw a brood of swallows: the young had very short tails, & had not been long out of their nests.

Friday 12.
29; 46; SE.
Shower, sun, grey & cool, red, dark.

Partridges, & pheasants are very shy, & wild.

Several swallows.

Bro.r Ben & wife left us, & went to Newton.

Saturday 13.
29; 52; SW.
Great dew, sun, sweet day.

Gathered knobbed russets, & the streaked apple.

Some swallows.

The *aurora* was very red & aweful.

Bat is out. Red N. *Aurora*.

We saw several Red-wings among the bushes on the N. side of the common. There were swallows about the village at the same time:

so that summer & winter birds of passage were seen on the same day.
    Two Wood-cocks killed at Swet-coomb.

Sunday 14.
29 3/10; 47½; NE, N.
Sun, warm, sweet day,
bright, & chill.

The ground covered with gossamer.

Monday 15.
29 4/10; 46½, 52; S,
S.
White frost, sun, heavy
clouds, small showers.

Gathered Cadillac pears, a small crop.

Tuesday 16.
29 5/10; 57; SW, W,
S; 62.
Sun, soft, small
showers, sun, pleasant.

Rain all night. Gathered the dearlings, apples, a moderate crop.
Celeri comes in.
Grapes grow better.

Wednesday 17.
29 3/10¼; 46; S; 18.
Rain in the night, sun,
showers, rain, rain.

Celeri large, & fine. Distant lightening.
Gathered-in the last apples, in all about 8 bush:

Thursday 18.
29 4/10; 53; W, NW;
24.
Grey, sun, sun &
clouds, bright & cold.

Planted 100 cabbages to stand the winter.

Bro.r Tho.s & Nep. Edm.d White have just fixed a barometer in the parlor at Newton against the wainscot. The tube was first filled here (at Selborne) twice, where it agreed, & stood exactly with mine: but being filled again twice at Newton, it stood, on account of the great elevation of that house, 3/10.ths of an Inch lower than the Barom.r at this place; & so continues. The plate of the Barom.r at Newton is set as low as 27; because in stormy weather the Mercury there will sometimes descent much below 28. We have supposed Newton-house to be 200 feet higher than this house: but if the rule holds good, which says, that Mercury sinks 1/10.th of an inch for every 199 feet elevation; then the Newton Barom.r which is 3/10.ths lower than that of Selborne, proves that Newton house must be 300 feet higher than mine at Selborne, instead of 200.

Friday 19.
29 6/10; 51; E, NW.
Great dew, sun,
pleasant, bright.

Saturday 20.
29 8/10; 48; NW.
White frost, sun, cool
& pleasant.

Sunday 21.
29 7/10; 45; NE, SE,
S.
Wh. frost, ice, sun,
sweet day, mackarel
sky.

Well very low.
Gossamer floats. The hangers, & my hedges are beautifully tinged.

William Dewye Sen.r¶ who is now living, has been a certificate man at Selborne ever since the year 1729, some time in the month of

April. He is a parishioner at the town of Wimborn-Minster in the County of Dorset.

The swallows mentioned Oct: 12 seem to have been the last that were seen.

Monday 22.
29 3/10; 52; SW, W; 26.
Rain, rain, grey & mild, bright.

Tuesday 23.
29 6/10; 50; W.
Sun, bright, & pleasant, moonshine.

The number of partridges remaining is very great. Pheasants do not abound.

Great Fieldfares seen on the down: Wood-pigeons, or Stock-doves seen about long coppice. These are the latest winter birds of passage.

Wednesday 24.
29 4/10; 48; S, W; 60.
Bright, clouds, rain, rain, yellow even.

Thursday 25.
29 1/10½; 48; S, SW; 62.
Rain, rain, rain & wind, dark & louring.

Saw several house-martins over my garden in the midst of the rain. I have observed none since the 12.th instant.

Friday 26.
29 3/10; 54; NE, SW, NE.
Grey & mild, gleams of sun, rain.
Full moon.

Well begins to rise: is risen one round of the rope.
Rain in the night.

Saturday 27.
29 5/10; 56, 59; SW; 38.
Driving rain, rain, rain.

Vast condensations on walls.
Warm & wet.

Sunday 28.
29 6/10; 60; SW, SW.
Grey, mild, pleasant gleams, wet.

Leaves fall very fast. Grapes very good.

Sam White saw three swallows at Oxford near Folly bridge.

Monday 29.
29 7/10; 58; S.
Dark & mild, moist & dark.

About four o'clock this afternoon a flight of house-martins appeared suddenly over my house, & continued feeding for half an hour, & then withdrew. Some thought that there were swallows among them.

Tuesday 30.
29 4/10; 58, 60; S.
Fog, mild, grey, sweet
sun, soft, moonshine.

Bro.ʳ Tho.ˢ left us, & went to London.
Planted-out Hollyhocks.

Wednesday 31.
29 2/10; 56; SW.
Sun, clouds, wind, &
showers.
N. *Aurora.*

Planted three rows of brown lettuce under the fruit wall to stand
the winter.
Split-out the great Monk's rhubarb ¶plant into 7, or 8 heads, &
planted them in a bed that they may produce stalks for tarts in the
spring.
Rain in Octob.ʳ . . . 5 inch: 4 hund:

NOVEMBER 1787

Thursday 1.
29 1/10; 54; SW.
Sun, mild, rain-bow,
wind, shower, yellow
even.

The N: *Aurora* made a particular appearance forming itself into a
broad, red, fiery belt, which extended from E: to W: across the
welkin: but the moon rising, at about 10 o'the clock, in unclouded
majesty in the E: put an end to this grand, but aweful meteorous
phenomenon.

Friday 2.
28 9/10½; 49; E.
Sun, mild, grey &
pleasant, rain, rain,
rain.

Farmer Hoar saw one cock ring-ousel at Nore hill.
Very windy, & wet till midnight.

Saturday 3.
29 6/10; N, NW; 95.
Sun, pleasant, clear &
cold.

The hanger is almost stripped of leaves.
Timothy the Tortoise begins to scrape a hole in the ground.

Sunday 4.
29 3/10; S.
Frost, ice, sun, grey,
rain, rain, rain.

Grapes good.

Monday 5.
29 4/10; 45, 47; W;
45.
Bright, cold air with
brisk gale, rain.

Two or three Wood-cocks seen in the hanger.
Saw one single house-martin flitting over my fields: it soon
withdrew towards the Plestor.

Tuesday 6.
29 2/10½; 50; SW;
16.
Blowing, vast showers,
wind.

Several wood-cocks in Harteley wood: they are in poor condition.

Wednesday 7.
29 3/10½; SW; 35.
Sun, fine, shower, sun,
pleasant.

FYFIELD
Saw several grey crows on the downs between Winchester, &
Andover; & four pheasants feeding at the corner of Whorwel-
wood.
Green wheat beautiful on the downs, but not forward sown.
The Fyfield Comedians¶ performed *Much ado about nothing*, with
the Romp.

Thursday 8.
28 7/10; S.
Rain, rain, blowing, &
showers, stormy, hail,
red, turbid.
Rain 84½.

N: *Aurora*.
About this time Timothy the tortoise buried himself in the laurel-
hedge.

Friday 9.
28 9/10; SW; 100.
Wind, & showers, sun
& clouds.

Broᵗ Henry's grapes did not ripen well.

Saturday 10.
29 3/10; S.
Sun, clouds.

The trufle-hunter comes about once in a fortnight, & tries
brother Henry's groves, where he finds a few trufles. The long
drought of last summer is supposed to have injured the crop.

Sunday 11.
29; S.
Rain, rain, sun &
clouds, mild, very wet
night.

Rain 10.
Great flocks of starlings on the downs attend the rooks.

Monday 12.
29 1/10; 53, 55; S; 94.
Rain, clouds, louring,
wet, showers.

Rain 83.

Tuesday 13.
29 3/10; S.
Deep fog, sun, grey &
pleasant.

The Fyfield players performed *Richard the third*.

Wednesday 14.
29 5/10; NW.
White frost, sun, grey
& pleasant.

The late hard winters killed the extreamities of my wallnut-trees,
so that they have born no fruit since: but the same severe seasons
killed many of the fyfield wallnut-trees quite down to the ground.

Thursday 15.
29 7/10; 38; NE.
Frost, bright, & sharp.

Friday 16.
29 8/10; NE.
Frost, sun, bright, &
pleasant.

WINTON
The stream at Fyfield encreases very fast.
Thomas finished tacking, & pruning the vines, which furnish good wood.

Spent three hours of this day, viz: from one o' the Clock till four, in the midst of the downs between Andover & Wintōn, where we should have suffered greatly from cold & hunger, had not the day proved very fine, & had not we been opposite the house of Mr Treadgold's down farm, where we were hospitably entertained by the labourer's wife with cold spare-rib, & good bread, & cheese & ale, while the driver went back to Andover to fetch a better horse. The case was, the saddle-horse, being new to his business, became jaded & restiff, & would not stir an inch; but was soon kept in countenance by the shaft-horse, who followed his example: so we were quite set-up 'till 4 o' the clock, when an other driver arrived with an other lean jaded horse, & with much difficulty assisted in dragging us to Wintōn, which we did not reach till six in the evening. We set out from Fyfield at eleven; so were seven hours in getting 19 miles. During our long conversation with the dame, we found that this lone farm-house, & it's buildings, tho' so sequestered from all neighbourhood, & so far removed from all streams, & water, are much annoyed with Norway rats:¶ the carter also told us that about 12 years ago he had seen a flock of 18 bustards at one time on that farm; & once since only two. The well at this house is deep. This is the only habitation to be met with on these downs in the road between Whorwel, & Winchester.

Saturday 17.
29 6/10; 40; NW, W.
Grey, dark, & still.

SELBORNE
Sam White was chosen, by the favour of the Provost & fellows of Oriel Coll: Bishop Robinson's Exhibitioner. This advantage will last him three years, 'till he takes his M^rs degree.

Sunday 18.
29 6/10; 39, 38; N.
Frost, sun, driving snow, bright & sharp.

Monday 19.
29 3/10; 40; NW.
Frost, rain, rain, bright.

Tuesday 20.
29 6/10; 36; N; 24.
Frost, sun, sharp wind, bright.

Wednesday 21.
29 7/10; 38; NW, W.   Thomas tacked the wall-honey-suckle, & the Virginian creepers.
Frost, sun, thaw, grey.

Thursday 22.
29 4/10; 43½; SW.
Fog, grey, brisk gale,
mild, moist.

Friday 23.
29 4/10¼; SW, W,
NW.
Grey, frost, sun,
pleasant, moonshine.

Saturday 24.
29 6/10¾; 38; N.   Housed all the billet-wood in dry, good order.
Frost, sun, sharp, but   Covered the lettuce under the fruit-wall with straw.
pleasant.

Sunday 25m
29 8/10½; 26; NE,
SE.
Hard frost, sun, still,
sharp, & bright.

Monday 26.
29 9/10; 31; SE.   Covered the asparagus-beds, & artichokes with dung, & straw.
Hard frost, sun,   Monthly roses now in bloom.
pleasant.

Tuesday 27.
29 9/10; 25, 31; SE,   Some wild-fowl appear in Wolmer-pond.
E.
Hard frost, sun, still &
pleasant, frost.

Wednesday 28.
29 9/10½; 25, 30; E.   Children slide on the ponds.
Hard frost, sun,   Rake up, & burn the leaves of the hedges.
pleasant, frost.

Thursday 29.
30¼; 27; E.
Hard frost, sun, sharp
wind, frost.

Friday 30.
29 9/10; 22, 31; E,   Frost comes within door: ice in the pantry, & chambers.

SE, NE.
Severe frost, sun,
pleasant.

Rain in Novem! . . . 4 inch. 9 h.

DECEMBER 1787

Saturday 1.
29 7/10; 39; S.
Grey & still, mild,
thaw, thaw.

Thomas begins to tack the fruit-trees on the wall.
Phalaenae flie abroad.

Sunday 2.
29 2/10½; 41; S.
Thick & moist, rain,
dark & mild.

Monday 3.
29 2/10½; SW; 12.
Mild, sun, pleasant,
shower.

The yellow Bantham pullet begins to lay.

Tuesday 4.
29 3/10; 39; SW.
Wh: frost, sun, sun,
mild, moist & dark,
rain.

Wednesday 5.
29 1/10½; 50; SW,
W; 86, 26.
Grey & soft, rain, rain,
dark & mild.

Heavy rains in the night.
Walls sweat.

Thursday 6.
29 5/10; NW.
Grey, still & mild.

Five or six bats were flying round my chimnies at the dawn of the
day. Bats come forth at all times of the year when the Therm! is at
50, because at such a temperament of the air *Phalaenae* are
stirring, on which they feed.

Friday 7.
29 5/10½; 30; SE, S.
Grey, wh. ftost,
shower, shower,
shower.

Saturday 8.
29 4/10; S, SE.
Rain, dark, rain, rain,
rain.

Rain in the night.

Sunday 9.
29 5/10; 52; SW; 118.
Blowing, sun, warm.

Thunder in the night.
Crocus's sprout.

Monday 10.
29 5/10; S.
Mild, & still.

A flight of wood-cocks in Harteley-wood, & Comb-wood.

Tuesday 11.
29 2/10; SE.
Sun, soft, & mild.

Bought a strong, stout, white Galloway mare, that walks well, &
seems to be gentle. She was lately the property of Mr Leech,
Surgeon at Alton, deceased.

Wednesday 12.
29 2/10; 51½; SW.
Showers, showers,
showers.

Thursday 13.
29 4/10; W, SE; 21.
Great dew, sun,
pleasant, still.

The air is full of Insects.

Friday 14.
29; 41; SW; 56.
Heavy showers,
showers.

Saturday 15.
29 1/10½; W; 33.
Grey, sun, pleasant.

Began to cut my new hay-rick.

Sunday 16.
29 3/10; 47; W, NW.
Grey, mild, sun,
pleasant.

Monday 17.
29 1/10; S, W; 30.
Rain, still, mild.

Tuesday 18.
29; 48; SW, W; 16.
Shower, heavy shower,
sun.

Very dark: some hail.

Wednesday 19.
29 1/10½; SW; 8.
Grey, still, mild.

NEWTON

Thursday 20.
28 8/10; W.
Grey, mild, sun.

Friday 21.
29 1/10, 29 4/10; 42;
N, NE.
Mild, sun, bright,
halo.

Saturday 22.
29 2/10; 31; E.
Frost, sharp, cutting
wind.

Sunday 23.
29 1/10; 28, 31; NE.
Hard frost, sun, sharp,
snow.

Monday 24.
28 9/10; 31, 32; NE,
N.
Deep snow, fierce
driving snow, snow.

Tuesday 25.
29 4/10; 32; N, NW;
100.
Snow, snow, bright.

Wednesday 26.
29 3/10¼; 24; SW,
SW.
Hard frost, bright sun,
sharp.

Thursday 27.
29 4/10; 34; N.
Gentle thaw, gentle
thaw.

Friday 28.
30; 31; NE.
Frost, still, sun, fog.

SELBORNE
Shortest day. Pleasant weather.

A hunted hind came down Galley-hill into the street: where being headed by the village dogs it turned back to Well-head, & was taken in Kirchen's farm yard, & put into the barn, being quite run down. One of the Gent: pursuers let it blood, & hired a man to watch it all night. In the morning by seven o' the clock a deer-cart came, & took it away. There were several Gent: in with the dogs when they took the deer. The dogs & hind were said to belong to Mr Delmee, who lives near Fareham.

The deer was turned-out in the morning on Stev†[?] Castle down near Bishop's Waltham, which is at least 18 miles from this place. The dogs were short & thick, but had shrill notes like fox-hounds, & when they ran hard opened but seldom, so that they made but little cry.

The Bantham fowls, when first let out, were so astonished at the snow that they flew over the house.¶

Snow all night.
The snow, where level, about one foot in depth: in some places much drifted.

Fly feeds on sugar.
Selborne teashop.

Many wild ducks at Wolmer-pond,
& occasionally some wild geese: some days ago some gulls.
The wildfowls are shy.
A *musca domestica*¶ by the warmth of my parlor has lengthened his life, & existence to this time: he usually basks on the jams of the chimney within the influence of the fire after dinner, & settles on the table, where he sips the wine & tastes the sugar, & baked

†Word illegible.

Saturday 29.
29 7/10½; 31; NE.
Frost, sun, thaw.

apples. If there comes a very severe day he withdraws, & is not
seen.

Sunday 30.
29 6/10½; 34; N, NE.
Gentle thaw, deep fog.

Some of our hollow lanes not yet passable.

Monday 31.
29 7/10¼; 36; S.
Dark & mild, gentle
thaw, fog.

Rain in Decemʳ . . 5 inch: 6 hund.
Rain at Selborne, the total in the Year 1787 . . . 36 inch 24 hund.

JANUARY   — 1788 —

SELBORNE

Contracted my great parlor chimney by placing stone-jams on the
top of the grate on each side, & building brick-work on the jams as
high as the work-man could reach. This expedient has entirely
cured the smoking, & given the chimney a draught equal to that in
the old parlor.

Tuesday 1.
29 5/10; 43; S.
Steady thaw, dark, wet.

Snow much melted.

Wednesday 2.
28 8/10; 50; S.
Driving rain, heavy
rain.

Snow almost gone.

Thursday 3.
28 6/10; 42; S; 99.
Dark & heavy, rain,
rain.

A flood at Gracious street.

Friday 4.
29; 39; SW; 20.
Sun, pleasant.

Snow gone except in the deep lanes.

Saturday 5.
29 1/10; 32; E, SW,
SE.
Grey, sun, mild.

Sunday 6.
29 1/10; SW, W; 17.
Mild, sun, pleasant.

Rain in the night.

Monday 7.
29 5/10; 35; N.
White frost, sun,
pleasant.

The woodmen begin to fell the beeches in the hanger for the second time: they now enter where they left off last year on the S.E. side of Shop-slidder.

Tuesday 8.
29 7/10; N.
Dark & blowing.

Old John Carpenter planted a Sycamore-tree on the Plestor near the pound. Furze blows.
The amenta of hasels open, & shed their farina.
Ivy-berries swell.

Wednesday 9.
29 8/10; 40; NE.
Dark, harsh, & wet.

Snow-drops bud.
Mr Churton left us, & went to Waverly.

Thursday 10.
29 8/10½; NE; 8.
Grey, & sharp.

NEWTON
The dry summer killed the new planted Sycamore on the Plestor.

Friday 11.
29 6/10; NE.
Grey, still, sharp.

Saturday 12.
29 7/10, 30; 34; NW.
Frost, sun, grey.

SELBORNE
Hepatica's blow.
Some snow remaining under hedges.

Sunday 13.
29 7/10; 38; 40; NW,
W.
Dark, still, & cold.

Helleborus foetidus, & winter aconites blow.

Monday 14.
29 8/10; 34; NW, N.
Frost, sun, hail, sharp.

Tuesday 15.
30/2; 23, 25; N.
Severe frost, cloudless,
sharp.

Barometer at Newton – 29-9.

Wednesday 16.
30/3; 26, 33; W, SW.
Frost, grey, sun, red.

Some thaw. Load of straw brought in.
Bar. at Newton – 30.

Thursday 17.
30/2; 33; W; SW.
Frost, sun sharp, red
even.

Polyanths blow. Cast an heap of dung for a hot bed. Wheeled much dung into the garden: housed earth for hot-beds.

Friday 18.
29; 6/10; 38; SW.   Thaw.
Dark, sun, small rain.

Saturday 19.
29 7/10; 37; N.   Sharp. Received from London a quarter of an hundred of Salt
Grey, & windy.   fish.

Sunday 20.
30; 33; NW, W.
Frost, sun, pleasant.

Monday 21.
29 7/10½; 41; SW.   Turned & cleansed the hot-bed mould.
Grey, dark & mild.

Tuesday 22.
29 7/10½; W, NW.   Driving showers in the night.
Sun, strong wind,   Broᵗ Thomas came from Fyfield.
bright.

Wednesday 23.
29 7/10; W.   Dan. Wheeler plants his field with beans.
Sun, strong wind,
yellow even.

Thursday 24.
29 3/10; SW.
Grey, windy, storms,
& rain.

Friday 25.
29 7/10; 39; W.   Made the seedling cucumber-bed.
Fair, pleasant.   Snow-drops blow.

Saturday 26.
29 5/10½, 44; S; 16.   Salt-fish proves good.
Grey & mild, small   The Creeper, *certhis familiaris*, appears in my orchard, & runs
rain.   up the trees like a mouse. Golden-crowned wren is also seen.

Sunday 27.
29 7/10; 42; S; SE.   The missel-thrush, or storm-cock, sings.
Dark, still, moist.   Snow lies still a yard deep at Stairs hill.

Monday 28.
29 9/10; 37; NE.   Several slow-worms found under the bottom of an old hay-rick in
Deep fog.   a torpid state, but not without some motion.

Tuesday 29.
29 9/10¼; 31½; SE,
NE.
Rime, sun, pleasant,
fog.

Rover sprung two brace of pheasants in long coppice.
Sowed some cucumberseed in the new-made bed.

Wednesday 30.
30; 36; NE.
Deep fog, still.

Vast flock of hen chaffinches.
Sowed radishes with a few carrots under the melon-screen.
Planted broad beans in the meadow-garden.

Thursday 31.
29 7/10; 34; NE.
Grey, & pleasant.

Tubbed half an hog, weighing 8 score: put half a bush: of salt, &
two ounces of salt petre. The pork was well trod into the tub, &
nicely stowed.

FEBRUARY 1788

Friday 1.
29; 4/10; 31; NE.
Hard frost, dark, &
cold.

Rain in January – 1 inch 60.
Received a brace of pheasants from Wood-house farm.

Saturday 2.
29 ½/10; 28; S, SE.
Frost, dark, & sharp,
rain.

Second Bantham pullet lays.
Cucumbers sprout.

Sunday 3.
29 1/10; 45; S, SW;
54.
Sun, showers, sun.

Rain & wind in the night.

Monday 4.
29 3/10; 30; E, NE.
Hard frost, still, &
bright, wet.

Potted the first sown cucumbers; sowed more.
Winter aconites, & snowdrops make a show.
Broʳ Thomas left us, & went to London.

Tuesday 5.
29 4/10½; S, W; 50,
19.
Rain, rain, bright.

Much rain in the night.
A couple of wood-cocks were given me.

Wednesday 6.
29 8/10; 41; SE.
Deep fog, sun, bright.

Daiseys blow.

Thursday 7.
29 8/10; 50; NE, N.

Bees come out, & gather on the snow-drops.

Fog, sun, pleasant, fog.   Some Gossamer appears on the grass.

Friday 8.
29 5/10½; NE, SE.
Fog, sun, wet.

Saturday 9.
29 4/10; 32, 29; NE.   Some Crocus's in bud.
Dark & freezing.

Sunday 10.
29 4/10½; 30; S; SW.
Frost, sleet, thaw.

Monday 11.
29 8/10; 44; S, SW; 7.   Bees gather on the winter-Aconites.
Rain, sun, pleasant,   Red *Aurora*. Some primroses blossom.
fog.

Tuesday 12.
29 8/10; 45; S.   Some Crocus's blown.
Fog, sun, dark.   Cucumber-plants show a rough leaf.

Wednesday 13.
29 7/10½; SW, W;   Some rain in the night. Some primroses blow. Trimmed the
20.   goose-berry trees, & planted more goose-berry & curran-trees.
Sun, pleasant.

Thursday 14.
29 6/10; SW.   Bro. Thomas, & Molly came from London.
Fog, grey, wet, wet.

Friday 15.
29 5/10; 48; W, NW.   Colts foot blows.
Dark, sun, pleasant,   Taw & hop-scotch come in fashion among the boys.
heavy clouds.

Saturday 16.
29 3/10½; 48; S, W;   White crocus's blow: Cucumbers thrive in their pots. Carted in
21.   six loads of hot dung for the bearing bed.
Rain, sun, pleasant.

                  Mʳ Ch: Etty sailed for Bombay, & Canton aboard the *Montrose*
                  India man in the capacity of third mate. – He was delayed, & did
                  not sail 'till the last week in March.

Sunday 17.
29 4/10½; 44½; W.   Storm-cock sings.
Sun, pleasant, dark.   Hail-showers about.

Monday 18.
29 3/10; 35; E, NE.
Snow, dark & chill.

Turnip-tops come into eating.
The ground dries at a wonderous rate.

Tuesday 19.
28 9/10; SE.
Sun, pleasant,
moonshine.

Bro.ʳ Tho.ˢ & Molly White went to London.
Mʳ & Mʳˢ Clement, & two children came, with Zebra the
Nursemaid.

Wednesday 20.
28 6/10½; 42; SE, E.
Rain, rain, rain.

Soft, still rain.

Thursday 21.
28 3/10! 3/10; 45; E,
SE; 60.
Rain, rain, rain.
Full moon.

At Newton – 28! No wind.
Turned the dung for the cucumber-bed.

Friday 22.
28 7/10; W; 8.
Dark, sun, dark.

Dug-up & new planted some rows of thrift.
Mʳˢ Edm.ᵈ White was brought to bed of a boy, who makes my
nephew & nieces 51 in number.

Saturday 23.
28 8/10; 52; SE; 8.
Grey, sun, & showers.

Black bird, & thrush sing.

Sunday 24.
28 6/10; 42; E.
Rain, rain, rain.

Partridges, & missel-thrushes are paired.
Mʳ & Mʳˢ Clement left us.

Monday 25.
29 3/10; 42; N; 26.
Grey, sun, grey.

Divided, & planted-out in two rows up the field-border several
fine polyanths of last Year: planted more rows of beans in the
meadow-garden.

Tuesday 26.
29 1/10½; 39; S, SE.
Wh: frost, sun, mild.

Cucumber-plants thrive. Large titmouse sings.
Turned the Cucumber dung the second time.
Made a hand-glass celeri-bed, & sowed the seed.

Wednesday 27.
29 1/10; NE.
Rain, dark & moist.

Dug-up the suckers of rose-trees, & planted them in a nursery.
Stone-curlew returns, & clamours.

Thursday 28.
29 1/10; 41; NE.
Dark, rain, rain.

Sowed the great mead, & Baker's hill with a good dressing of
ashes: of my own 31 bushels: . . . bought 54 . . .

Grey squirrel
Priory Lane.

Friday 29.
28 8/10¾; 39; E, SE;
64.
Rain, grey, rain.

Winter aconites going out of bloom: crocus's in high beauty.
Spread Mrs Etty's coal-ashes on the bank, & other borders.
Rain in February – 3 inch: 37.

MARCH 1788

Saturday 1.
29 2/10; SE, NE.
Wh: frost, sun,
pleasant, red even.

Radishes come up.
Stone-curlew passes over the village in the dark with a quick
short note.

Sunday 2.
29 4/10; 41; NE.
Dark, & harsh.

A strong smell of London smoke.

Monday 3.
29 7/10; 33; NE, N.
Sharp air, sun &
clouds.

Turned the cucumber-dung the third time, & divided in into
three heaps.
A squirrel in my hedges.

Tuesday 4.
29 6/10; W.
Wh. frost, sun &
clouds, bright.

Made the bearing cucumber-bed with six cart-loads of dung,
which had been turned thrice.

Wednesday 5.
29 4/10; N, W, S.
Hard frost, sun,
pleasant.

Pile-wort begins to blow.

Thursday 6.
29 3/10; 31; NW.
Hard frost, snow, &
hail, cutting wind,
frost, bright.

Strong, severe wind.

Friday 7.
29 2/10; 30; N, S; 14.
Frost, harsh, snow.

Saturday 8.
29 2/10; 28; NE, E.
Hard frost, snow on the
ground, sun, & clouds.

Earthed the bearing cucumber-bed. The bed comes gently to it's heat.

Sunday 9.
29 4/10; 31, 30; NE.
Hard frost, dark &
harsh.

Monday 10.
29 6/10; 27½; NE.
Fierce frost, cloudless,
frost.

Turned-out some pots of cucumbers into the bearing-bed, which is in fine order. The plants are good.

Tuesday 11.
29 7/10; 25, 29; NE,
E.
Fierce frost, cloudless,
frost.

Trenched up ground in kitchen-garden.
Freezing all day.

Wednesday 12.
29 6/10; 24, 31; NE,
SE.
Fierce frost, sun, flisky
clouds.

The violent frost injured the Crocus bloom.
The sun mounts, & looks down on the hanger.
The air is milder.

Thursday 13.
29 3/10; 30; E.
Hard frost, dark &
sharp, frost.

Friday 14.
29 1/10; 30; E.
Hard frost, dark, thaw,
rain.

The frost has entered the ground.
Cucumber-bed hot: plants look well, & show rudiments of bloom, & fruit.

Saturday 15.
29 1/10¼; 38, 39; NE;

Snowdrops go out of bloom.

14.
Rain, dark, mild, &
still.

The hot-bed steams very much; but the plants thrive, & put out
their roots down the sides of the hills; & the weeds spring in the
bed. Yet a little neglect, should there come hot sun-shine, would
burn the plants. Holes are bored on every side in the dung.

Sunday 16.
29 1/10; 41; E, NE.
Dark, & harsh.

Cucumber-bed steams much.

Monday 17.
29 2/10; 31, 31; E.
Ice, dark & harsh,
frost, snow.

Early crocus's are going out of bloom.
Sowed the border opposite the great parlor-windows with dwarf
upright larkspurs; a fine sort.

Tuesday 18.
29 5/10; 31½; NE.
Frost, snow gone, dark
& still.

The wheat-ear, a bird so called, returns & appears on Selborne
down.

Wednesday 19.
29 7/10; 35; SE, S.
Frost, dark, sun, mild.

Violets blow.

On the 27th of February Stone-curlews were heard to pipe: & on
March 1st after it was dark some were passing over the village, as
might be perceived by their quick, short note, which they use in
their nocturnal excursions by way of watch-word, that they may
not stray, & lose their companions. Thus we see, that retire whither
so ever they may in the winter, they return again early in the
spring, & are, as it now appears, the first summer birds that come
back. The smallest uncrested wren has been deemed the earliest
migrator, but is never heard 'till about the 20th of March. Perhaps
the mildness of the season may have quickened the emigration of
the curlews this year. They spend the day in high elevated fields &
sheep-walks; but seem to descend in the night to streams &
meadows, perhaps for water which their upland haunts do not
afford them.

Thursday 20.
29 4/10½; 43; S, W,
S.
Rain, sun, hail, bright.

A violent hail-storm, which filled the gutter, & came in, &
flooded the stair-case; & came down the chimnies & wetted the
floors.

Friday 21.
29 3/10½; 44; S; 50.
Grey, sun, mild.
Full moon.

Added more mould to the cucumber-bed, which seems to be
growing mild.
Showers about.
Young squab red-breasts were found this day in a nest built in a
hollow tree.

Saturday 22.
29 1/10; NE.
Dark, moist, rain,
warm.

Cucumber-plants shew male-bloom.
Sowed balsom-seeds in pots.
Wry-neck returns, & pipes.
Flies come out in windows.

Sunday 23.
29 3/10; 36; NE, N.
Dark, sun, bright.

Mr Churton, who was this week on a visit at Waverley, took the opportunity of examining some of the holes in the sand-banks with which that district abounds. As these are undoubtedly bored by bank-martins,¶ & are the places where they avowedly breed, he was in hopes that they might have slept there also; & that he might have surprised them just as they were awakening from their winter slumbers. When he had dug for some time he found the holes were horizontal, & serpentine, as I had observed before; & that the nests were deposited at the inner end, & had been occupied by broods in former summers: but no torpid birds were to be found. He opened & examined about a dozen holes.

Mr Peter Collinson made the same search many years ago with as little success.

These holes were in depth about two feet.

Monday 24.
29 2/10½; S; 17.
Bright, grey, wet.

ALTON

Tuesday 25.
43, 56; SW.
Fine day.

OXFORD

Wednesday 26.
47.
Bright, wet.

Large Mackarel.

Thursday 27.
41; SE; 11.
Sun, showers.

Friday 28.
44; NW; 25.
Fine, showers.

Saturday 29.
49.
White dew.

Sunday 30.
29 6/10.
Foggy, clouds, rain.

Daffodils by the edge of a wood.
Selborne parish.

Monday 31.
W.
Windy with showers.

READING
Mr Loveday's tortoise at Caversham is come-out.
Young goslins. Rain in March – 1–31.

APRIL 1788

Tuesday 1.
29 7/10; 50; W; 40.
Showers, windy &
cloudy.

SELBORNE
Daffodils in bloom. Apricots in bloom.
Mr Churton came. Sowed polyanth-seed.

Wednesday 2.
29 7/10; W.
Windy, cloudy, windy.

Sowed a bed of Onions. Mr Churton left us.
Cucumbers show fruit; fruit in bloom.
Crocus's are gone off.

Thursday 3.
29 2/10; W.
Blowing, strong gales
with showers.

Dogs-tooth violets blow.

Friday 4.
29 5/10; 35; NW; 15.
Windy, with snow-
showers.

Saturday 5.
29 8/10; 34; N.
Sharp wind, sun, &
dark clouds.

Sowed a crop of parsnips with lettuce, & radishes. The first
radishes failed.
After all Mr Charles Etty did not sail f^m St Hellens 'till this
morning.

Sunday 6.
29 9/10; 40; N.
Sharp wind, sun &
clouds.

Peaches & nectarines in bloom.
Nightingale heard in the church-litten coppice. qu.

Monday 7.
30; 45, 51; NW, N.
Sun, mild, clouds, wet.

Cucumbers begin to set.
Put some honey in the frames to tempt the bees.

Tuesday 8.
30 1/10; 48, 57; W,
NW, N.
Wet, grey, sun, bright.

Sowed a crop of lettuce, & carrots.
Insects swarm in the air. Ants come forth.
Timothy heaves up the earth.

Wednesday 9.
30 1/10; 46, 65; NE.

Grass now grows. Planted cabbages.

Dew, grey, warm,
dark.

Timothy the tortoise comes out. Cucumbers swell.
Bat out.

Thursday 10.
29 9/10; 50, 62, 49;
SE.
Great dew, sun,
summer, yellow even.

Crown Imperials blow, & stink.
The chif-chaf is heard.
Much gossamer. Sweet weather. Bat.
Cucumbers swell. Water, & line the cucumbᵣ beds.

Friday 11.
29 6/10; 46, SE.
Fog, sun, brisk air,
dark clouds.

Men prepare for poling their hops: women hoe the wheat. Sweet
weather. Butterflies.

Saturday 12.
29 8/10; 45, 45; SW.
Sun & clouds, sweet
even.

Rain-bow. Showers about.
Apricots begin to set.
Mowed the grass of the fairey-ring on the grass-plot.
Sent Mᵣ White of Newton some male cucumber-blossoms in a
box, to set some fruit in bloom in his frames.
Fritillaria blows.

Sunday 13.
29 8/10½; 36; SW.
White frost, bright,
sweet red even.

The bees frequent the cucumber-frames.
Nightingales heard below Temple.

Monday 14.
29 6/10½, 7/10; 45;
SW, NW.
Sun, clouds, rain,
bright.

Cut a brace of Cucumbers, one a large one.
Ivy-berries are ripe, & drop-off.

Mᵣ Ventris observed at Faringdon a little whirl-wind, which
originated in the road before his house, taking up the dust & straws
that came in it's way. After mounting up thro' one of the elms
before the Yard, & carrying away two of the rooks nests in which
were young squabs; it then went off, leaving the court-yard
strewed with dust & straws, & scraps of twigs, & the little naked
rooks sprawling on the ground. A pair of rooks belonging to one of
these nests built again, & had a late brood.

Tuesday 15.
29 7/10½; 48; N,
NW; 6.
Wh: frost, sun, red
even.

Pronged the asparagus-beds. Sowed Mʳˢ Eveleigh's curious asters
in a hot-bed; & several perannials in the cold ground. Men pole
hops.

Wednesday 16.
29 7/10½; 41; NW.
Cold air, dark, grey.

Swallow seen at Selborne; one yesterday at Faringdon.

Thursday 17.
29 7/10¼; 42; W.
Dark & harsh, dark.

Cut a cucumber. Celeri under a hand-glass very forward.

Friday 18.
29; 8/10; 45; NW.
No dew, grey, dark.

Nightingale sings in my outlet.
Cucumbers swell. Polyanths very gay.

Saturday 19.
29 8/10¾; 45, 62; W,
NW, N, W.
Sun, summer day,
Mackarel sky.

Mowed the grass-plot. Wall-cherries begin to blow.
Mended the fences this week all round my outlet.
Black snails come out. Insects abound; yet no swallows to be seen.
The voice of the Cuckoo is heard in the land.¶

Sunday 20.
29 8/10; 55, 63; S.
Good dew, summer
weather.
Full moon.

Cuckow about the village: no hirundines.
Insects abound.
Sweet evening.

Cuckoo.
Newton Valence.

Monday 21.
29 5/10; 45, 63; S,
SW.
Cloudless, gale,
louring.

Some beeches in leaf in the hanger.
Cut a brace of fine cucumbers.
Timothy begins to eat: he crops the daisies, & walks down to the
fruit-wall to browze on the lettuces.

Tuesday 22.
29 5/10; 40; W, NW.
Showers, & wind.

Sowed nasturtiums. Mountain snow-drops, & early tulips blow.
Mowed the garden round. Cut a brace of fine cucumbers.
No hirundines. Some vine-shoots so forward as to shew
rudiments of fruit.

Wednesday 23.
29 5/10¼; 42; SW,

Cut five brace of fine Cucumbers.

W.
Grey, dark, rain.

Gave away 24 eggs of the Bantham kind among my neighbours.

Thursday 24.
29 6/10; 42; W.
Sun with strong gale.

Grass-hopper-lark whispers.
Cut two brace of cucumbers.
Cowslips blow.

Friday 25.
29 7/10½; 40; W.
Blowing, & harsh.

Apricots swell. Mowed the grass-plot. Wall-cherries loaded with bloom. The wild meris, cherry, blossoms.

Saturday 26.
29 7/10, 42; W, SW.
Blowing, sprinklings.

Cut two brace, & half of fine cucumbers: in all this week ten brace & an half.
Harsh, windy, unpleasing weather for many days.

Sunday 27.
29 8/10¾; 48; W.
Grey, sun, pleasant, red even.

No hirundines of any sort, tho' this month is so far advanced.
Polyanths continue in high beauty.

Monday 28.
29 9/10½; 48; SW.
Sun, summer weather.

Cut two brace of fine cucumbers. Watered the linings of the beds.
Redstart appears. Two house-martins.
Nightingale in my outlet.

Tuesday 29.
29 9/10; 64; SE.
Wh: dew, hot sun, red.

Cut four brace of cucumbers.
A pair of Swifts. Swallows.
Water the garden much. Well sinks. Rain wanted.

Wednesday 30.
29 8/10; 49, 68; NE,
SE, E.
Sun, hot sun, cloudless, red even.

Cut 3 brace & half of cucumbers.
Began to mow the orchard for the horses.
Timothy weighs 6 pds 13 oz 10.
Rain in April – 0 inch: 61 h.
Mole-cricket churs.

MAY 1788

Thursday 1.
29 8/10; 50, 73; N, S.
Sun, hot, clouds, red even.

Antirrhinum cymbalaria blows.
Cut five brace of cucumbers. Rain much wanted.
Made the large annual bed. First asparagus.

Mrs Ben White was brought to bed of a boy, who encreases my nephews, & nieces to the number of 52.

The bloom of cherries, pears, & apples is great; of plums, bullace, sloes, little. Currans promise for much fruit, gooseberries for little. Peaches & nectarines are set: cherries begin to set.

Friday 2.
29 8/10½; 50, 73;
NE, S, N.
Fine dew, sultry,
clouds, thunder-like.

Hops grow; & are now tying to their poles.
Young ducks.
Cut two brace of cucumbers. Flowers hurried out of bloom by the heat.
Best tulips are shaded.
Bro.ʳ Tho.ˢ White's tulips from South Lambeth make a gaudy appearance.

Saturday 3.
29 9/10; 48; NE, NE.
Gale, cool, sun, red
even.

Earthed-out the Cucumber-bed: the lining is hot.
Men cart peat & chalk. The deepest roads are quite dry.

Sunday 4.
29 8/10; NE.
Dark & harsh, sun, red
even.

Shade the best tulips from the vehemence of the sun. Polyanths are hurryed out of bloom. Vine-shoots are forward. Sowed the great annual-frame with flower-seeds: sowed two hand-glasses with cucumbers, green & white. Timothy wanders round the garden, & strives to get out: he is shut-up in the brew-house to prevent an escape.

Monday 5.
29 7/10; 66; NE.
Sun, sultry, cloudless,
red even, lightening.

Several swifts. Many swallows.
Cut seven brace, & half of cucumbers.
The great oak in the mead abounds with male bloom.
Timothy is very voracious; he devours the lettuce.

Tuesday 6.
29 6/10; SE.
Clouds, sprinklings.

The woodlark sings in the air at three in the morning: Stone-curlews pass over the village at that hour.
Distant showers. Watered the garden much.

Wednesday 7.
29 6/10; 64; W, N; 17.
Clouds, shower,
shower.

Honey-suckles against walls begins to blow.
Cut five brace of cucumbers, small ones.
Copious showers. We have enjoyed no good rain since April 1.ˢᵗ

Thursday 8.
29 6/10½; 63; W, S.
Dew, sun, pleasant,
gale.

Raked down the borders, which are softened by the rain. Mowed the walks well. Sowed cucumbers green & white, radishes, lettuce; several sorts of flowers.

Friday 9.
29 5/10¾; 58; SW.
Dew, sun, dark, rain.

Blowing.

Saturday 10.
29 8/10; W, NW.
Sun, clouds, pleasant.

Cut three brace & half of cucumbers.
Sowed two rows of large white kidney-beans.

Mr Burbey's brown owl, which was a great washer, was drowned
at last in a tub where there was too much water.

Sunday 11.
29 8/10¼; 51; SW.
Grey, dark, cool.

In some districts chafers swarm: I see none at Selborne. Cotton
blows from the willows, & fills the air: with this substance some
birds line their nests.

Monday 12.
29 9/10; 63; E, S, SE.
Sun, hot sun, red even.

Cut two brace of cucumbers.
Fern-owl chatters: it comes early this year.

Tuesday 13.
29 8/10½; 49, 65; SE,
NE.
Dew, sun, cloudless,
red even.

Cut four brace of Cucumbers. 8 brace of swifts.
Apple-trees in beautiful bloom.
Watered much. Not many martins.
My great oak in the meadow abounds with male bloom.

Wednesday 14.
29 8/10; 59; NE.
Fog, grey, sun,
cloudless, red even.

Vine-shoots very forward. Cut two brace of cucumbers. Honey-
suckles blow.
Two nightingales in my out-let.
Very few house-martins about the village.

Thursday 15.
29 7/10; 46; NE.
Dry mist, sun, clouds.

Cold wind. Cut two brace of cucumbers.
A brace more of cucumbers.

Sheared my mongrel dog Rover,¶ & made use of his white hair in
plaster for ceilings. His coat weighed four ounces. The N:E: wind
makes Rover shrink.
    A black bird has made a nest in my barn on some poles that lie
on a scaffold.

Friday 16.
29 5/10; 49; NE.
Shower, gale, sun, red
even.

Laburnums make a fine show. Haw-thorns blow.

Saturday 17.
29 5/10; NE.
Shower, sun, fine even.

Cinnamon-rose blows.
Heavy clouds about.

Sunday 18.
29 5/10½; 62; NE, N.
Grey, clouds, shower.

The Fly-catcher appears: it usually comes about the 20th of this
month, & is the latest summer bird of passage.

Orange-lilly blows.
A thunder-storm at London that damaged houses.
Very small shower.
Rain at S. Lambeth . . 40.

Monday 19.
29 7/10; 63; N, NW.
Grey, sun, clouds,
shower.

Cut two brace, & half of Cucumbers.
Showers about. Thunder. Mountain-ash blows.

Tuesday 20.
29 9/10; 61; N; 9.
Sun, hot.

Fly-catcher begins to make a nest in my vine.
Cut five brace of cucumbers: small ones.

Wednesday 21.
29 9/10; 58, 66; N,
SW. Sun, cloudless,
sultry, gale.

The rudiments of wall-nuts appear.
Watered the garden much.

Thursday 22.
29 9/10; 60, 66; W.
Dew, sun, sultry, grey.

Saint-foin, & fiery lilly begin to blow. Rain much wanted.
House-martins much encreased in number within these two days.

Friday 23.
29 8/10; 54; S.
No dew, dark, sun,
sultry.

Wheat in some fields seems to be injured by the drought. Cut
four brace of Cucumbers: by much bearing the plants begin to be
almost exhausted.

Many ponds round the neighbourhood are dry, & cleaned out.
Newton pond almost full of water. Mr White's tank reduced to two
feet of water.

Saturday 24.
29 6/10½; 58, 68; SE.
Sun, sultry, red even.

Began to tack the vines, the shoots of which are very long. My
vines do not shew much bloom. N. *Aurora*.

Sunday 25.
29 6/10; 59, 72; SE,
E.
Cloudless, gale, red
even.

My winter lettuces all run-off to seed.

The Culture of Virgil's vines corresponds very exactly with the
modern management of hops. I might instance in the perpetual
diggings, & hoeings, in the tying to the stakes, & poles, in pruning
of the superfluous shoots, &c: but lately I have observed a new
circumstance, which was Farmer Spencer harrowing the alleys
between the rows of hops with a small triangular harrow, drawn
by one horse, & guided by two handles. This occurrence brought
to my mind the following passage:
. . . "*ipsa*
"*Flectere luctantes inter vineta juvencos.*"
    Second Georgic.¶

Monday 26.
29 6/10; 61, 72; SE.
Cloudless, gale, red
even.

Sultry. Showers to the S.E. & E. Sprinkling.

Tuesday 27.
29 4/10½; 62, 75; SE,
E. Sun, sultry, clouds.

Grass burns. Mr White of Newton fetches water from Newton
pond to put into his tank.

Wednesday 28.
29 3/10; 63, 72; SE.
Grey, sultry, louring,
rain.

The Flycatcher, which was not seen 'till the 18th has got a nest, &
four eggs.
Thinned & tacked the vines.
Thunder heard at a distance. Showers round.

Thursday 29.
29 3/10½; 62; W,
NW, N.
Sun, gale, dark.

Monthly roses in bloom.
No sign of the rain of last night.

Friday 30.
29 4/10; 52; E.
Dark, rain, dark &
cool, rain.

Soft showers.

On this day there was a tempest of thunder & lightening at Lyndon
in the County of Rutland, which was followed by a rain that lasted
24 hours. The rain that fell was 1 in. 40 h.

Saturday 31.
29 6/10½; 48; E; 50.
Rain, dark, & cool.

Elders, & corn-flags, solstitial plants, now in bloom!
Rain in May – 0 in. 76 h.

JUNE 1788

Sunday 1.
29 6/10¼; 59; E.
Sun, clouds, sweet
even.

Monday 2.
29 6/10¼; E.
White frost, sun, fine.

ALTON
Mr Edm^d White, & Captain Dumaresque cut their Saint foin.

Tuesday 3.
E.
Sun, blue mist, fine.

S. LAMBETH
Hay-making is general about Clapham, & South Lambeth: Bro^r
Benjn has eight acres of hay down, & making.

Wednesday 4.
NW, N.
Dingy.

Saw some red-backed butcher-birds about Farnham.

Thursday 5.
NW.
Sun, sultry.

LONDON

Friday 6.
S, SW.
Sun, sultry.

Scarlet strawberries at 2s. p^r pottle.¶
Red-backed butcher-bird, or Flusher, in Bro. Ben's outlet.

Saturday 7.
N.
Sun, dark, rain.

S. LAMBETH
Bro. Ben ricked ye hay of eleven acres of ground in delicate order.
Rain . . . 0 in. 8 h.

Sunday 8.
NE.
Sun, strong gale.

The black cluster vines from Selborne are in bloom, & smell delicately!
Dust flies. Cucumbers bear.

The *scarabaei solstitiales* begin to swarm in my Brother's outlet. My Bro.^{r} this spring turned one of his grass-fields into a kitchen-garden, & sowed it with crops: but the ground so abounded with the maggots of these chafers, that few things escaped their ravages. The lettuces, beans, & cabbages were mostly devoured: & yet in trenching this enclosure his people had destroyed multitudes of these noxious grubs.
    The stalks & ribs of the leaves of the Lombardy poplar are embossed with large tumors¶ of an oblong shape, which by incurious observers have been taken for the fruit of the tree. These Galls are full of small insects, some of which are winged & some not. The parent insect is of the Genus of *Cynips*. Some poplars in this garden are quite loaded with these excrescencies.

Monday 9.
NE.
Sun, sharp wind,
cloudless, & cold.

Many swallows, & a few swifts. Mazagon-beans come in.
Cauliflowers are small for want of rain.

Tuesday 10.
NE.
Cloudless, sharp wind.

Scarlet straw-berries very dry, & tasteless.
Hemerocallis blows.

Wednesday 11.
NE.
Sun, sharp wind.

Some good oats about S. Lambeth.

Thursday 12.
NE.
Sun, brisk gale.

My Brother's gardener cut his first melon, a Romagna.
Gardens, & fields quite scorched up.

Friday 13.
NE.

The bloom of the vines fills the chambers with an agreeable scent

Sun, gale.

some what like that of mignonette.

Saturday 14.
N.
Dark, gale.

Barometer all this week about 30. The constant N.E. winds have much dryed, & exhausted the fields, & gardens.
Latter orange-lillies blow. Red pinks in full bloom.

Bro. B. has in his grounds 77 rows of Lucerne,¶ which are each 48 yards in length. This plot furnishes his three horses with green meat the summer thro', & is cut at an average four times in the Year. His gardener cuts-up three rows at a time several evenings in the week, & observes that one row fodders one horse for 24 hours.

The crop is kept clean at considerable expense: & would soon be over-run with weeds, was not care & attention bestowed. As soon as the whole rows are gone thro', those that were cut first are ready to be cut again.

He has 15 lights of melons, & 16 lights for cucumbers; & 40 hand-glasses for ridge-Cucumbers, & other purposes.

Sunday 15.
NE.
Sun, sultry, clouds.

The double scarlet Pomegranade buds for bloom.
A bunting appears about the walks: this is a very rare bird at Selborne.

The solstitial chafers swarm by thousands in my Brother's grounds. They begin to flie about sun-set, but withdraw soon after nine, & probably settle on the trees, to feed & to engender.

Monday 16.
NE.
Shower, sun,
sprinklings, red even.

My chamber at S. Lambeth is much annoyed with gnats.
Cut a melon. Rain – 0 –6.
The dust is laid. Passion flower buds for bloom.

Tuesday 17.
78; NE.
Cloudless, sultry,
distant thunder.

Cherries turn colour, & begin to be eatable; but are small for want of moisture: are netted.
Therm.ʳ at Fyfield 82. Nights are very hot.

Wednesday 18.
71; E, NE, S.
Sun, grey, dark.
Full moon.

Neither the pease or beans have the same flavour, or sweetness as in moist summers.
Therm.ʳ at Fyfield 88!!
A cat gets down the pots of a neighbour's chimney after the Swallows nests.

Thursday 19.
N; 9
Dark, rain, dark.

LONDON

Muscae domesticae swarm in every room. I have often heard my Brothers complain how much they were annoyed with flies at this place. They are destroyed by a poisonous water called fly-water, set in basons; & by bird-lime twigs laid across pans of water.

Friday 20.
N. Rain, rain, rain.

Saturday 21.
N.
Dark, & still.

Rain – 0 – 24.

Sunday 22.
N, NW.
Sun, clouds, fine even.

S. LAMBETH
My fly-catchers left their nest this day.
Hollyhocks, Sweet Williams, Nasturtiums, & everlasting-pease,
blossom. Gooseberries, & cherries appear at table: the latter are
very small, & have not much flavour.

The cuckoo is heard every day. Black-bird sings. Swift is abroad at
half hour after three in the morning. About this time swifts hatch.
    Black-caps sing.

Monday 23.
SW.
Sun, clouds, rain.

The dwarf, upright lark-spurs make a fine show. Rasps begin to
turn colour.

Tuesday 24.
SW; 6.
Clouds, sprinklings,
cool.

Rain – 0 – 8. The dust is laid, & the gardens, & fields some what
refreshed. Four women gather my Bro.^{rs} goose-berries for sale.
Gardener sows turnips.

Wednesday 25.
65; W; 63.
Grey, clouds, rain.

Rain – 0 – 2. Grapes set.
Dark, heavy weather to the S. & S.W.

Mr Reeve, a master Carpenter in the town of Lambeth, is employed
in building a Conservatory for the Queen of Naples, the dimensions
of which are 117 feet in length, 40 feet in breadth, 20 feet to the
angle of the roof, & 10 feet to the eaves. This noble green-house
(the largest that has been constructed in this kingdom) is to be
roofed with sash-work on both sides, the upper sashes of every
other one of which are so contrived as to slide down with pullies:
the sides also are to be lined with sashes which pull up & down: the
South end also is to be sashed, but the N. end is to be close, thro'
which there is an entrance by a pair of large doors. That there
might be no beams across to obstruct the view, the roof is
supported by 16 pillars of cast iron, weighing 500 weight each,
which are so ramifyed at the top as to give the roof something of a
Gothic air, & to add to it's strength. The area is to contain two
beds or borders of earth, of 100 feet by 11 feet, around & between
which there are roomy alleys, or paths. This whole deal frame-
work, when finished, is to be taken to pieces, & so sent by sea to
Naples. The whole area of this house will contain 4680 square feet,
& the two beds, or borders 2200 square feet. As the soft &
southern climate of Naples produces oranges, lemons,
pomgranades, citrons, & many trees & plants with which we croud
our green-houses; we are to suppose that this royal conservatory
will be furnished only with the most fragrant, choice, & rare

vegetable productions of the Tropics. The Gardener of the King of the two Sicilies is a Scotchman, who went over two years ago; & had been partner, or assistant to Mr Gordon.

If there is any defect in this edifice, it seems to lie in the sash-roofing, which appears to be rather too slight & delicate for the length of the bearings; tho' each sash is stiffened by a small iron-rod: however heavy snows, we may suppose, are seldom or never seen in Lat: 40–50 so as to weigh in the glass. But with regard to the brittle healing, large hail-storms from off the Apennine may some times be dreaded, which would occasion almost as great an havock among that fragil tiling, as a shower of cinders from the neighbouring Vesuvius. The clatter & jingle on such an occasion would put a man in mind of that beautiful, & expressive line in Virgil,

"Tam multa in tectis crepitans salit horrida grando."¶

Thursday 26. W, @; 3. Showers, heavy rain.	Rain – 0 – 12. Fly-catcher. Thunder. Rain – 0 – 50. Kidney-beans come in: dwarfs.
Friday 27. 29 2/10; 63; SE. Sun, pleasant.	SELBORNE Pomgranade, & Passion-flower blossom. Dust laid all the way. Met a cart of whortel-berries on the road.
Saturday 28. 63; NE; 46. Rain, gleams, rain.	Roses almost out. Pinks, red garden valerian, orange & white lillies, make a fine show. Annuals are all planted out. The fields & gardens are much refreshed by the rains. Wood-strawberries, but not ripe. Young partridges.
Sunday 29. 29 4/10½; 60; N. Dark & cool, gleam.	Spotted martagons blow. Grapes set. Young nightingales in the walks.
Monday 30. 29 7/10; 60; NW, W. Dark & louring, gleam.	Crop of apples general. The parsonage-orchard at Faringdon, that has failed for many years, has now a full burthen. The rain in June was 1 in. 27 h.

JULY 1788

Tuesday 1. 29 7/10½; SW, S. Small showers, showers, vast clouds in the horizon.	Lime-trees in full bloom, & frequented by bees. Ponds in bottoms that had been dry, & cleaned-out, have now some water.

Wednesday 2.
29 7/10; 63½; S.
Grey, sun, clouds,
gleam.

The rasps begin to ripen: white currans are eatable. Turned-out the ridge-cucumbers from under the glasses: they begin to blow.

Thursday 3.
29 5/10¾; 66½; S.
Grey, sun, sultry, sun.

Red-backed butcher-bird, or flusher at Little comb.
Gathered a good mess of Rasps for jam.

Friday 4.
29 4/10½; 63; SE,
SW; 10.
Rain, sun & wind.

Gathered cherries for preserving.
Cut a doz: of artichokes.
Broad beans come in. Sowed endive.
Wheat in general looks very fine.

Saturday 5.
29 4/10; 61; 21.
Showers, showers.

The fly-catchers build again in the vines with a view to a second brood.
Timothy grazes on the grass-plot.
Finished cutting several of the tall hedges.
Some dishes of wood straw-berries are brought to the door.

Sunday 6.
29 6/10; 62; SW, S.
Sun, clouds, wet.

Young martins come out of their nests.
Lime-trees very beautiful with their golden tassels.
Some young wasps appear.

The late burning season has proved fatal to many deer in elevated situations, where the turf being quite scorched up, the stock in part perished for want. This is said in particular to have been the case at Up-park in Sussex. A want of water might probably have been one occasion of this mortality. Some fallow-deer have dyed in the Holt.

Monday 7.
29 6/10; 62; SW, W;
40, 19.
Showers, showers,
gleam.

Young partridges flyers.
M.ʳˢ White made much Rasp, & curran jams.

Tuesday 8.
29 4/10½; 62; SW;
25.
Sun, clouds, rain.

Made cherry-jam. H.W. & Anne Woods came.
Some wasps eat the cherries.
Grass grows. Rasps, & cherries very fine.
D.L.

Wednesday 9.
29 4/10; 62; SW.
Dark, rain, rain.

Bunches of snakes eggs are found under some straw near the hot-beds. Several snakes haunted my out-let this summer, & cast their sloughs in the garden, & elsewhere.

Deer glimpsed
Selborne High Wood

Thursday 10.
29 5/10; 63; S; 38.
Rain, rain, rain, rain.

Cran-berries are offered at the door.
There are now some fallow-deer, & a red deer in Hartley wood.

Friday 11.
29 6/10; 65; SW, SE;
19.
Wet, sun, clouds.

Grass grows on the walks. The meadow-grass should be cut.
White apples stew.
Scarlet martagons blow.

Saturday 12.
29 5/10; 66, 71, 70; S,
S; 13.
Shower, thunder,
sultry, vast thunder,
clouds, sultry.

Codlins come in for stewing.
Wasps encrease & gnaw the cherries: hung bottles to take the
wasps. Straw-berries offered.
Cucumbers under the hand-glasses begin to set.
Many swifts: but it does not appear that their young are yet out.

"*Contemplator item, cum se Nux plurima silvis Induet in florem,*
& ramos curvabit olentes: Si superant foetus, pariter frumenta
sequenter; Magnaque cum magno veniet tritura calore".¶

    If by *Nux*¶ in this passage Virgil meant the Wall-nut, then it
must follow, that he must also mean that a good wall-nut year
usually proves a good year for wheat. This remark is verifyed in a
remarkable manner this summer with us: for the wallnut trees are
loaded with myriads of nuts, which hang in vast clusters; & the
crop of wheat is such as has not been known for many seasons.
The last line seems also to imply, that this coincident, even in Italy,
does not befall but only in a dry, sultry summer. Tho' wall-nut-
trees in England blow long before wheat; yet it is probable that in
Italy, where wheat is more early than with us, they may blossom
together. And indeed unless these vegetables had accorded in the

time of their bloom, the Poet would scarce have introduced them
together as an instance of concomitant fertility.

Sunday 13.
29 4/10½; 68; SW.   Young swallows out.
Rain, rain, rain.

Monday 14.
29 5/10; 64; SW, SE;   Boys bring their first wasps nest, a small one. Wasps, & honey-
13.   bees gnaw the Cherries.
Grey, dark, rain.   Housed the frames, & lights of the early cucumber-beds.
                           Piped many shoots of elegant pinks.¶
Tuesday 15.   Dripping weather now for three weeks.
29 4/10; 62; S, SW;   There are some buntings in the N. field: a very rare bird at
63, 16.   Selborne. They love open fields, without enclosures.
Rain, rain, moon shine.   Jennetings,¶ apples so called, come in to be eaten. Potatoes
                           come in.

Wednesday 16.
29 5/10; 63; SW; 21.   Bull-finch eats the berries of the honey-suckles.
Rain, rain, gleams,   Bro.ʳ Tho.ˢ came.
showers.

Thursday 17.
29 7/10; 63; SW, NW,   Mushrooms come in.
W; 60.
Showers, showers,
bright.

Friday 18.
29 8/10½; 60; N,   Fly-catcher feeds his sitting hen.
NW.   M.ʳˢ H. W. Bessy, & Lucy came.
Fine dew, sun, grey.   Mushrooms.
Full moon.

Saturday 19.
29 7/10; 63, 66; SW.   Poultry begin to moult.
Sun, small shower,   Some men begin to cut their meadows.
grey.

Sunday 20.
29 8/10½; 63; NW.   Turnips come up well.
Grey, dark, gleams.
                           The fields are now finely diversifyed with ripe corn, hay & harvest
                           scenes, & hops. The whole country round is a charming land-
                           scape, & puts me in mind of the following lovely lines in the first
                           book of the *Cyder* of John Philips.
                           "Nor are the hills unamiable, whose tops
                           To heaven aspire, affording prospect sweet
                           To human ken: nor at their feet the vales

Descending gently, where the lowing herd
Chews verdurous pasture; nor the yellow fields
Gaily interchang'd, with rich variety
Pleasing; as when an Emerald green, enchas'd
In flamy gold, from the bright foil mass acquires
A nobler hue, more delicate to sight".

Monday 21.
29 8/10¾; 60, NW,
W.
Sun, clouds, gleams.

Began to cut my meadow-grass. Farmer Parsons begins wheat-harvest in the Ewel: farmer Hewet at the forest side. Cool. A young man brings a large wasps nest, found in my meadow.

Tuesday 22.
29 8/10½; 63; NW.
Grey, sun, dark.
gleam.

An other wasps-nest brought.
Soft & mild.
Sweet gleam.

Wednesday 23.
29 7/10¼; 66; E, S,
W.
Grey, hot, dark.

An other wasps nest. Wheat blited at Oakhanger.
Oakhanger-ponds empty: they were sewed in the spring. Hay makes.

Thursday 24.
29 7/10½; 66; SW,
NW.
Showers, sun, cool.

Thunder.
Farmer Parsons binds some wheat. Hay makes.

Friday 25.
29 8/10; 60; W, NW.
Sun, dark clouds,
gleam, cool.

Apricots come in. Wheat-harvest general.
Ricked my hay in nice order.

Saturday 26.
29 8/10, 58½; SW.
Dark, louring, gleam.

Hops shew bloom: some gardens look well.
Much hay ricked. No swifts.

Sunday 27.
29 7/10½; 51; SW,
W.
Cold dew, sun, louring,
gleam.

White frost.
No swifts.

We have had a few chilly mornings & evenings, which have sent off the swifts. I have remarked before, many times, how early they are in their retreat. Surely they must be influenced by the failure of some particular insect, which ceases to fly thus early, being checked by the first cool autumnal sensations; since their congeners will not depart yet these eight or nine weeks.

Monday 28.
29 7/10½; 52; NW.
Sun, dark, shower,
gleam.

Two swifts sipping the surface of Bin's pond.
The bed of Oakhanger pond covered with large muscle shells.
The stint or summer snipe. Large flock of Lapwings in the

S. Loe¶ thunder.   Forest. No swifts at Selborne.
Sweet harvest weather.

Tuesday 29.
29 8/10; @; 62.   Fly-catchers have got a second brood.
Sun, sultry, louring.   Sweet harvest weather.
Thatched the hay rick.
No swifts.
Men hoe turnips.

Wednesday 30.
29 8/10¾; 62, 77; S,   Some reapers/workmen are made sick by the heat.
W. Sun, hot, sultry,   Sowed second crop of endive. Trenched five rows of celeri.
sweet even.   Much wheat bound. Some houses by John Carpenter.

Thursday 31.
29 8/10½; 72; W.   Rain in July – 3 – 58.
Dark, hot.   Much wheat housed. Two swifts. N. *Aurora*.

AUGUST 1788

Friday 1.
30 ¼; 74; N.   Four swifts. Much wheat bound. Watered Celeri, & cucumbers.
Dark, spitting, louring.   Nightingales appear in my walks.
Aurora.

Saturday 2.
30 1/10; 74, 75; E, S.   Many bats breed under the tiles of my house.
Sun, sultry, red even.   Much wheat housed.
Watered celeri, & cucumbers.
Many reapers are made sick by the heat.
Five gallons, & one pint of brandy from London.

Sunday 3.
30 ½; 78½; E, SE.   The air swarms with flying ants.
Sun, cloudless, sultry,
red even.

Monday 4.
29 9/10¾; 82; SE,   Sowed a good bed of winter spinage, & rolled it down with the
SW.   garden stone-roller.
Cloudless, sultry,   Ants swarm at the bottom of my stair-case.
yellow even.   Gale. Much wheat gleaned. One swift.

Tuesday 5.
29 9/10; 73; N.   Cucumbers bear. Flying ants from the stair-case.
Sun, gale, gleam.   Farmer Spencer's rick slipped down as it was building.
Much wheat gleaned. Preserved some apricots.

Wednesday 6.
29 8/10; 64; N.
Sun & clouds, cool.

Many coveys of partridges. Flight of lapwings comes up into the malm fallows.
Much wheat gleaned.

Thursday 7.
29 8/10; 62; N, E.
Dark & cool.

Peat brought in. One swift.
Some men have finished wheat-harvest.
Fly-catcher brings out his second brood.

Friday 8.
29 8/10¼; 53, 61; N.
Sun, dark, & cool.

Two or three beeches below Bradshot are quite loaded with mast.
The King's field is cleared, & thrown open. Farmer Spencer finished wheat-harvest.
Some beeches tinged with yellow.

Saturday 9.
29 8/10; 64; E.
Dark & cool, gleam, dark.

Wheat housed all day. Wheat-harvest will be finished by Monday, viz in old July.¶

Sunday 10.
29 7/10; 63; E.
Spitting, dark & louring, grey.

Hops come unequally; some are full formed, & some in blossom.
Rain is wanted: grass-walks burn.
Colchicum blows. Wheat-harvest mostly over.

Monday 11.
29 7/10; 72; E.
Sun, sultry, gleam.

Many lapwings at French-meer. Single swift at Fyfield.
Soft & still. Watered the garden. Many ponds are almost dry the second time. Finished cutting the tall hedges.
The walks burn.

Tuesday 12.
29 5/10; 72, 65; SE, S, SW.
Great dew, sun, dark & louring, rain.

Wednesday 13.
29 2/10; 66; 46.
Sun & clouds, moonshine.

Fine rain in the night.
Trenched out the sixth row of celeri.

Thursday 14.
28 9/10¾; 58; SW, W; 51.
Rain, sun & wind, bright.

Trenched-out an other row of celeri: planted-out a bed of endive.
The wind has blown down several hop-poles.
H: W. & Miss W. left us, & went to Newton. Bro. Henry, & B. White, & wife came with little Tom, & Nurse Johnson.

Friday 15.
29 3/10½; W.
Heavy showers & thunder.

Saturday 16.
29 4/10½; SW; 39.
Sun, showers.
Full moon.

Oats mowed by Farmer Spencer.

Sunday 17.
29 3/10; SW.
Showers, gleams, wet.

Monday 18.
29 4/10; SW; 18.
Showers, sun & wind.

Some wheat that is out, lies in a sad wet state.
Grapes begin to turn colour.

Tuesday 19.
29 3/10½; 65; SW;
26.
Heavy showers, clouds.

Farmer Lasham has much wheat out, which was not ripe when
other people cut, & housed.

Wednesday 20.
29 6/10; SW.
Sun, pleasant.

Martins have young, a second brood.
Sowed brown Dutch lettuce to stand the winter under the fruit-
wall. A vast flock of Lapwings haunts the pastures & low grounds
of Norton farm.
Nep. Ben returned to London.

Thursday 21.
29 6/10; 67; S.
Grey, & mild, soft,
dark.

Mushrooms now come again.
Bro.ʳ Henry left us.

Friday 22.
29 4/10; 66; SW.
Wet, wet, sun &
clouds.

The swallows are very busy skimming & hovering over a fallow
that has been penned: probably the dung of the sheep attracts
many insects, particularly scarabs.

Saturday 23.
29 5/10½; SW, W;
32.
Showers, sun, pleasant.

Many pieces of oats cut in the N. field.
Mʳ Prowling gathers his most early hops at Chawton.
Some mushrooms spring on my hot-beds.
Mʳ Sam Barker, from a measurement taken, adjudged Wolmer
pond to contain 66 acres, & an half, exclusive of the arm at the E.
end: the pond-keeper at Frinsham avers that his pond measures
80 acres.

Zizania aquatica, Linn: called by the English setlers wild Rice; &
by the Canadian French *Folle Avoine*.
    In consequence of an application to a Gentleman at Quebec, my
Bro. Thomas White received a cask of the seed of this plant, part of

which was sent down to Selborne. His desire was to have received it in the ear, as it then would have been much more likely to have retain'd it's vegetative faculty: but this part of his request was not attended to; for the seed arrived stript even of it's husk. It has a pleasant taste, & makes a pudding equal to rice, or millet. This kind of corn, growing naturally in the water, is of great service to the wild natives of the south west part of N. America: for as Carver in his travels says, they have no farther care & trouble with it than only to tye it up in bunches when it first comes into ear, & when ripe to gather it into their boats; every person or family knowing their own by some distinction in the bandage. Carver observes, that it would be very advantageous to new settlers in that country, as it furnishes at once a store of corn the first year: & by that means removes the distress & difficulty incident to new colonies till their first crop begins to ripen. Linnaeus has given this plant the name of *Zizania*: but what could induce the celebrated Botanist to degrade this very beneficial grain with the title of that pernicious weed which the Enemy in the parable sowed among the good corn while men slept, does not so easily appear. (Math. 13 chapter.)

Sunday 24.
29 6/10½; 62; W,S.
Grey, sun, showers.

The coveys of partridges that I have seen are not large.
A splendid rain-bow.

A stag, which has haunted Hartley wood the summer thro', was roused by a man that was mowing oats just at the back of the village. Several young persons pursued him with guns, & happening to rouse him again on the side of Nore hill, shot at him; & then collecting some hounds from Emshot, & Hawkley, they drove him to a large wood in the parish of West Meon, where they lost him, & called-off their dogs.

Monday 25.
29 5/10¾; 59; SW.
Sun, pleasant.

Oats housed.

Tuesday 26.
29 6/10; 66; NE; 10.
Sun, warm, cool.

Mʳ Hale & Tim. Turner begin to pick hops in the Fore down.
Hale picked 350 bushels: his hops are large & fine.

Wednesday 27.
29 7/10; 60; W.
Dark, & still, wet.

Many hops picked.
Cool.

Thursday 28.
29 7/10; 67; SW.
Grey, sun, sultry,
showers.

A bat comes-out many times in a day, even in sunshine to catch flies: it is probably a female that has young, & is hungry from giving suck: the swallows strike at the bat.

Friday 29.
29 4/10¾; 61; SW, S.

Farmers are much busied with oat-harvest & hopping. Far:

Wet, wet, rain, rain, blowing.

Fielder has cut a field of grass at Breche. Hops picked in the forenoon.
N. *Aurora.*

Saturday 30.
29 5/10½; 59; W; 48.
Sun, pleasant, dark.

Many hops gathered.
Few partridges seen in Selborne.
Leaves of the black-cluster-vine turn purple.

Sunday 31.
29 5/10; 68; SW, W;
52. Rain, rain,
thunder, rain.

Rain in August . . . 3 inch: 22 h.

SEPTEMBER 1788

Monday 1.
29 6/10½; 65; W.
Sun, sultry, sun &
clouds.

My monthly rose-trees are covered with bloom.
Many hops picked: the crop is great in some gardens.
A sand-piper shot at Hawkley.

Tuesday 2.
29 7/10; 61; W.
Dark, & warm.

J. Hale's crop of hops under the S. corner of the hanger is prodigious: many hills together produce a bushel each, some two, & some three!
N. *Aurora.*
Mʳ White of Newton cuts some Saint foin a second time.

Wednesday 3.
29 5/10; 65, 69; S, SE.
Dark, sun, sweet day.

China asters, & Mich: daiseys blow.
Nep. Ben came from London.
Barley, & seed-clover are housed.

Thursday 4.
29 3/10½; 4/10; 70; S.
Sun, sultry, louring,
rain.

Prodigious dew! Gathered-in the white pippins, a large crop.
Vast showers about.
Were all wet thro' in our return from Faringdon.

Friday 5.
29 5/10; 64; S; 6.
Grey, clouds,
sprinklings, rain.

Under the eaves of an house at Faringdon are 22 martins nests, 12 of which contain second broods now nearly fledge: they put out their heads, & seem to long to be on the wing.
Peaches & nectarines are crude, & tasteless.

Saturday 6.
29 7/10; 63; S.
Sun, dark & mild,
gleam.

Sunday 7.
29 8/10; 68; S, SW.
Sun, pleasant, moon
shine.

Hot sun.

Monday 8.
29 7/10½; 65; S, W.
Sun, sprinkling, sun,
sweet moonshine.

Tuesday 9.
29 7/10½; N.
Dark, sun, sweet day.

On the brow of the cliff that looks down on Candover's farm-house my Brother found a lime tree which had been cut down to a stool when the coppice was cut formerly. Was this a wild tree¶ or planted?

Wednesday 10.
29 7/10¼; W, SW.
Vast dew, sun, dark &
mild.

Tim. Turner cuts the grass of Baker's hill.
Peaches & Nectarines are over, & grapes come in. Partridges are wild: some pheasants are seen about.

Thursday 11.
29 8/10½; N, NE.
Rain, fog, sun, yellow,
sweet afternoon.

Barley housed. Turned the horses into the great mead. Many hops picked.
Second broods of swallows & martins mostly flown.
Nep. Ben & Wife, & nurse & baby left us, & went to Newton.

Friday 12.
29 7/10½; E.
Vast dew, sun, pleasant,
sweet moon-light.

Hop-picking in general is at an end.

Saturday 13.
29 5/10; S.
Dew, sun, soft &
louring.

Men house vetches.
Kidney-beans, & Cucumbers bear well.
Gathered in my golden pippins, a small quantity.
Mr Churton came from Cheshire.

Sunday 14.
29 8/10; N.
Sun, brisk air.

The gale snapped off a large bough from my Cadillac pear-tree, which is heavily laden with fruit.
Grapes are good, but the crop is very small.

Monday 15.
29 6/10; 49; E.
White dew, sun, cool.
Full moon.

Chilly air.
Gathered many of the baking pears to disburthen the boughs, & keep them from breaking.
Wells are very low.

Tuesday 16.
29 4/10½; S; 32.

Men bag their hops.

Looking south from Selborne Common.

Grey, showers about, rain.

Some martins have young still in their nests: fly-catchers seem to have withdrawn themselves.

Wednesday 17.
29 4/10¾; SE, S. White frost, sun & clouds.

China asters make a fine shew.

Thursday 18.
29 2/10; 67; NE, E; 87. Rain & wind, rain, rain.

Lightening. Thunder.
Lightening. Thunder.

Friday 19.
29 3/10; 67; E; 146. Rain, sun, sultry, rain.

Much rain in the night.
Grapes very good.

Saturday 20.
29 2/10; 60; N, NE; 46. Rain, rain, gleam.

China-asters are damaged by the wet.

Sunday 21.
29 1/10¾; 48; SW; 60. Rain, rain, rain.

Began to light fires in the parlor.

Monday 22.
29 4/10; 42; SW. Cold & wet, cold, wet.

The swallows seem to be distressed for food this cold, wet weather, & to hawk up & down the street among the houses for flies with great earnestness.

Tuesday 23.
29 3/10½; 60; SW. Grey & mild, wet.

Some of my rasps bears twice in the year, & have now ripe fruit: these berries the partridges have found out, & have eaten most of them. Thomas sprung two brace & an half among the bushes this morning. These birds were hatched in Baker's hill.

Wednesday 24.
29 3/10½; SW, S; 180. Grey, mild, gleam.

Much rain in the night.
The grass cut in Baker's hill rots. Tyed-up some large endives.
The leaves of the Virginian creeper turn of a blood-colour.

Thursday 25.
29 6/10; SW. Grey, mild, shower, mild.

A flood last week at Hedleigh mills. The miller at Hawkley has long been distressed for want of water.
Spinage very fine. Herrings are brought to the door.

Friday 26.
29 6/10; 60; SW; 55. Rain, rain, gleam, mackerel sky.

Saturday 27.
29 7/10; 43; NE, E.
Sun, gale, sprinkling,
bright.

Gathered the swans-egg pears, & some apples.

Sunday 28.
29 6/10; 62; S, SW.
Sun, showers, blowing,
showers.

Rain in the night.

Monday 29.
29 3/10; SW; W; 59.
Rain, rain, blowing.

Mr Churton left us.
T: H: White came from Fyfield.

Tuesday 30.
29 6/10¾; 55; NW,
SW.
Grey, & cool.

Gathered such of the Cadillac pears, as could readily be reached
by ladders. Thomas says there are 13 bushels on my only tree.
Rain in Septem^r . . . 5 in. 71 h. More than five inches of this
quantity fell in eleven days.

OCTOBER 1788

Wednesday 1.
29 6/10½; 62; W.
Grey & blowing.

Mild. Grapes are now finely flavoured.
H. H. White came from Fyfield.

Thursday 2.
29 7/10; W, W.
Grey, louring, with
gale.

Gathered six bush: & half of dearlings from the meadow-tree:
four or five bush: remain on the tree.
The foliage of the Virginian creeper of a fine blood-colour.

Friday 3.
29 8/10; 59, 67; W.
Grey, mild, warm,
moist.

A wood-cock was killed in the hanger: one was seen there Sep:
29. Endive is blanched for the table: tyed-up more. Martins
about. Timothy comes-out to the verge of the laurel-hedge.

Saturday 4.
29 7/10½; 60; W,
SW.
Dark, mild, still.

Earthed up the celeri which is grown large.
Fyfield, the spaniel, rejects the bones of a wood-cock with horror.
Gathered in non pareils.
The prodigious crop of apples this year verified in some measure
the words of Virgil made use of in the description of the Corycian
garden . . .
"*Quotq in flore novo pomis se fertilis arbos*
Induerat, totidem autumno matura tenebat."¶

Sunday 5.
29 6/10; S.
Dark, still, mild.

Several swallows, & martins.
The foliage of the Virginian creeper makes a singular appearance
being of a very bloody colour.

Monday 6.
29 5/10; S, W.
Mist, showers, gale,
cool.

The beech-trees turn very fast. Gathered-in some royal russets, very fine.
Swallows & Martins, a few.

Tuesday 7.
30 1/10; 45; N.
Cool dew, sun, sharp.

Many gulls, & wild fowls on Wolmer-pond.
Gathered-in more royal russets.
Men sow wheat. Whitings brought.

Wednesday 8.
30 2/10, 2/10; 39; N.
White frost, sun, &
sharp air.

Brisk wind. Several swallows & martins play round the church & catch the flies on the sunny sides of the tower.
Bought of bright hops 21 pounds; of brown 49.

Thursday 9.
30 ½/10; 49; NE.
Cloudless, red even.
D.L.

Paths dry, & clean.
Virginian Creeper sheds it's leaves. It's leaves have a silky appearance.
Tho. H. White, & H. H. W. went to Fyfield.
Strong cutting wind. Some Martins.

Friday 10.
30 1/10; 43; NE, E.
Sun, gale, pleasant.

Nailed-up a Greek, & an Italian inscription on the front of the alcove on ye hanger. Leaves fall.
Boys took a large round wasps nest in the Ewel, nearly as large as a gallon measure.

Saturday 11.
30; 52, 53; NE.
Dark & mild.

Several martins round the church. Many flies on the tower, which come out from the felfry to sun themselves.
Several snipes on the forest. The water in my well rises.

Sunday 12.
29 9/10; NE.
Dark, sharp, gleam.

Some swallows, & several martins round the tower.

Monday 13.
29 9/10; 56; NE.
Sun, pleasant.

Roads & paths dry like as in Summer.
Some hirundines round the Church.

Tuesday 14.
29 8/10½; E.
Grey, sun, pleasant.

Some house-martins.
Women & children go a acorning, & sell their acorns at one shilling p^r bushel.

Wednesday 15.
29 5/10; 39; E, SE.
Deep fog, vast dew,
sun, sweet day.
Full moon.

No Hirundines. Vast quantities of gossamer; the fields are covered with it:
. . . . . . slow thro' the air
The gossamer floats; or stretch'd from blade

to blade
The wavy net-work whitens all the fields.

Thursday 16.
29 3/10½; 38; SE.
Frost, sun, sweet day.

Celeri comes in, very good.

Friday 17.
29 6/10; NW.
Wet, fog, grey & cool.

Two ring-ousels seen at Nore-hill.
Men pull turnips, & stack them.

Saturday 18.
29 9/10; 34; NE.
Frost, ice, sun, sharp.

Planted an hundred cabbages to stand the winter. Planted two rows of brown Dutch lettuces under the fruit-wall to stand the winter. No Hirundines.

Sunday 19.
30; 28! NE.
Thick ice, sun,
pleasant.

Broᵗ T. White planted two Lombardy poplars in the corners of the pound: & a Sycomore on the Plestor near the pound. ¶

Monday 20.
29 9/10/ 28; SW.
Thick ice, grey, sun,
yellow even.

Leaves fall.
The pound-field is sown with American wheat.

Tuesday 21.
29 8/10; SW, W, NW.
Grey, windy.

The Hanger deeply tinged, yet beautiful.
Children go a acorning.

Wednesday 22.
30; 46; NE.
Grey, still, mild.

Much wheat is sown. The fallows are very dry: & the roads clean as in summer.

Thursday 23.
29 9/10; 49; NW.
Grey, mild, gleams.

Much peat carted thro' the village.

Friday 24.
29 8/10; NW.
Grey & sharp, louring.

Gave away many stone-less berberries: the tree every year bears vast burdens.

Saturday 25.
29 8/10½; N.
Sun & clouds, sharp.

Leaves fall in showers. Virginian-creeper naked.

Sunday 26.
29 8/10; 36; W, NE.
Grey, & sharp, sun.

Some woodcocks shot on the Barnet lately.

Monday 27.
29 7/10½; 44; NE.
Grey, gleams, louring.

Set up again my stone dial, blown down many years ago, on a thick Portland slab in the angle of the terrass. The column is very old, came from Sarson house near Amport, & was hewn from the quarries of Chilmarke. The dial was regulated by my meridian line.¶

Tuesday 28.
29 7/10; NE.
Frost, dark, dark.

Wednesday 29.
29 7/10½; NW, NE.
Sun, dark & still.

Meridian line, & dial accord well.
The lettuces, planted to stand the winter, seem half dead for want of moisture.

Thursday 30.
29 9/10; 41; NE.
Fog, sun, pleasant.

Larches turn yellow: Ash leaves fall; the hanger gets thin: my tall hedges finely diversifyed.

Friday 31.
30 1/10, 1/10½; 42;
E, NE.
Sun, pleasant, red even.

Timothy the tortoise seems to have withdrawn himself into the laurel-hedge ever since tuesday.
Rain in October – 0 inc. 0 h.! none that could be measured!

NOVEMBER 1788

Saturday 1.
30; 35; E.
Frost, fog, cloudless,
red even.

Planted on the bank in the garden several dames violets raised from cuttings under hand-glasses. Sowed some seed of the *Zizania aquatica* in Comb-wood pond.
The wheat-season seems to have been finished with the last month.

The King's stag-hounds came down to Alton, attended by a Huntsman & six yeoman prickers¶ with horns, to try for the Stag that has haunted Hartley wood, & it's environs for so long a time. Many hundreds of people, horse & foot, attended the dogs to see the deer unharboured: but tho' the huntsmen drew Hartley wood & long coppice, & shrub-wood, & Temple hangers; & in their way back Hartley, & Ward le ham hangers; yet no Stag could be found. Lord Hinchinbroke, the master of the hounds, & some other Nobleman attended.

The royal pack, accustomed to have the deer turned-out before them, never drew the coverts with any address or spirit, as many people that were present observed: & this remark the event has proved to be a just one. For as Harry Bright was lately pursuing a pheasant that was wing-broken in Hartley wood, he stumbled upon the stag by accident, & ran in upon him as he lay concealed amidst a thick brake of brambles, & bushes.

Sunday 2.
29 7/10; 53; S.

Vast dew, sun, dark & still.

Monday 3.
29 3/10; 54; S.
Dark & mild, blowing, wet.

Bro. Tho. sowed many acorns, & some seeds of an ash in a plot dug in Baker's hill.
The King's hounds tryed our coverts for the stag, but with no success.

Tuesday 4.
29 5/10; W; 21.
Sun, gale, sun.

Rain in the night.
Strong wind.

Wednesday 5.
29 9/10; 33; NW.
No frost, sun, sweet day.

Gossamer & insects abound. Swarms of sporting gnats come streaming out from the tops of the hedges, just as at Midsum.ʳ On this soft summer-like day some h. martins might have been expected along the hanger; but none appeared.

Thursday 6.
29 8/10½; 29; SE.
Thick ice, sun, sharp.

Bro. Tho. & T. H. W. left us, & went to London.

Friday 7.
29 5/10½; SE.
No frost, sun & gale.

Saturday 8.
29 7/10½; 44; NW, E; 10.
Sun, sweet day, white fog.

Rain in the night.
No martins.

Sunday 9.
29 4/10½; 40; S.
Deep fog, sun, pleasant.

Many people are sick.

Monday 10.
29 6/10½; 48; SE, E.
Grey, sun, pleasant.

Planted 10 roses, 2 cypresses, 6 viola tricolores, 3 sent from S. Lambeth by Bro. Ben.

Tuesday 11.
29 8/10½; 41; SE, W.
Grey, soft & pleasant.

Men have taken advantage of this dry season, & have chalked their hop-gardens, & fields.
The chalk at the foot of the Hill is called marl, but it is only a hard grey chalk. This chalk is of service on the malms.

Wednesday 12.
29 8/10; W.
Sun, soft, pleasant.

Clear to the S.

Thursday 13.
29 4/10; S, W, NW.
Rain, rain, sharp
shower, dark, bright.
Full moon.

The horses began to lie within.

Friday 14.
29 8/10; 35; NW, N;
49.
Frost, sun, sharp, frost.

Furze in bloom.

Saturday 15.
29 8/10½; N; 6.
Rain, sun, sharp.

Sunday 16.
30; 28; N.
Sharp frost, sun, frost.

Monday 17.
29 8/10½; 45; NW.
No frost, sun, grey.

Tuesday 18.
29 8/10¾; 39; N,
NW. No frost, sun,
sweet day.

Farmer Lasham's Dorsetshire ewes have produced several lambs.
Insects abound. Wheat comes up well.

Wednesday 19.
29 8/10; NW.
Dark & mild, wet,
dark.

Wild wood-pigeons.
Mr Hale continues to chalk the black malm field opposite to
J. Berriman's house, called Hasteds. He has laid on about 120
loads on less than 3 acres.

Thursday 20.
29 8/10¾; 42; N, NE,
E. Deep fog, sun, soft.

Charming weather.

Friday 21.
29 8/10¾; 43; E, SE.
Dark & soft.

Saturday 22.
29 8/10¾; 41; SE.
Grey & mild.

The fields are very dry, & the paths clean.
Began to dress the vines: the new wood well ripened.
The smoke of the new lighted lime-kilns this evening crept along
the ground in long trails: a token of a dry, heavy atmosphere.

Sunday 23.
29 7/10; SE, E.

The downy seeds of traveller's joy fill the air, & driving before a

Sun, sharp, clouds.

gale appear like insects on the wing.

Nov.ʳ 23. Mrs Clement brought to bed of a boy. My nephews & nieces now 53.

Monday 24.
29 8/10; 32; E.
White frost, cloudless, red even.

Liss hounds are hunting on the common.
My well very low: some wells are dry.
We have taken away much of the old wood from the vines.
Wheeled dung.

Tuesday 25.
29 9/10; 32½; E.
Hard frost, sun, sharp.

Took-off the mould from the old hot-beds; trenched the ridges of mould in the melon-ground.

Wednesday 26.
29 8/10¾; 21, 28: E.
Hard frost, sun, freezing all day.

Finished shovelling the zigzag, & bostal.
Wildfowl on Wolmer pond.

Thursday 27.
29 6/10½; 20½, 25; NE.
Hard frost, sun, frost.

Some light snow. Boys slide on lakes.
Finished dressing, & tacking the vines. Turned up much fine rotten earth from among the rubbish carryed out of the garden.

Friday 28.
29 5/10¾; 26, 24; E.
Dark & still.

NEWTON
Ther. at Newton 26.

Saturday 29.
29 7/10; 26; NE.
Dark, still & frosty.

SELBORNE
M.ʳ White's tank at Newton has been empty some days.

A vast flock of hen chaffinches are to be seen in the fields along by the sides of Newton-lane, interspersed, I think, with a few bramblings, which being rare birds in these parts, probably attended the finches in their emigration. They feed in the stubbles on the seeds of knot-grass, the great support of small, hard-billed birds in the winter.

Sunday 30.
29 8/10½; 33; NW, N.
Dark, still, thaw.

Many wild fowls haunt Wolmer pond: in the evenings they come forth & feed in the barley-stubbles.
Rain in November – 0 inch 86 h.

DECEMBER 1788

Monday 1.
29 7/10½; 33; N.
Frost, thaw, dark & still.

Several wells in the village are dry, & some ponds in the neighbourhood. Well-head runs much as usual. There is a fine perennial spring at the bottom of Hasteds. Men cart earth, & marl from Clays pond.

Tuesday 2.
29 4/10½; 31, 23;
NE.
Rime, sun, sharp.

Wednesday 3.
29 2/10½; 26; N, NE.   The grey chalk carried-out upon Hasteds falls to pieces. Good
Fog, sun, clouds.   mackarel brought to the door.

Thursday 4.   The plows have been stopped by the frost some days. Men cart
29 3/10; 21, 28; NE.   earth & dung for their hop-grounds.
Rime, sun, frost.   Covered the lettuces, artichokes, spinage, & celeri with straw.
                          Took in the urns.

Friday 5.
29 4/10; 32; NE.
Sleet, dark & sharp.

Saturday 6.
29 5/10; 31; NE.   The millers around complain that their streams fail, & they have
Frost, dark & sharp.   no water for grinding.

Sunday 7.
29 6/10; 32, 33; NE.   The wind & frost cut down the wheat, which seems to want a
Grey, severe & sharp   mantle of snow.
wind.

Monday 8.
29 6/10; 32, 28; NE.   Great want of water on the downs about Andover.
Grey, & sharp, sun,   The ponds, wells, & brooks fail.
sharp.

Tuesday 9.
29 5/10¾; 33, 37;   J. Hale cleans out the pond at Littlecomb.
NE.
Grey, small snow, sun,
dark.

Wednesday 10.
29 6/10; 33; NE.   Great complaint for want of rain, & water, round Dublin in
Wet, thaw, sun.   Ireland.

Thursday 11.
29 8/10; 31; NW.
Deep fog, fog, thaw,
bright.

Friday 12.
29 7/10; 21, 24; NW.
Vast rime, sun, still.

Saturday 13.
29 4/10; 25, 30; NE.
Deep fog, & rime, dark
& wintry.
Full moon.

The Stag seen again about Oakhanger. He some times haunts about Hartley wood, & some times about the Holt.

Sunday 14.
29 2/10; 27; 22; E, SE.
Frost, vast rime, sun,
still & sharp.

The navigation of the Thames is much interrupted thro' the want of water occasioned by the long dry season.

Monday 15.
29 2/10½; 20, 23, 17.
Dark, small snow,
severe, & cutting.

Therm! at Newton 21.
Many have been disordered with bad colds & fevers at Oxford. The water in the apparatus for making mineral water froze in the red room.

Tuesday 16.
29 3/10½; 20, 19, 24;
NE, E.
Severe, sun, sharp &
cutting.

The wind is so piercing that labourers cannot stand to their work. Ice in all the chambers. The perforated stopple¶ belonging to the apparatus broke in two by the frost.
Apples preserved with difficulty. Potatoes & carrots in the cellar.

Wednesday 17.
29 8/10; 24, 18, 20;
NE. Snow, snow,
gleam, severe.

Ice in all the chambers. Shallow snow covers the ground, enough to shelter the wheat.

Thursday 18.
29 6/10; 10, 28, 25;
NW, W.
Severe, grey, cutting.

Most of the wells in the street are dry! among the rest my own is so shallow as not to admit the bucket to dip!
Moved some apples & pears into the kitchen closet. The horse-roads are dusty. Many ponds are dry.

Friday 19.
29 6/10½; 23, 31; N.
Frost, sun, pleasant,
dark.

Saturday 20.
29 6/10; 24, 28; NW,
W. Frost, sun,
pleasant, red even.

The frost has lasted now five weeks.

Sunday 21.
29 5/10; 35, 32; W,
NW. Rain, drifts of
snow, sun, frost.

Fierce drift of snow, but of short continuance.
Shortest day.

Monday 22.
29 7/10½; 26, 29;

A considerable flight of wood-cocks round the Barnet.

NW.
Frost, sun, still, red
even.

Small snow on the ground.

Tuesday 23.
30; 18, 21, 28; NE.
Fierce frost, sun,
pleasant, frost.

Moles work, & heave up their hillocks.

Wednesday 24.
29 6/10¾; 39; W.
Thaw, moist & dark,
thaw.

Thursday 25.
29 4/10; 38; W.
Grey, & mild, sun,
gale.

Thaw.

Friday 26.
29 6/10½; 30, 32½;
W, N.
Frost, snow shower,
sun, frost.

Snow covers the ground. Snow.

Saturday 27.
29 6/10; 29, 32; N.
Grey, sharp, snow.

Snow on the Ground.

Sunday 28.
29 9/10; 20, 24; N.
Severe frost, sun, sharp
wind, frost.

Snow covers the ground.

Monday 29.
29 9/10; 19, 19; N,
NW.
Severe frost, sun, frost.

Ice in chambers, & in the kitchen.
Many wild geese in the moors of the forest.

Tuesday 30.
29 9/10; 14, 25; NE,
SE.
Fierce frost, snow,
snow.

Ice within doors. Rime.
Snow on the Ground.

Wednesday 31.
29 4/10; 28, 35; SE, S.
Thaw, snow, snow.

Rain in December – 0 inch 23 hund.

Rain in 1788 – 22 inch. 50 hund.

JANUARY — 1789 —

Thursday 1.
29 1/10, 29 3/10; 33,
25; SE, S, NW; 21.
Snow, thaw, sun, frost.

SELBORNE
Heavy snow. Snow thick on the ground.
Timothy begins to sink his well¶ at the malt-house.

Friday 2.
29 7/10½; 25, 18, 14;
N.
Frost, sun, pleasant.

Snow covers the ground.

Saturday 3.
30; 18, 27; NE, SE.
Vast rime, dark, &
still.

Rime hangs on the trees all day.
Turner's well-diggers have sunk his well about six feet. It is now
about on a level with mine, viz: 63 feet deep. They came to day to
a hard blue rag,¶ & a little water.
Began the new hay-rick.

Sunday 4.
30 2/10¾; 23, 23, 18;
NE, E.
Frost, dark & still.

Snow on the ground; but the quantity little in comparison with
what has fallen in most parts.

Monday 5.
30 3/10½! 15, 23, 15;
NE.
Severe frost, sun, still,
frost.

Turner's well-diggers advance slowly thro' a blue rag.
M⁅ Churton left us, & went to Waverly.

Tuesday 6.
30 1/10⅓; 25, 18;
NE.
Fierce frost, sun,
cutting wind.

Severe day.

Wednesday 7.
29 8/10; 22, 27; NE.
Severe, sun, sharp
wind.

Salted-up a small hog in the pickling tub: weight 8 scores, &
8 pounds: the meat was young, & delicate.
The people of Fraxfield fetch their water from Petersfield up
Stoner hill.

Thursday 8.
29 4/10; 16, 17; NE.
Fierce frost, sun, keen
air.

A severe frost prevails all over the Continent.

Friday 9.
29 2/10⅓; 24, 25;

The farmers are in pain about their turnips, both those of the

NE.
Hard frost, snow,
snow.

Saturday 10.
29; 23, 28; NE, NW,
@.
Fog & rime, snow,
snow.

ground, & those that are stacked under hedges.
The people at Forestside drive all their cattle to be watered at a
spring issuing out of Temple grounds at the foot of Temple
hanger: Oakhanger ponds, & Cranmer ponds are dry.
The frost has lasted now just seven weeks: it began Nov.ʳ 23.
T. Turner has sunk his well nine feet without coming to water.
He now desists on account of the expence. My well, I now find,
has more than three feet of water; but the rope is too short to
reach it.

As one of my neighbours was traversing Wolmer-forest from
Bramshot across the moors, he found a large uncommon bird
fluttering in the heath, but not wounded, which he brought home
alive. On examination this proved to be *Colymbus glacialis* Linn:
the great speckled Diver or Loon,¶ which is most excellently
described in Willughby's *Ornithology*.

Every part & proportion of this bird is so incomparably adapted
to it's mode of life, that in no instance do we see the wisdom of God
in the Creation to more advantage. The head is sharp, & smaller
than the part of the neck adjoining, in order that it may pierce the
water; the wings are placed forward, & out of the center of gravity,
for a purpose that shall be noticed here after; the thighs quite at the
podex, in order to facilitate diving; & the legs are flat, & as sharp
backward almost as the edge of a knife, that in striking they may
easily cut the water: while the feet are palmated, & broad for
swimming, yet so folded up when advanced forward to take a fresh
stroke, as to be full as narrow as the shank. The two exterior toes of
the feet are longest; the nails flat & broad resembling the human,
which gives strength, & increase the power of swimming. The foot,
when expanded, is not at right angles to the leg or body of the bird:
but the exterior part inclining towards the head, forms an acute
angle with the body; the intention being not to give motion in the
line of the legs themselves, but, by the combined impulse of both in
an intermediate line, the line of the body.

Most people know, that have observed at all, that the swimming
of birds is nothing more than a walking in the water, where one
foot succeeds the other as on the land: yet no one, as far as I am
aware, has remarked that diving fowls, while under water, impell
& row themselves forward by a motion of their wings, as well as by
the impulse of their feet: but such is really the case, as any person
may easily be convinced who will observe ducks when hunted by
dogs in a clear pond: Nor do I know that any one has given a
reason why the wings of diving fowls are placed so forward.
Doubtless not for the purpose of promoting their speed in flying,
since that position certainly impedes it: but probably for the
encrease of their motion under water by the use of four oars instead
of two: yet were the wings & feet nearer together, as in land birds,
they would, when in action, rather hinder than assist each other.

This *Colymbus* was of considerable bulk weighing only three drachms short of three pounds averdupoise. It measured in length from the bill to the tail (which was very short) two feet; & to the extremities of the toes four inches more; & the breadth of the wings expanded was 42 inches. A person attempted to eat the body, but found it very strong & rancid, as is the flesh of all birds living on fish. Divers, or Loons, tho' bred in the most northerly parts of Europe, yet are seen with us in very severe winters; & on the Thames are called *Sprat-loons*, because they prey much on that sort of fish.

The legs of the *Colymbi* & *mergi* are placed so very backward, & so out of all center of gravity, that these birds cannot walk at all. They are called by Linnaeus *Compedes*, because they move on the ground as if shackled, or fettered.

Sunday 11.
29 2/10½; 25½; 27;
N.
Dark & still, snow,
bright.
Full moon.

Hares frequent the garden, & nibble the pinks.
The trees are all covered with snow, & make a most winter-like appearance. Snow thick on the ground.

Monday 12.
29 3/10¼; 8, 23; NE,
E.
Fierce frost, sun, frost.

Therm.^{r} at South Lambeth – 2½. This frost, as frosts usually do, went-off soon after the Therm^r was at the lowest.
Much wind with snow.

Tuesday 13.
28 7/10; 27, 38; E,
SE.
Snow, rain, rain.

Deep snow. Snow drifted thro' every crevice.
Swift thaw. Snow that had been driven in now melts & drips thro' the garret-ceiling.

Wednesday 14.
28 8/10½; 38; S; 100.
Thaw, sun, mild.

The snow drifted in thro' the tiling now melts, & floats the ceilings.
A Goosander, & a Dun diver,¶ a drake & a duck of the same species, *Mergus Merganser*, were brought me this morning. They are beautiful birds, never seen in the South but in hard frosts: were shot on the stream at Hedleigh.

Thursday 15.
29; 35; SW; 37.
Rain, sun, mild.

Snow melts very fast. The frost, where a grave was dug, appeared to have ent'red the ground¶ about 12 inches.

Friday 16.
29 5/10; 35, 39; SW.
Frost, sun, dark.

Snow on the ground. Now the rope is lengthened my well furnishes us with water.

Saturday 17.
28 9/10½; 35; S.
Dark & mild.

Fine thaw. Snow decreased.

Sunday 18.
28 3/10½; SW.
Rain, rain, blowing.

Snow melts very fast.
A swan came flying up the Lythe, & without regarding objects
before it, dashed itself against Dorton-house, & fell down
stunned. It recovered, & was sold to the miller at Hawkley.

Monday 19.
29; 35, 39; SW; 47.
Small frost, sun, rain,
rain.

Insects dance, & play about in the sun.

Tuesday 20.
29 3/10½; 32; SW;
51.
Deep fog, sun, clouds.

Snow gone, except under hedges.

Wednesday 21.
29 4/10; 42; SW, S.
Dark & mild, rain,
rain.

Walls sweat: dew on windows on the outside.
Lettuces under the fruit-wall, & spinage look well: cabbages not
hurt: Laurels, portugal laurels, & laurustines seem not to be
injured.
Wells rise.

Thursday 22.
29 3/10; 48; S; 73.
Rain, rain, rain, rain.

Now the ice is melted on Hartley-pond, many dead fish come
floating ashore, which were stifled under the ice for want of air.

Friday 23.
29; S; 31.
Grey, mild, sun,
shower, wind.

Rain-bow.
Blowing night. Worms lie out on grass-walks.

Saturday 24.
28 7/10½; 42; S; 50.
Wind, rain, rain,
windy.

Sunday 25.
29 2/10½; 42; W; 9.
Sun, pleasant.

Monday 26.
29 4/10; 48; SW.
Dark, & mild, wet.

Tuesday 27.
29 5/10½; 47; SW.
Grey & mild, rain,
rain.

Bees come out. Snow-drops bud. Crocus's sprout. Tulips begin
to peep.

Wednesday 28.
29 6/10½; 47; SW,
W; 50.
Dark, wet, rain, dark.

Begin to trim, & tack the trees on the fruit-wall.
Winter-aconite blows.
Well rises.

Thursday 29.
29 9/10; 42; S.
Deep fog, mild, fog.

NEWTON
Bantam-hens make a pleasant little note, expressive of a
propensity towards laying.
Fog so deep that we could not see the alcove in the garden.

Friday 30.
29 9/10; SE.
Fog SE, fog.

Saturday 31.
29 8/10; 50; SW.
Sun, sweet day.

SELBORNE
Farmer Knight's wheat of a beautiful colour.
Children play at hop-scotch.
Rain in Jan: − 4 inc: 48 h.

I now see, that after the greatest droughts have exhausted the
wells, & streams, & ponds, four or five inches of rain will
compleatly replenish them.

FEBRUARY 1789

Sunday 1.
29 3/10; 47; S.
Fog, sun, spring-like.

Snow-drops, hepatica's, daiseys blow. The catkins of some hazels
open, & the female bloom appears.
Boys play at taw on the plestor.

Monday 2.
29 3/10; 40; S; 36.
Sun, sun & clouds.

Rain in the night.

Tuesday 3.
29 1/10½; SW, W.
Showers, sun, &
showers.

Rain & wind in the night.
Two of the †Bantham hens lay each an egg.

Wednesday 4.
29 2/10; SW; 33.
Showers, showers,
stormy.

Green rye has a delicate soft tinge in its colour, distinguishable
from that of wheat at a considerable distance.
Made a seedling hot-bed for cucumbers.

Thursday 5.
29 4/10; 34, 33; SW,

Fierce storms of snow in the night.

---

†Correction made by GW.

W; 7.
Snow, sun & wind.

As one of farmer Spencer's cows was gamboling, & frisking about last summer on the edge of the short Lythe, she fell, & rolled over to the bottom. Yet so far was she from receiving any injury by this dangerous tumble, that she fattened very kindly, & being killed this spring proved fine beef.

Friday 6.
29 5/10; 34; W; 41.
Frost, sun & wind,
rain.

Saturday 7.
29 4/10; 40; NW.
Blowing, sun, frost.

Sunday 8.
29 3/10; 38; S, SW.
Wh. frost, rain, bright.

The open catkins illuminate the hazels; these are the male blossoms: the female are so minute as to be scarce discernible.

Monday 9.
29 2/10½; 34; SW.
Snow, sun, rain, snow,
bright.

Sowed some cucumber-seeds in the seedling bed.

Tuesday 10.
29 1/10; SW.
Ice, sun.
Full moon.

Wednesday 11.
29 4/10; 33; NW; 20.
Frost, sun, snow-
showers.

Crocus's begin to swell for bloom.

Thursday 12.
29 8/10; 31½; N.
Hard frost, ice, sun,
frost.

About this time Miss Chase, & Miss Rebecca Chase sailed for Madras in the *Nottingham* Indiaman.

Friday 13.
29 8/10½; 35; W.
Frost, dark & still.

Lined the hot-bed screen with reeds. Cucumbers come up well: bed works well.

Saturday 14.
29 7/10½; 45, 48; W.
Dark, sun, dark.

Potted the cucumbers.

Sunday 15.
29 6/10; 45; SW.
Dark, wet, wet &
windy.

Polyanths begin to blow.

Monday 16.
29 8/10½; 36; W,
NW; 10.
Sun, sun & clouds,
yellow even.

Rain in the night.
Some crocus's blow.

Tuesday 17.
29 7/10; W.
Dark, wind, blowing.

Sowed two ounces of radish-seed under the cucumber-screen.
Some flies come out.
Strong wind.

Wednesday 18.
29 7/10½; 43; W.
Dark, & mild.

No missel-thrush, or song-thrush to be heard: onely one black
bird about my out-let.

Thursday 19.
29 5/10; 44; S, SW.
Fog, wet, wet, dark.

A large bank in Burrant garden covered with winter-aconites,
which have been there more than 40 years.
Missel-thrush sings on one of the firs.

Friday 20.
29 6/10½; 36; NE,
SE.
Frost, grey & mild.

Dug a plot of ground for beans.
Spring-like.

Saturday 21.
29 1/10½; SW, S; 33.
Rain, showers, gleams,
wet.

Yesterday I fixed some nuts in the chinks of some gate-posts in a
part of my outlet where Nut-hatches used to haunt: & to day I
found that several of them were drilled, & the kernels gone.

Sunday 22.
29 2/10; 41; SW; 83.
Rain, gleams, hail.

Much rain, & wind in the night.

Monday 23.
28 8/10½; S.
Dark, wind & rain.

Stormy wind, with fierce drifting rain.

Tuesday 24.
29 1/10; SW; 82.
Sun, showers, rain,
rain.

Carted six loads of dung for the hot-bed.
Crocus's make a show.

Wednesday 25.
28 1/10; S, W; 57.
Rain, storms, hail.

Thursday 26.
28 1/10; 36; NW, N.

Our butcher began to kill grass-lamb.

Rain & snow, gleams,
dark & cold.

Friday 27.
29 2/10; N, NW, W.   Cucumber-plants thrive.
Sun, pleasant, clouds.   Daffodils bud.

Saturday 28.
29 6/10; 35; N; 9.   Rain in Feb: – 4 inch: 11 h.
Dark, gleams, dark.

MARCH 1789

Sunday 1.
29 7/10½; N.
Sleet, cold, dark &
still.

Monday 2.
29 7/10; 34; NE.   Sowed the great meadow with ashes: with 49 bushels bought of
Dark, & harsh.   neighbours, & with 28 bushels of our own: total 77.

Tuesday 3.
29 7/10; 32½; NE,   Sowed a hand-glass with Celeri.
NW.   Planted five rows of beans.
Frost, ice, sun, grey.

Wednesday 4.
29 5/10; 34; N.   Still. Good weather for the spring-corn season. Paths dry.
Small sleet, dark, &
harsh.

Thursday 5.
29 5/10; 31½; NE.   Male yew-trees shed their farina in clouds.
Frost, dark, & still.

Friday 6.
29 6/10½; 30½; N.   Mʳ Richardson came.
Frost, snow, sun,
sharp.

Saturday 7.
29 6/10½; 25, 29; N.   Ice in chambers.
Hard frost, snow,   Snow on the ground.
snow, snow.

Sunday 8.
29 6/10½; 27, 31; N.   Mʳ Richardson left us.

Snow, snow, frost,
sharp.

Monday 9.
29 4/10; 28; 35; NW.   Turned the dung for the bearing cucumber-bed.
Frost, ice, sun, hail,   Cucumbers thrive.
snow.   Loud thunder at Kinchley in Leicestershire, & lightening that
                             did some damage: it happened in the midst of snow.

Tuesday 10.
29 2/10½; 23½; N.   Snow on the hill.
Frost, severe, sun,   Mr & Mrs Clement, & 3 children came.
harsh.

Wednesday 11.
28 9/10; 30; SE, E.   Snow covers the ground.
Snow, snow, snow.
Full moon.

Thursday 12.
29; 34; NE.   Snow lies three inches deep. Snow on the roofs melts in the sun
Frost, bright, frost.   very fast.
                             Cucumber plants are very fine: stopped down several pots.

Friday 13.
28 5/10½; 34; SW;   Snow in the night: snow five inches deep.
48.   Snow melts on the roofs very fast: & runs thro' the ceiling of the
Sun, vast clouds.   garret.

Saturday 14.
28 8/10; S, SE.   Snow covers the ground. Thaw.
Sun, showers, showers.   Cucumbers thrive. The bloom of the apricot-trees appears to be
                             injured in the bud by the frost.

Sunday 15.
28 9/10; E.   Snow on the ground.
Rain, rain, rain.   Raw, & cold. Mrs Clement left us.

Monday 16.
29 4/10; 30, 31; NE,   Snow all night.
N; 73.   Mended the cucumber-frames.
Frost, dark & freezing.

Tuesday 17.
29 3/10½; 30, 34;   Icicles hang on eaves all day.
NW, W, S.   Snow melts in the sun.
Frost, sun, heavy
clouds.

Wednesday 18.
29; 35; S, NW, N; 56.
Snow, fog, rain.

Snow all night. Deep snow.
Swift thaw.

Thursday 19.
29 4/10; 33, 35; NE.
Dark, & still.

Snow lies on the hill.
Made the bearing cucumber-bed: the dung is full wet, but warm.

Friday 20.
29 1/10½; S, NW.
Rain, rain, bright.

Saturday 21.
29 3/10; 38; W, SW;
21.
Sun, clouds, dark,
mild.

Snow almost gone on the hill.
Crocus's make a show. Violets.

Sunday 22.
28 9/10¾; SW, W.
Showers, bright, heavy
showers.

Bees gather on the crocus's.

Monday 23.
29 6/10; 34; N; 49.
Dark, & harsh.

Some snow under hedges.
The cucumber-bed heats, & smokes.

Tuesday 24.
29 5/10; 31½; NE, E,
SE.
Frost, ice, sun, dark, &
chill.

Some snow on the hill.
About this time sailed for Antigua Ned White, aboard the *Lady Jane Halliday*, Captain Martin.

Wednesday 25.
29 1/10½; 31½; E, N.
Snow, snow, snow.

Snow all night. Snow melts.

Thursday 26.
29 6/10; 30, 34; N, E.
Hard frost, sun &
clouds.

Snow on the ground.
Icicles hang all day. Hot-bed smokes.

Friday 27.
29 6/10; 25; NE, S.
Severe frost, sun, &
clouds.

Bees gather on the crocus's. Violets smell. ¶
Vivid N. *Aurora.*

Saturday 28.
29 2/10½; 34, 36; SE,

Snow did not lie. Apricots begin to blow.

NE.
Heavy snow, dark &
cold.

Earthed the bearing cucumber-bed. The plants in the seedling-bed grow, & want room.
N. *Aurora*.

Sunday 29.
29 3/10½; 34; NE, E.
Dark & cold, sleet,
gleams, bright.

Wheat looks poorly, & hardly shows on the ground.

Monday 30.
29 7/10; 32; N.
Ice, sun, & clouds,
sharp.

Sowed dwarf lark-spurs.
Turned-out a pot of cucumbers in each hill: the plants turned-out well; were well rooted.

Tuesday 31.
29 6/10; 32; NW, W,
SW.
Hard frost, sun, hail,
clouds, wet, rain.

Sowed a crop of onions, lettuce, & radishes.
Rain in March – 2 inc. 47 h.

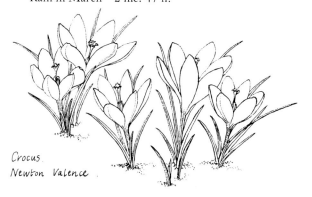

*Crocus
Newton Valence*

APRIL 1789

Wednesday 1.
29 3/10½; SW, W;
66.
Sun, sun & clouds.

Rain in the night. Spring-like.
Crocus's make a gaudy show.
Some little snow under hedges.

Thursday 2.
28 9/10; 49; SW; 37.
Rain, rain, sun &
wind, rain.

Much rain early.
Very little spring-corn sown: the season will be very backward.

Friday 3.
29 ½/10; 42; SW; 12.
Showers, sun & clouds.

Some wood-cocks are now found in Hartley wood: as soon as the weather grows a little warm, they will pair, & leave us.

Saturday 4.
29 6/10; 33; N.
Sleet, snow, snow, hail.

Snow all melts as it falls.
Celeri comes up well under the hand-glass.
Cucumbers thrive, & throw-out side-shoots.

Sunday 5.
29 8/10; 30; N, NE.
Wh. frost, ice, sun,
pleasant.

Wry-neck pipes. The smallest uncrested wren chirps loudly, & sharply in the hanger.

Monday 6.
29 7/10½; 36; NE, E, SE.
Frost, grey & pleasant.

Pile-wort blows: ivy-berries turn black, & ripen. Apricots blossom.
Timothy the tortoise heaves up the sod under which he is buried.

Tuesday 7.
29 6/10; 35; SE, S, SW.
Frost, sun, grey, rain.

Daffodil blows.

Wednesday 8.
29 7/10½; 39; N, NW.
Grey, gleams, fine even.

Sowed more green cucumber seeds. Cucumbers thrive.

Thursday 9.
29 8/10; 61; NE.
Frost, ice, sun, spring-like, red even.
Full moon.

Brimstone butter-fly. The tortoise comes out.
Dogs violets blow. Summer like.

Friday 10.
29 6/10; 35; NE.
Deep fog, hot sun, sweet even.

Cucumber blows. Picked & sweeped the grass-walks.

Saturday 11.
29 4/10; N.
Wh. frost, sun, sweet even.

Timothy the tortoise weighs 6 pd. 14 oz.
Cucumbers show rudiments of fruit.
Dug several plots of garden ground: ground digs well.

Sunday 12.
29 5/10; 40; N.
Sun, bright, red even.

Peaches & nectarines begin to blow.

A cuckoo was seen on Kingsley green.
Nightingale heard below Temple.

Monday 13.
29 7/10; 30; N.
Frost, ice, sun, dark & still.

Sowed a large bed of carrots with radishes, & lettuce: sowed a bed of parsnips.
Bombylius medius, a bee-like insect, appears in the walks, & lays it's eggs by bobbing it's tail against the grass.
Swallow seen at Candovers.

Tuesday 14.
29 6/10; 33; NE, E, E.
White frost, bright,
sharp, red even.

Pulled down the old forsaken martin's nests, in some of which we found dead young. They grow fetid, & foul from long use.
Redstart appears in my tall hedges.

Wednesday 15.
29 3/10½; 49; E, SE.
White frost, sun, gale,
grey & still.

Planted a plot of beans, broad beans, & a plot of potatoes.
Crocus's out of bloom.

Thursday 16.
29 3/10; 49; SW, S.
Sun, warm, dark &
mild, rain.

Sent four pots of large cucumber-plants to M.ʳ White of Newton: they shewed fruit.
Great bloom of apricots.
Sowed hollyhocks, columbines, snap-dragons, stocks, mignonette, all from S. Lambeth, in a bed in the garden: also sweet williams, & Canterbury bells.

Friday 17.
29 3/10; 49; SW; 38.
Rain, clouds & sun,
fine even.

Five gallons of french brandy from London.
Cucumbers shew fruit in bloom.

Cuculus cuculat: the voice of the cuckoo is heard in Blackmoor woods.

Saturday 18.
29 3/10½; 45; SW.
Showers, sun & clouds,
shower, clouds.

Fine growing weather.
Set some cucumbers, by putting male bloom.
The cucumber-frames are earthed every day.
House-martin is seen.

Sunday 19.
29 6/10; SW, NW.
Grey, sun, sweet even.

Several house-martins. Second uncrested wren, or laughing wren is heard.

The vines of John Stevens, which were trimmed late, not till March, bleed much, & will continue so to do untill the leaf is fully expanded. It is remarkable, that tho' this is the case while the trees are leafless, yet lop them as much as you please when the foliage is out, they will not shed one drop. Dᵣ Hales was not acquainted with this circumstance when he cut-off a large bough of his vine at Teddington late in the spring; & it was lucky for science that he was not. For his sollicitude for his vine, & his various attempts to stop the effusion of the sap, led him step by step to many expedients, which by degrees brought on abundance of curious experiments, & ended in that learned publication known by the name of *Vegetable Statics*, a work which has done much honour to the Author, & has been translated into many modern languages.

Monday 20.
29 8/10; 43; NW, SW, W.
White dew, sun, yellow even.

Apricots set very fast. The willows in bloom are very beautiful. Men pole their hops: barley is sowing at the forest side.

Several swallows, h: martins, & bank-martins play over Oakhanger ponds. The horses wade belly deep over those ponds, to crop the grass floating on the surface of the water.

Tuesday 21.
29 7/10¾; 45; W, S.
Grey, sun, louring & warm.

Crown imperials, & fritillaria's blow: wall cherries begin to blow.

Wednesday 22.
29 7/10; 49; W.
Sun, gale, grey.

Young broods of goslings. Wood sorrel & anemony blow. The cuckoo cries along the hanger.
Wheat thrives.

Wood Anemone.
Short Lythe.
April.

Thursday 23.
29 3/10; 46, 51; W.
Wet, strong gale.

Apricots set: cucumbers thrive. Swallows & martins do not yet frequent houses.
Women hoe wheat.

Friday 24.
29 4/10; 43; NW.
Gale, sun, clouds, sharp wind.

Lined the cucumber-bed well with hot dung at the back. Swallows at Oakhanger ponds: none yet frequent the village.

Saturday 25.
29 1/10½, SW, S.
Sun, pleasant, rain, rain.

Began to mow the grass-plots: grass grows.
Black-thorn blows. Two cuckoos along the hanger.

Sunday 26.
28 9/10; 41; SW.
Sun, hail, showers.

Most of the artichokes were killed by the long frost, except some few basons.
Vast shower of hail.

This morning I saw a certificate from the town of Wymburn Minster in the country of Dorset to the parish of Selborne, acknowledging William Dewye to be parishioner of the said town. This paper is dated Apr: 20, 1729: so that Will: Dewye, & wife, both still living, have been certificate people¶ here exactly 60 years.
  The long frost of last winter has proved very destructive to pond-fish the kingdom over, except in those pools & lakes thro' which passed a constant current of water: nor did the expedient of breaking holes in the ice avail. Mr Barker, who has been writing an account of the late frost, thinks that it did mischief. A current of water introduces a constant current of fresh air, which refreshes continually the air of the pools & ponds, & renders it fit for respiration.

Monday 27.
28 9/10½; S; 28.
Showers, windy.

ALTON
One beech in the hanger shows some foliage.

Tuesday 28.
41; S.
Sun & clouds, cold wind.

Timothy the tortoise begins to eat dandelion.
A pair of Swifts at Alton.

Wednesday 29.
29 3/10½; 43; SW.
Fog, sun, bright even.

SELBORNE
Scarce an *hirundo* has been seen about this village.
Cucumbers swell.

Thursday 30.
29 4/10; S, SE.
Wh. dew, sun, fine even.

Many beeches in yᵉ hanger look green.
Pair of swifts. Several swallows, & martins round the village.
Rain in April – 1 inch 81 hund.
Brother Thomas White, & daughter, & little Tom came.

MAY 1789

Friday 1.
29 5/10; 45; NE.
Grey, wet, wet, still.

Lined the front of the cucumber-bed.
Mountain snow-crops blow.

Saturday 2.
29 6/10; 45; NE, E, 17.
Dark & still, fine even.

Cucumbers swell.

Sunday 3.
29 3/10; NE.   Lettuces, which have stood the winter, now come in.
Rain, dark, mild.   Shell-snails begin to come out.

Monday 4.
29 4/10; 50; S; 23.   Beat the grass-banks in the garden. Put up the urns.
Sun, sweet summer.   Martins come into the old nests.
                    Bat out. Nightingale in my out-let.
                    Black snail.

Tuesday 5.
29 3/10¾; 59; S.   Bees at last frequent my cucumber-frames.
Wh. dew, sun, dark, Foward tulips blow. Cucumbers swell.
gleams.   Black-thorns covered with bloom.
                    Snails come out.
                    The Fern-owl, or Goat-sucker chatters in the hanger. This
                    curious bird is never heard till warm weather comes: it is the
                    latest summer bird except the fly-catcher.

Wednesday 6.
29 6/10½; SW, NW. Black-cap sings. Swallows frequent houses.
Wet, sun, summer.   Hardly a swift to be seen.

Thursday 7.
29 9/10; 59; SW.   Cut two brace & half of cucumbers.
Sun, summer.   Timothy eats out the hearts of the lettuces.
                    The foliage in the hanger almost fully out.
                    Ten or 12 swifts round the church.

Friday 8.
29 7/10¼; 64; SE.   Cut the first mess of asparagus. The bloom of plums is very
Wh. dew, summer,   great. Peat-carting begins.
sweet even.

Saturday 9.
29 7/10; 50, 69; SE. Cut a cucumber. Several swifts. Swallows frequent chimneys.
Vast dew, cloudless, Some hops are said to be infested with insects.
gale, red even.
Full moon.

Sunday 10.
29 8/10¾; 53, 65;   Vines shoot, & shew rudiments of much fruit. Nep. Ben came.
NW.
Sun, cloudless, brisk The beeches on the hanger, now in full leaf, when shone down on
gale.   by the sun about noon, exhibit most lovely lights & shades, not to
                    be expressed by the most masterly pencil.
                      The hops are infested by the *Chrysomela oleracea*,¶ called by
                    the country people the turnip fly, or black dolphin, which eats
                    holes in their leaves. This species is *"saltatoria, femoribus posticis*

*crassissimis": chrysomelae saltatoriae plantarum cotyledonibus,
& tenellis foliis infestae sunt."* Linn:

Monday 11.
29 8/10½; 55, 69; SE.
Sun, cloudless, red
even.

The bloom of cherries is prodigious.

Tuesday 12.
29 7/10½; 50, 69; E.
Cloudless, gale, red
even.

Levant weather. Dragon-fly.
Scarabeaus melolontha, the may chafer: bats prey on the chafers.

Great tempest at Winchester.

Wednesday 13.
29 5/10; 50, 69; @.
Sun, sultry, thunder,
rain.

The bloom of apples in many orchards great.
Monks rhubarb blows. Viburnum blows.
Nep. Ben & wife left us.

Thursday 14.
28 6/10; 68; SW; 7.
Sun & clouds, gale.

Pear-bloom great.
Sowed scarlet, & white kidney-beans.
Mice infest the hot beds, & spoil the plants.
Sycamore blows. Began to cut grass for the horses.
Stoparola, the fly-catcher, the latest summer bird of passage:
appears usually about the 20th

Friday 15.
29 2/10½; 52; SW;
43.
Rain, clouds, gales,
clouds.

Caught a mouse in the hot-bed: cut several cucumbers, but they
are ill-shapen.
Sowed two hand-glasses on the cucumber-ridge with white, &
green cucumbers.

Saturday 16.
29 6/10½; 52; W,
NW; 17.
Rain, blowing, gleams,
fine even.

Narcissus blows. Very few house-martins appear.
Sowed the large three-light annual frame with various flower-
seeds. Few black snails.

*Mouse in the herb garden.
Wakes.*

Sunday 17.
29 4/10; SW.
Rain, rain, wind.

The mice have infested my garden much by nestling in my hot-beds, devouring my balsoms, & burrouging under my cucumber basons: so that I may say with Martial . . .
"Fines Mus populatur, & colono"
"Tanquam Sus Calydonius timetur."
Epigramm: †XIX lib: XI.¶

Monday 18.
29 7/10½; 46; W; 57.
Strong wind, with showers, bright.

Very blowing all day.

Tuesday 19.
29 9/10; NW, S.
Sun, summer, mackarel sky.

Stellaria holostea, greater stitchwort, blows: a regular, periodical plant.

Wednesday 20.
29 6/10; E.
Sun, summer, dark.

Martins build briskly at the Priory, & in the street.
Oaks show prodigious bloom.
Showers about.

Thursday 21.
29 6/10; 50; E, S; 18.
Shower, wet, wet.

Annuals come-up: hand-glass cucumbers spring-up.

Friday 22.
29 5/10; SE, S.
Wet, wet, rain, rain.

Hirundines keep out in the rain: when the rain is considerable, Swifts skim with their wings inclining, to shoot off the wet.

Saturday 23.
29 6/10; 64, S; 42.
Sweet, lovely weather.

White thorn blows. The air is filled with floating willow-down.
Martins begin to build against the end of my brew-house.
Columbines blow. N. *Aurora.*
Timothy the tortoise begins to travel about, & be restless.

Sunday 24.
29 3/10; 71; E, S.
Rain, heavy shower, soft & growing.

Dr Chandler by letter dated Rolle en Suisse April 4th 1789. "The Swallows disappeared here about the end of September 1787, the weather being cold: but Octr 17th I saw a pair as we passed among the mountains towards Fort le Cluse on the road to Lyons; & my servant saw a pair on the 19th when we had got thro' the mountains into Bresse. Passing an islet of the Rhone Octr 23 near Pont St Esprit, again I saw a swallow, which dipped to drink. As we approached nearer Marseilles, we saw wasps, dragon-flies, butter-flies, & other summer-insects. I was ashore Novr 10 at Porto Longona, in the isle of St Elbe, off the coast of Italy, towards

---

† The correct attribution is XVIII.

the evening. Philip declared that a swallow had passed over his head, of which I doubted: but presently after saw three crossing the Port towards us. They flew almost strait, very swiftly; & I should have supposed were going to Italy, if the distance had been less, or the Sun not so near setting. Wasps were in full vigour, & numerous there.

"I was assured by a friend at Rome, March 16 1788, that he had seen swallows at Naples six weeks before. M[r] Morris informed me that the martins had been busy under the eaves of the house, where he lodged, about a week. I saw there, two days after, four nests which they had began to repair, & on the 26th a couple of the birds: but M[r] M. declared that he had heard them twitter at least as early as the first of March. The first swift I observed was over the river Liris on my return from Naples, April 27th Nightingales sung there.

"On the 20th of last March Philip saw two martins about the lake of Geneva: & was assured by a man that he had seen them on the 18th On the 25th he saw several swallows; & supposes the martins to have perished with the cold, as they have not been seen since, & the weather has been bad. They seem to have disappeared again, as I have not yet seen one. I remarked bees, & a brimstone-butterfly, March 15th & about the same time Magpies building in the trees opposite to my windows. I am told that a single martin commonly arrives first, as it were to explore: & again withdraws, as it were to fetch a colony.

"M[r] Morris, who has lived several years at Rome, related, that the boys there angle for the Swallows with a line at the end of a reed, &, instead of a hook, a noose baited with a feather, & hung out at the corners of the streets. Many are taken by this method, & carried home to be roasted & eaten: . . . or to supply the markets, where they are commonly sold in the season."

"At Chamberry in Savoy I observed in the evening a joyous croud, & a great bustle. My curiosity led me to see what was the matter. A net was spread from one house to an other across a street. Those brutes tied the birds they intercepted (chiefly swifts) in pairs by two of their legs, & dismissed them from the windows to flutter down, & become the sport of the mob below. I turned away with horror, & disgust!

The first quail that I have heard this year 1787 was near Rolle, on May 20th in the evening."

Monday 25.
29 3/10; 71; E, SE; 42.
Rain, thunder, dark, moist, & hot.

Sowed a hand-glass of green, & white cucumbers.

Tuesday 26.
29 3/10; 65; E, S.
Dark, warm, rain, rain.

Ophrys nidus avis in the hanger budding for bloom.
Vast rain.

Wednesday 27.
29 5/10; SE, W; 82.
Dark & moist, gleam.

Honey-suckle, mountain-ash, & laburnum blow.
Hippobosca equina.

Thursday 28.
29 4/10; 53; S.
Sun, warm, wet.

A fly-catcher has built a nest in the great apricot-tree, in which there is one egg.

Friday 29.
29 4/10½; SW; 25.
Showers, rain in the
night, sun & clouds.

Saturday 30.
29 3/10½; 59; SE.
Dark, shower, rain.

Early orange-lillies, & fiery lillies blow.
Some heads of S! foin begin to open.

Sunday 31.
29 3/10; S; 32.
Showers, showers, sun.

House-martins now abound, & are busy in building.
Rain in May – 4 inch: 5 hun.

JUNE 1789

Monday 1.
29 4/10; 51; S, SE.
Sun, & clouds, sweet
even.

Dame's violets blow. Monks rhubarb seven feet high; makes a noble appearance in bloom. Thunder.
Horses begin to lie out. Hops thrive: have been tyed to the poles twice.

Tuesday 2.
29 5/10½; 48, 55; @.
Vast dew, sun, sweet
even.

Many showers about. A heavy shower at Oakwoods.

Wednesday 3.
29 3/10½; 46; S.
Fine dew, sun, dark,
rain.

Vast bloom of haw-thorns. Peonies blow.

Thursday 4.
29 1/10; 50; W, NW;
19.
Windy, hail, rain, dark
& windy.

Friday 5.
29 5/10; 56; NW, N;
44.

Wind & rain all night.
Sowed some white cucumber-seeds from S. Lambeth under a

Rain, wind, sun, still & dark.

hand-glass.
Moon-shine.

Saturday 6.
29 4/10¾; 49, 57;
NW.
Strong, cold, wind, wind.

Pricked-out celeri from the hand-glass.
Aphides begin to appear on the hops: in some places they are called smother-flies. Farmer Spencers Foredown hops are much injured, & eaten by the *chrysomēlae*: while Mʳ Hale's adjoining are not much touched.

Sunday 7.
29 8/10; 51; N, NW.
Cold dew, strong wind, sun, bright.
Full moon.

Wood-strawberries show much bloom.

Monday 8.
29 8/10; 64; N.
Sun, brisk air, dark, wet.

The bloom of hawthorns is vast: every bush appears as if covered with snow.
Brother Thomas left us, & went to Fyfield.

Tuesday 9.
29 7/10; SW.
Grey, pleasant, mild.

Field-crickets shrill on the verge of the forest. Cuckoos abound there.

Wednesday 10.
NW, N.

SOUTH LAMBETH
Thinned the apricots, & took-off many hundreds.
Young Cygnets on the Mole river at Cobham.
Hay made, & carrying at Wandsworth.
Roses, & sweet-briars beginning to blow in my brother's outlet.
Rye in ear.
Green pease at supper, a large dish.

Dog roses in the churchyard. Selborne.

Thursday 11.
30½ 1/10; NE.
Grey, cool, pleasant.

Straw-berries cryed about. ¶
Fraxinellas in bloom.

My Niece Hannah's squirrel is much delighted with the fruit of the coniferous trees, such as the pine, the fir, the larch, & the birch; &, had it an opportunity, would probably be pleased with the cones of alders.

As to Scotch firs, Squirrels not only devour the cones, but they also bark large boughs, & gnaw off the tops of the leading shoots; so that the pine-groves belonging to Mr Beckford at Basing-park are much injured & defaced by those little mischievous quadrupeds, which are too subtile, & too nimble to be easily taken, or destroyed.

Friday 12.
30 2/10; 57; NE.
Grey, & cool, bright.

Cucumbers do not thrive: melon-plants look well; some fruit well grown.
Bro.^r Benjn cuts his grass, clover & rye, a decent burden, but much infested with wild chamomile, vulg: margweed: may weed.
The Cypress trees, & passion flowers mostly killed by the late hard winter.

Saturday 13.
30 2/10; 55; N.
Grey & cool, bright, cool.

My brother's barley begins to come into ear.
The squirrel is very fond of the cones of various trees.

Sunday 14.
30 1/10; 56; NE.
Dark, & chill.

Cucumbers do not thrive, nor is the fruit fair, & shapely.
Nothing grows in the garden.

A patent machine, called a Fire escape, (rather perhaps a Scape fire) was brought one evening along Fleet street. It consisted of a Ladder, perhaps 36 feet in length, which turned on a pivot, so as to be elevated or depressed at will, & was supported on timber-frame-work, drawn on wheels. A groove in each rail of this ladder-like construction admitted a box or hutch to be drawn up or let down by a pulley fixed at the top round & by a windlass at the bottom. When the ladder is set against a wall, the person in danger is to escape into the hutch, then drawn to the top. That the ladder may not take fire from any flames breaking out below, it is defended all the way by a sheathing of tin. Several people, it seems, had illiberally refused the Patentee the priviledge of trying his machine against their houses: but Mr White, on application, immediately consented; when the ladder was applyed to a sash on the second story, & a man was hoisted up & let down with great expedition, & safety, & then a couple of boys together. Some spectators were of opinion that the hutch or box was too scanty or shallow, & that for security it ought to be raised on the sides, &

lower end by a treillis of strong wire, or iron-work, least people in terror & confusion should miss of their aim, & fall over to the ground. This machine was easily drawn by four men only. The ladder, the owner told us, would reach to a third story, when properly elevated. The name of the Inventor is Mon.^r Dufour.

Monday 15.
30; 65; E.
Haze, sun & air.

Hay makes very fast.

Tuesday 16.
29 8/10½; E.
Sun, breeze, sun, hot.

Wednesday 17.
70; E; 82.
Sun & clouds,
sprinkling, rain.

LONDON
My brother's hay ricked in fine order, just before the wet season.
Cauliflowers.
The Opera-house in the Hay-market burnt down.

Thursday 18.
27; @.
Rain, rain, rain.

Rain 5. Rain 31.

Friday 19.
S.
Sun & clouds, sultry.

Saturday 20.
SE.
Rain, sun, & clouds.

Rain 20.

Sunday 21.
29 4/10½; SE.
Sun, clouds, rain,
thunder.

S. LAMBETH
Vines begin to blossom: corn-flags blow.

Monday 22.
SE; 67.
Rain, & wind, dark &
chilly.

Rain 30.
Elder trees blossom.

My brother trenched his field, & sowed it with barley, but the corn seems as if it would be too big, & begins already to lodge. The Product, when thrash'd, was 9 Quarters, one Bushel, & an half, viz. 73½ Bushels.
My brother has set up a may-pole 55 feet in height: it is constructed out of two slender deal spars, & for support cramped to the corner of a garden wall.

Tuesday 23.
29 5/10½; S; 37.
Rain, rain, wind &

Rain 17. Much hay lies abroad in a bad way.
Scarlet strawberries are cryed about at six pence the pottle:¶ they

rain.

are not finely flavoured.

Wednesday 24.
29 5/10; SW.
Showers, showers,
heavy showers.

Rain 40.
Mazagan beans come in.
The barley much lodged.

No House-martins appear at S.L., a very few swallows, & only three pairs of Swifts that seem to belong to the place. No wonder therefore that flies abound so in the autumn, as to become a nuisance.

Thursday 25.
29 6/10½; 56; E,
NW, SW; 97.
Dark & cold, rain,
heavy showers.

Rain 54. Crop-gardeners sell their pease at market at 20^d the sack, & their cauliflowers at 18^d per dozen: pease abound, so as hardly to pay for gathering.

Friday 26.
29 8/10; 60; W; 23.
Cool, clouds, sun.

Rain 34.

Saturday 27.
29 9/10; S; 28.
Grey, sun.

My brother cuts his first melon, a small cantaleupe.
Barley in bloom: that which was lodged rises a little.

Sunday 28.
29 7/10; 53; SW, W.
Clouds, wind, &
showers, cold air.

Rain 25. Cut a fine melon, a cantaleupe.
Daws come on the cherry-trees, for the fruit.

While Mrs J. White & I were at S. Lambeth, we visited a Mrs Delhust of that place, the wife of an officer, who being at Gibraltar all the time of the siege, underwent all the horrors of that long blockade, & bombardment. Even at this distance of time some what of terror, & uneasiness seem to be imprinted on her features, so as to occasion a lasting impression. Nor is there any room for wonder: for fear is a violent passion, which frequently repeated, like other strong emotions, must leave traces behind. Thus, thro' the transports of inebriation, where men habituate themselves to excess in strong liquors, their faces contract an air of intoxication, even when they are cool & sober. This Lady, with many others, lodged for more than a twelve month in a cave of the rock to avoid the bombs & shot from the gun-boats, which annoyed the Southern part of the Istmus every night, as soon as it began to grow dark.

Monday 29.
29 8/10¾; 54; NW,
NW.
Clear, cloudy, shower,
dark & cool.

Rain 21. Raw & cold.
Marrow-fat pease come in.

Tuesday 30.
30, 30, 1/10; 54; NW.
Sun, clouds, grey &
still.

Rain 5. Cold air. Raspberries turn colour.
A few of the *Scarabaei solstitiales* begin to appear. Their time of
flight is the month of July.
Rain in June – 4 - 24.

JULY 1789

Wednesday 1.
30 ½/10; 56; SW.
Wet, dark & cold, rain.

LONDON
The price of wheat rises on account of the cold, wet ungenial
season. The wet & wind injures the bloom of the wheat.

Thursday 2.
30; SW, NW.
Wet, grey, sun,
pleasant.

S. LAMBETH
Cherries sold in the streets, but very bad.
Young fly-catchers come out at Selborne.

Friday 3.
NW, SE.
Sun, cloudless, sultry.

ALTON
Young swallows on the top of a chimney.
The western sun almost roasted us between Guildford &
Farnham, shining directly into our chaise.

Saturday 4.
29 5/10; 65; SE, S.
Sun, wet, rain.

SELBORNE
Distant thunder. A cock red-backed butcher-bird, or flusher, was
shot in Hartley gardens, where it had a nest. Wood-straw-berries
come in.
Planted out annuals down the field & in the garden.

My garden is in high beauty, abounding with solstitial flowers,
such as roses, corn-flags, late orange-lillies, pinks, scarlet lychnises,
&c, &c. The early honey-suckles were in their day full of blossoms,
& so fragrant, that they perfumed the street with their odour: the
late yellow honey-suckle is still in high perfection, & is a most
lovely shrub; the only objection is that having a limber stem, &
branches, it does not make a good standard.

Flower border at the Wakes.
July.

Sunday 5.
29 4/10½; 65; SW, S.
Rain, rain, sun.

My scarlet straw-berries are good: what we eat at S. Lambeth were stale, & bad.
Vines not much in bloom.

Monday 6.
29 6/10; 65; SW; 43.
Sun, heavy showers,
fine even.

Wheat is very backward, & in some fields hardly in bloom.
Began to cut my tall hedges.
Took in the hot-bed frames, & lights.

Tuesday 7.
29 5/10; 64; S.
Sun & clouds, rain,
rain, thunder, wind.
Full moon.

All fruits are very backward.

Wednesday 8.
29 6/10⅓; 63; S; 41.
Sun, & clouds, louring.

Rasps begin to turn.

Thursday 9.
29 7/10⅓; 65; W, S.
Sun, pleasant, louring.

My wall-cherries are now very good.
Much hay ricked, currans tending to be ripe.

Friday 10.
29 5/10; 64; S; 10.
Louring, rain, sun.

A peat-cutter brought me lately from Cranmoor a couple of snipe's eggs, which are beautifully marbled. They are rather large, & long for the size of the bird, & not bigger at the one end than the other. The parent birds had not sat on them. Some say, that they are not snipes eggs; but to what bird they belong they do not pretend to determine.

These eggs, I find since, were the eggs of a Churn-owl: the eggs of Snipes differ much from the former in size, shape, & colour. The peat-cutter was led into the mistake by finding his eggs in a bog, or moor.

Saturday 11.
29 5/10½; SW.
Sun, showers, fine.

The fly-catchers in the vine bring out their Young.

Sunday 12.
29 3/10; 62; S.
Louring, rain, vast
showers.

Wag-tails bring their young to the grass-plots, where they catch insects to feed them.

Monday 13.
29 2/10; 63; SW, W;
102.
Rain, showers, louring.

Cucumber-plants come to nothing: my neighbours have not cut one cucumber.
Took away the annual-frame.

Tuesday 14.
29 5/10; 63; W.
Grey, sun, pleasant,
rain.

Benham skims the horse-fields.
Rasps come in: not well flavoured.
Planted-out more annuals.

On this day a woman brought me two eggs of a fern-owl, or eve-jar, which she found on the verge of the hanger to the left of the hermitage, under a beechen-shrubb. This person, who lives just at the foot of the hanger, seems well acquainted with these nocturnal swallows, & says she has often found their eggs near that place, & that they lay only two at a time on the bare ground. The eggs were oblong, dusky, & streaked some what in the manner of the plumage of the parent bird, & were equal in size at each end. The dam was sitting on the eggs when found, which contained the rudiments of young, & would have been hatched perhaps in a week. From hence we may see the time of their breeding, which corresponds pretty well with that of the Swift, as does also the period of their arrival. Each species is usually seen about the beginning of May: each breeds but once in a summer: each lays only two eggs.

Wednesday 15.
29 4/10; 63; SW; 50.
Rain, rain, rain, rain.

We have planted-out vast quantities of annuals, but none of them thrive. Grapes do not blow, nor make any progress.
The wet season has continued just a month this day. Dismal weather!

Thursday 16.
29 3/10; 62; SW, S.
Grey, sun, pleasant,
louring.

Some young h: martins are out, & fed in the air by their dams.
Wall-cherries are excellent.
Lime-trees blossom, & smell very sweet.
M^r & Mrs Sam. Barker, & Miss Eliz: Barker came from the county of Rutland.

Friday 17.
29 3/10; SW.
Showers, sun, pleasant.

Saturday 18.
29 3/10½; SW.
Deep fog, sun &
clouds, pleasant.

Sunday 19.
29 4/10; 58; S.
Sun, pleasant, sweet
even.

Where old beech trees are cleared away, the naked ground in a year or two becomes covered with straw-berry plants, the seeds of which must have lain in the ground for an age at lest. One of the slidders¶ or trenches down the middle of the hanger, close covered over with lofty beeches near a century old, is still called strawberry slidder, tho no strawberries have grown there in the memory of man. That sort of fruit, no doubt, did once abound there, & will again when the obstruction is removed.

Monday 20.
29 5/10, 6/10; 62; N, @.
Vast dew, sun, clouds, fine.

Began to cut my hay, a vast burden, but over-ripe.
Vast clouds to the SE, E, & NE.

Tuesday 21.
29 6/10; 68; S, SE.
Bright, sun & clouds, rain.

Hay makes well. Heavy weather to the NE.
Hot: heavy weather to the SE.

Wednesday 22.
29 3/10½; 62; SW; 21.
Showers, sun & wind, showers about.

Anthericum ossifragum, Lancashire asphodel, a beautiful plant, found by Mr Barker in bloom among the bogs of Wolmer forest. *Monotropa Hypopithys* blossoms on the hanger.

Thursday 23.
29 5/10; 62; NW.
Dark, sun & clouds, sweet even.

Farmer Knight sold two loads of wheat for £36!
Brisk gale. Hay makes well.
Heavy cloud to the E.

Thistles begin to blow. The naked part of the hanger is now covered with thistles; but mostly with the *Carduus lanceolatus*. There are also the *Carduus nutans*, the musk thistle; *Carduus crispus*,¶ the thistle on thistle; *Carduus palustris*, the marsh thistle. The seeds of these thistles may have lain probably under the thick shade of the beeches for many Years; but could not vegetate till the sun & air were admitted.

Friday 24.
29 5/10½; 59½; SW.
Sun, showers, louring.

Ricked four large jobbs of hay in good order.
Rain in the night.

Saturday 25.
29 4; S.
Rain, sun, louring, wet.

No garden-beans gathered yet.
Threw the hay in the meadows into large cocks.
The lime-trees with their golden tassels make a most beautiful show. Hops throw out their side branches, which are to bear the fruit.

Sunday 26.
29 5/10; 63; S.
Sun, pleasant, fine even.

Cran-berries at bins pond not ripe.
Hog pease are hacking at Oakhanger.

By observing two glow-worms, which were brought from the field to the bank in the garden, it appeared to us, that those little creatures put-out their lamps between eleven & twelve, & shine no more for the rest of the night.

Farmer Spencer & Farmer Knight are beginning to lime their respective farms at Grange, & Norton.

Monday 27.
29 4/10½; 61; @.
Fog, sun, thunder,
rain.

Few swifts have appeared for some days past; but more are seen this hot morning. H. martins continue to bring-out their Young. Bees gather on the limes, which smell very sweet.
Ricked two large jobbs of hay, & a small jobb, & finished my rick in good order.

Tuesday 28.
29 7/10; NW; 16.
Bright, sun, sweet
even.

Hay still about.
Lapwings leave the bogs, & moors in large flocks, & frequent the uplands.

Wednesday 29.
29 7/10; 64; SW.
Sun, shady, fine even.

Many young swallows out: few swifts remain.
The land-springs have run for some time, & especially in the hollow lane that leads from the village to Rood.

Thursday 30.
29 7/10¼; NW, W.
Grey, sweet day.

Much hay is making: those that are late with their hay will succeed best.
Roads much dryed.

John Hale brings home a waggon-load of woollen-rags, with [which] are to be strewed on his hopgrounds in the spring, & dug in as manure. These rags weighed a ton weight, & cost brought home near six pounds. They came from Gosport.

Friday 31.
29 3/10; 61¼; S, W;
86.
Louring, vast rain,
blowing.

This rain was very great at Malpas in Cheshire.
Rain in July – 3 inch: 69 hun:

AUGUST 1789

Saturday 1.
29 7/10; NW.
Blowing, sun & clouds.

Strong wind in the night which has injured the hops; & particularly farmer Spencer's in Culver croft.
Trenched out several rows of celeri, but the plants are of a red ugly colour, & seem not to be a good sort. The seed came from the gardener at Alton.
Artichokes, & garden-beans come in.
The rain of yesterday has lodged some of the wheat.

Sunday 2.
29 7/10½; 67; S.
Sun, grey, warm.

The goose berries are bent to the ground with loads of fruit.
Four swifts remain: several of them seemed to withdraw by the third week in July.

These swifts proved to be the last seen this season.

Monday 3.
29 7/10; 69; S, SE, E.
Sun, summer, sweet
even.

Wheat reaped at Ropley.
Ripening weather. Ant-flies begin to come forth on their business
of emigration.

Tuesday 4.
29 6/10; 69; E, SE.
Sun, sultry, broken
clouds.

Holly hocks, scarlet martagons, & sunflowers blow.

Wednesday 5.
29 6/10¾; 68; SW.
Sun, sultry, wet.
Full moon.

Forest-fuel brought in. Beechen fuel brought in.
Wood-straw-berries are over.

Augst 5th Mrs Brown brought to bed of a daughter, who makes the
number of my nephews & nieces 54.

Thursday 6.
29 9/10; 65; W, NW.
Sun, gale, clouds,
bright even.

Swifts seem to be gone.
Roads much dryed.

Sedum Telephium, orpine, & *Hypericum Androsaemum*, tutsan,
growing in Emshot lane leading to Hawkley mill.
Rhus Cotinus, sive Coccygria, blows: it's blossom is very minute, &
stands on the extremities of it's filiform bracteals, which have a sort
of feather-like appearance that gives the shrub a singular, &
beautiful grace. This tree does not ripen it's berries with us. Is a
native of Lombardy, & to be found at the foot of the Apennine, &
in Carniola.

Friday 7.
29 8/10¾; 66; NW.
Sun, summer weather.

M^r & Mrs Barker, & Miss Eliz. Barker rode to Blackdown to see
the prospect, & returned by three o'clock: they set out at six in the
morning.

Saturday 8.
29 8/10; 68; E.
Vast dew, sun, sultry,
red even.

Two poor, half-fledged fern-owls¶ were brought me: they were
found out in the forest among the heath.
Farmer Hewet of Temple cut 30 acres of wheat this week. This
wheat was lodged before it came into ear, & was much blighted.
It grew on low grounds: the wheat on the high malms at Temple
is not ripe.

The country people have a notion that the Fern-owl, or Churn-
owl, or Eve-jarr, which they also call a Puckeridge, is very
injurious to weanling calves by inflicting, as it strikes at them, the
fatal distemper known to cow-leeches by the name of puckeridge.
Thus does this harmless, ill-fated bird fall under a double
inputation, which it by no means deserves; in Italy of sucking the
teats of goats, where it is called *Caprimulgus*; & with us, of
communicating a deadly disorder to cattle. But the truth of the
matter is, the malady above-mentioned is occasioned by the

Oestrus bovis, a dipterous insect, which lays it's eggs along the backs/chines¶ of kine, where the maggots, when hatched, eat their way thro' the hide of the beast into the flesh, & grow to a very large size. I have just talked with a man, who says he has, more than once, stripped calves that have dyed of the puckeridge; that the ail, or complaint lay along the chine, where the flesh was much swelled, & filled with purulent matter. Once myself I saw a large maggot of this sort taken/squeezed out of the back of a cow. These maggots in Essex are called wornils.

The least observation & attention would convince men that these birds neither injure the goat-herd, nor the grazier; but that they are perfectly harmless, & subsist alone, being night birds, on night-insects, such as *scarabaei*, & *phalaenae*; & thro' the month of July mostly on the *scarabaeus solstitialis*, which in many districts abounds at that season. Those that we have opened have always had their craws stuffed with large night-moths & their eggs, & pieces of chafers: nor does it any wise appear how they can, weak & unarmed as they seem, inflict any harm on kine, unless they possess the powers of animal magnetism, & can affect them by fluttering over them.

Mr Churton informs me, "that the disease along the chines of calves, or rather the maggots that cause them, are called by the graziers in Cheshire worry brees, & a single one worry bree." No doubt they mean a breese, or breeze, one name for the gad-fly or *Oestrus*, which is the parent of these maggots, & lays it's eggs on the backs of kine.

Sunday 9.
29 8/10; 68½; E.
Dew, sun, brisk air, red even.

Dogs come into my garden in the night, & eat my goose-berries.
Levant weather.

Monday 10.
29 8/10; 70½; E.
Fog, sun & gale, red even.

Monotropa Hypopithus abounds in the hanger beyond Maiden dance, opposite to coney-croft hanger.
Ripening weather.

Tuesday 11.
29 8/10; 69½; NE.
Grey, sun, sultry, red even.

Wheat-harvest not much begun. Got-in forest-fuel in nice order.
Farmer Knight begins wheat-harvest.
Lovely weather.
Mr Barker, who measured the great oak in the Holt this day, finds the circumference to be 33 feet, & four inches.
Comb-wood pond fished. There were some large carps, & some tench, & many eels.

Wednesday 12.
29 7/10½; 70½; NE.
Fog, sun, hot, heavy

Apricots turn colour: peaches, & nectarines are yet very small.
The hand-glass cucumbers grow much, & begin to bear.

clouds.

The planters think these foggy mornings, & sunny days injurious to their hops.
The wheat about the village hardly ripe.

Thursday 13.
29 7/10½; 68; NE.
Fog, sun, heavy clouds.

Sowed a crop of spinage seed to stand the winter, & trod it, & rolled it well: sowed also turnip-radishes.
Apricots come in. Men house pease.

Friday 14.
29 7/10; 66, 69; NE.
Heavy, sun, sultry, red even.

Flying ants come forth from under the stairs.

Saturday 15.
29 7/10; 69; N, NE.
Sun, sultry, heavy clouds.

Sunday 16.
29 6/10½; NE; 32.
Sun, dark, heavy shower, sun.

China asters begin to blow.

Brimstone butterfly
Church meadow

Monday 17.
29 9/10; N; 8.
Sun, sun & clouds.

Cool air.
Wheat gleaned.

Tuesday 18.
29 9/10; 66½; N.
Sun, hot, red even.

Many pease housed.
Harvest-scenes are now very beautiful!
Turnips thrive since the shower.

Wednesday 19.
29 7/10½; 66; E.
Grey, sun, red even.

Timothy Turner's brew-house on fire: but much help coming in & pulling off the thatch, the fire was extinguished, without any farther damage than the loss of roofing. The flames burst thro' the thatch in many places.

Thursday 20.
29 5/10; 71; E, SW.
Sun, sultry, dark clouds.

Hirundines cluster on the tower.
Apricots ripen very fast. Cucumbers bear well.
We are this day much annoyed in the brown parlor by multitudes of flying ants, which come forth, as usual, from under the stairs.

Friday 21.
29 3/10½; 66½; @.
Sun, sultry, dark, thunder around.

Much wheat housed. Kidney-beans come in.
Two thunder-clouds in sight. Heavy rain.

Saturday 22.
29 5/10; 62; NW, W; 15.

Vast rain, & much thunder at London.
Much wheat housed & ricked. Thunder.

Sun, shower, sun, shower.

M.rs Ben White came to us from Newton.

Sunday 23.
29 7/10½; 59; NW, N.
Sun, clouds, showers, dark & louring.

Boy brought me the rudiments of a hornet's nest, with some maggots in it.
Some of the hop-gardens are beautifully adorned with hops, which are not yet come to their full growth.

Every ant-hill usually about this time is in a strange hurry, & confusion, & all the winged ants, agitated by some violent impulse, are leaving their homes; & bent on emigration, swarm by myriads in the air, to the great emolument of the Hirundines, which fare luxuriously. Those that escape the Swallows return no more to their nests, but looking out for fresh settlements, lay a foundation for future colonies. All the females at these times are pregnant: the males that escape being eaten, wander away, & die.

Monday 24.
29 8/10½; 61; W, S.
Sun, dark & louring.

Butterflies swarm in my fields, & garden.
Cucumbers abound. A fernowl sits about on my field walks.

Tuesday 25.
29 8/10; 63½; S, W.
Sun, dark, sun.

Sweet harvest weather. Wheat ricked, & housed.
M.r & M.rs S. Barker, & Miss E. Barker left us.

Wednesday 26.
29 7/10; 62; SW, N.
Dark, wet, dark & still.

Much wheat cut. Young hirundines abound, & many continue to come-out.

Thursday 27.
29 7/10; 61; E, SW.
Vast dew, sun, sweet day.

Tho. Holt White comes from Fyfield.
Began to turn the horses into the great meadow.

Friday 28.
29 6/10; 68; SE, S.
Deep fog, sun, sweet even.

Colchicum autumnale, naked boys, blows.
Wheat-harvest goes on finely.

Saturday 29.
29 4/10; 70; S.
Fog, sun, sultry, clouds.

The tops of the beeches begin to be tinged.
Wheat housed.

Sunday 30.
29 3/10½; 65; S, SE.
Rain, wet, wet.

Michaelmass daiseys begin to blow.

Monday 31.

65; SE, S; 44.
Dark, louring, sun,
louring.

Rain in the night. Gathered a bushel-basket of well-grown cucumbers, 238 in number.
Molly White, & T. H. White left us, & went to London.
Rain in August – 0 inch. 99 hund.
Hop picking would have taken place in the Hartley gardens had the weather permitted.

SEPTEMBER 1789

Tuesday 1.

29 2/10½; SE.
Rain, rain, rain.

Sowed lettuces to stand the winter: planted-out endives.
Rain in the night.

Wednesday 2.

29 2/10½; 63; SE, E; 65.
Rain, sun, hot, pleasant.

Bees feed on the plums, & the mellow-goose-berries. They often devour the peaches, & nectarines.
Mʳ Hammond begins to pick his hops at Wardleham.

Wry-necks, birds so called, appear on the grass-plots, & walks: they walk a little as well as hop, & thrust their bills into the turf in quest, I conclude, of ants, which are their food. While they hold their bills in the grass, they draw out their prey with their tongues, which are so long as to be coiled round their heads.

Thursday 3.

29 1/10; 64; S, SE.
Showers, sun, showers, yellow gleam.

Some peaches grow soft.
Mʳ Charles Etty returns from Canton.

Friday 4.

29; 62; SW; 59.
Heavy showers, gale.
Full moon.

Fly-catchers still appear: hirundines abound.
Farmer Knight, & farmer Lasham have much wheat abroad.
Mʳ Thomas Mulso comes from London.

Saturday 5.

29 5/10; 63; SW, S; 24.
Showers, sun, showers, pleasant.

Hopping begins in many gardens.

Sunday 6.

29 6/10¾; 58; SW.
Fog, sun, pleasant, showers.
Moonshine.

Rain in the night.
Mushrooms begin to come.
I see only now & then a wasp.

Footbridge over Oakhanger Stream.
ate August.

Monday 7.
29 7/10¼; 63½; SW, W.
Fog, sun, louring.

Wheat abroad injured; some begins to grow.
Many hops picked. Mᵣ Thomas Mulso left us, & went to Winton.
Some wheat housed, but cold & damp.

Tuesday 8.
29 8/10; 62½; W, SW.
Louring, sun, pleasant.

Gathered many cucumbers. Gale all night.
Brisk gale all day. Wheat housed.
Broᵣ T. W. & Th. H. W. came from London.

Wednesday 9.
29 8/10; 60, 65; SW.
Sun, pleasant.

Hops are not large.
The fly-catchers which abounded in my outlet seem to have withdrawn themselves.
Some grapes begin to turn colour. Men bind wheat.

Sweet harvest, & hop-picking weather. Hirundines congregate on barns, & trees, & on the tower. The hops are smaller than they were last Year. There is fine clover in many fields.

Thursday 10.
29 5/10; 66; S.
Grey, sun, hot.

Wheat housed, & pease.

Friday 11.
29 8/10¼; 63; N, NW; 41.
Rain, gale, sun, cool.

Ophrys spiralis, ladies traces, in bloom in the long Lythe, & on the top of the short Lythe.
Sent 12 plants of the *Ophrys spiralis* to Mʳ Curtis of Lambeth marsh.

Saturday 12.
30; 58; NW.
Cold dew, sun, clouds, bright even:

Some wheat is out. W. Trimming has a large field not cut.
Gentiana Amarella, autumnal gentian, or fell-wort, buds for bloom on the hill.
Wasps seize on butter-flies, & shearing off their wings, carry their bodies home as food for their young: they prey much on flies.

Sunday 13.
29 7/10½; 62; S.
Sun, pleasant, louring.

Monday 14.
29 5/10; 61; S, W.
Dark, rain, yellow even.

After a bright night, & vast dew, the sky usually becomes cloudy by eleven or twelve o'clock in the forenoon; & clear again towards the decline of the day. The reason seems to be, that the dew, drawn-up by evaporation, occasions the clouds, which towards evening being no longer rendered buoyant by the warmth of the sun, melt away, & fall down again in dews. If clouds are watched of a still, warm evening, they will be seen to melt away, & disappear.
    Several nests of gold-finches, with fledged young, were found among the vines of the hops: these nestlings must be second broods.

Tuesday 15.
29 4/10; 48; S; 19.
Dark clouds, rain,
chilly.

Showers about. The hops at Kimbers grow dingy, & lose their colour.
T. H .W. left us, & went to Fyfield.

Wednesday 16.
29 4/10; NW.
Clouds, showers,
showers, thunder, hail,
cold air.

Timothy the tortoise is very dull, & inactive, & spends his time on the border under the fruit-wall.

Thursday 17.
29 5/10½; 43; W, N.
White dew, clouds,
sun, pleasant, bright.

Barley & oats housed.
No mushrooms on the down.
Some young martins in a nest at the end of the brew-house.

Friday 18.
29 2/10; 48; W; 18.
Wet, cold air, rain,
chilly.

Young martins come-out, & are fed on the wing.
Began to light fires in the parlors.
Small uncrested wrens, chif-chaffs, are seen in the garden.
The furze-seed, which Bro. Tho. sowed last may on the naked part of the hanger, comes up well.
Some rasp-berry-trees in the bushes on the common. Trees keep their verdure well.

Saturday 19.
29; 55; N, W.
Sun, pleasant, shower.

Vast clouds about. Oats are housed.
Several people have finished their hops.
Many martins, & swallows round the village; but, in appearance, not the whole flock which used to congregate on trees & roofs some days ago.
No mushrooms in the pastures below Burrant hangers.
Here & there a wasp.

Sunday 20.
29 2/10½; N.
Rain, clouds, cool air.

Black-birds feed on the elder-berries.

Monday 21.
29 6/10½; 55, 59; N,
NW.
Deep fog, hot sun,
sweet afternoon.

Myriads of Insects sporting in the sun-beams.
The foliage of the woods, & coppices is very little tinged, or discoloured.

Tuesday 22.
29 7/10; 57; SW.
Dark & louring, wet,
dark.

Swallows abound; but the bulk of the house-martins seem to be withdrawn.
Turnips are delicate.

Wednesday 23.
29 8/10; 58; N.
Grey, & pleasant.

We find no mushrooms on the down, nor on Nore hill. Women continue to glean, but the corn is grown in the ears. Many martins again.
Will. Trimming has wheat still abroad.
Gather-in the white pippins, a large crop.

As we were walking this day, Septr 22nd being the King's coronation,¶ on Nore-hill at one o'the clock in the afternoon, we heard great guns on each side of us, viz. from the S. & from the NE., which undoubtedly were the cannons of Portsmouth & Windsor; the former of which is at least 26 miles distant, & the latter 30.
If the guns heard from the NE. were not the Windsor, they must be those of the Tower at London.

Thursday 24.
29 8/10¾; 59; NE,
SW.
Great dew, hot sun,
pleasant.

Many hirundines.
M.^r & Mrs Ben White came from London.

Friday 25.
29 8/10¾; 59; E, SE,
S.
Vast dew, sun, pleasant.

Men bag their hops; & house seed-clover.
A fern-owl plays round the Plestor.

Saturday 26.
29 8/10½; 65; E, S.
Dark, gleam, bright.

Multitudes of Hirundines.
Sweet Mich: summer.

Sunday 27.
29 6/10¾; 61; SW.
Fog, sun, pleasant,
clouds.

Peaches & nectarines abound, but are not finely flavoured.

Monday 28.
29 6/10; SW.
Sun, louring, grey.

Men bag their hops.

Tuesday 29.
29 3/10; 60; S, SW.
Rain, rain, rain.

Swallows not seen; they withdraw in bad weather, & perhaps sleep most of their time away like dogs & cats, who have a power of accumulating rest, when the season does not permit them to be active.

Wednesday 30.
29 4/10; 55; SW; 56.
Sun, windy, bright.

Rain in September – 2 inch. 82 hund.

OCTOBER 1789

Thursday 1.
28 9/10; 55; SW; 96.
Heavy clouds, & wind,
thunder, hail.
Moonshine.

Storm in the night! Apples, & pears blown down.
Some swallows & martins.

Friday 2.
28 8/10; 52; W.
Sun & clouds, shower.
Moonshine.

The foliage of the Virginian creeper turns very fast.
Showers about: vivid rain-bow.

Saturday 3.
28 8/10; 50; W, NW.
Blowing, sun, shower.
Moonshine.

Gathered in bergamot, & Cresan bergamot pears.
Gathered some grapes, but they are not good.
B. Th. White sowed two pounds of furze-seed from Ireland on
the naked part of the hanger. The furze-seed sown by him on the
same space in May last is come-up well.

A man brought me a land-rail,¶ or daker-hen, a bird so rare in this
district, that we seldom see more than one or two in a season, &
those only in autumn. This is deemed a bird of passage by all the
writers: yet from it's formation seems to be poorly qualifyed for
migration; for it's wings are short, & placed so forward, & out of
the center of gravity, that it flies in a very heavy & embarrassed
manner, with it's legs hanging down; & can hardly be sprung a
second time, as it runs very fast, & seems to depend more on the
swiftness of it's feet, than on it's flying. When we came to draw it,
we found the entrails so soft & tender, that in appearance they
might have been dressed like the ropes of an wood-cock. The craw
or crop was small & lank, containing a mucus; the gizzard thick &
strong, & filled with small shell-snails, some whole & many
ground to pieces thro' the attrition which is occasioned by the
muscular force & motion of that intestine. We saw no gravels
among the food: perhaps the snail-shells might perform the
function of of gravels or pebbles, & might grind one an other.
Land-rails used to abound formerly, I remember, in the low wet
bean-fields of Aetian Malford in North Wilts; & in the meadows
near Paradise gardens at Oxford, where I have often heard them
cry, Crex, Crex. The bird mentioned above weighed seven ounces
& an half; was fat & tender, & in flavour like the flesh of a wood-
cock. The liver was very large, & delicate.

Sunday 4.
29 3/10; NW.
Sun, bright & pleasant.

No hirundines seen.
Full moon.

The breed of hares is great: last year there were few. Some have
remarked that hares abound most in wet summers.

Monday 5.
28 7/10½; 49; S, SW.
Sun, vast shower, hail,
bright, rain.

Gathered in Chaumontel pears: tyed endive.
Some martins, several martins, & swallows.
Mꞃ Ben, & Mꞃˢ Ben White left us.

Tuesday 6.
28 9/10; 49; W, NW;
52.
Sun & clouds, pleasant.

Grapes do not ripen: they are as backward as in the bad summer
1782. The crop is large.
Some hirundines.

Timothy the tortoise is very dull, & never stirs from the border of
the fruit-wall. Many loads of hops set-out for wey hill.

Wednesday 7.
29; 48; W.
Sun, wind, showers,
moonshine.

No mushrooms to be seen. Men sow wheat.
Swallows about the Plestor.

Thursday 8.
28 8/10½; 50; N, NE,
W; 143, 18.
Rain, rain, rain.

Vast rain in the night! Thunder.
Flood at Gracious street. No wind.

Friday 9.
29 ¾; 50, 52; S; 5.
Dark, mild, sun,
pleasant.

Many martins.
A bag of hops from Master Hale, weight 36 pounds, & an half.

Saturday 10.
29 2/10½; 50; S.
Sun, pleasant, rain.

Many house-martins, & some swallows.
Two hop-waggons return with loads of woollen rags, to be spread
& dug in as manure for the hop-gardens.

Sunday 11.
29 3/10½; 53; S.
Sun, mild, pleasant,
rain.

Some few bunches of grapes just eatable.
Some of the latter nectarines well flavoured.
A few swallows.

A trufle-hunter called on us, having in his pocket several large
trufles found in this neighbourhood. He says these roots are not to
be found in deep woods, but in narrow hedge-rows, & the skirts of
coppices. Some trufles, he informed us, lie two feet within the
earth; & some quite on the surface: the latter, he added, have little
or no smell, & are not so easily discovered by the dogs as those that
lie deeper. Half a crown a pound was the price, which he asked for
this commodity.

Monday 12.
29 3/10; SW; 83.
Sun, pleasant.

Much rain in the night with wind. No swallows.
Gathered Cadillac, & Swans-egg pears.

Octob.ʳ 11. On this day D.ʳ Chandler saw several swallows, flying as usual, near Cologne: he had observed none at Rolle since the beginning of September, nor none in his way to Cologne.
On the 12. in his way to Brussels, he saw more.

Tuesday 13.
29; 53; S.
Dark, rain, rain.

No mushrooms to be found.
Several martins.

Wednesday 14.
29 1/10; 52½; NE, E;
45.
Grey, pleasant, red
even, rain.

Much rain in the night. Saw one martin. Gathered apples.
One martin.
Bat out.

Thursday 15.
29 1/10¾; 54; NW; 8.
Grey, sun, warm &
pleasant.

Mackarel sky. A wheat-ear seen on the down.
Gathered pears & apples.

Friday 16.
29 5/10; 54; NW, SW.
Cold dew, sun, soft &
pleasant.

Colchicums, a fine double sort, still in bloom.
Ivy blows. Some mushrooms with thick stems, & pale gills.

Saturday 17.
29 5/10; 53; SE, S.
Dark, grey, pleasant,
clouds.

Gathered pears.

Sunday 18.
29 4/10; 57; S.
Rain, sun, pleasant.

Monthly roses are full of bloom. Great fieldfares are seen on the down. Beeches turn colour.

Monday 19.
29 3/10; SE.
Clouds, gale, rain,
rain.

NEWTON
Fierce, driving rain!

Tuesday 20.
29 5/10½; 62; S; 54.
Gale, sun, warm.

[SELBORNE]
Gathered in nonpareils, & some royal russets.

Wednesday 21.
29 5/10½; 61; S.
Sun, gale, soft.

Woodcock seen on the down, among the fern.
Finished gathering the apples, many of which are fair fruit. Shoveled the zigzag. Leaves fall. My wall-nut trees & some ashes are naked.

Thursday 22.
29 7/10; 57; N, NE.
Vast dew, sun, dark &
still.

Mended the planks of the zigzag.

Bro. Tho. White sowed the naked part of the hanger with great
quantities of hips, haws, sloes, & holly-berries. In May last he
sowed a pound of furze seeds on the same naked space; many of
which appear to have grown: & lately he sowed two pounds more.
　　Decem.ʳ 1790. As fast as any of these seeds have sprouted, they
have constantly been browzed off, & bitten down by the sheep,
which lie very hard on them, & will not suffer them to thrive.

Friday 23.
29 8/10; NE.
Fog, sun, mild, calm,
& dark.

The quantity of haws is prodigious!

Saturday 24.
29 8/10½; 53; NE.
Fog, dark, still, &
mild.

Men plow, & sow wheat.

Sunday 25.
29 8/10¾; 52; NE.
Dark & still, mild.

Fine weather for the wheat-season.
Red-wings seen on the down.

Monday 26.
29 8/10½; 50; NE.
Sun, grey & mild.

Bro.ʳ Th. W. sows laburnum seeds on the hanger, & down.
Men sow wheat.
A wood-cock killed in the high wood.

Tuesday 27.
29 9/10; 49; NE.
Dark, still & mild.

Planted out many young laurustines, & Portugal laurels from the
old stools.

Wednesday 28.
29 8/10½; 48; N.
Shower, sun, shower.
Moonshine.

Bright in the night. Rain-bow.

The young men of this place found a stray fallow deer at the back
of the village, which they roused, & hunted with grey hounds, &
other dogs. When taken it proved to be a buck of three years old.

Thursday 29.
29 8/10; 44, 49; NW.
Dew, cool, sun,
pleasant.

Bro.ʳ Th. W. left us, & went to London.
Men sow wheat.

Friday 30.
29 4/10; 45; SW, W.
Wet, dark & blowing,
stormy.

My horses taken into the stable, & not to lie out any more a
nights.
Leaves fall very fast.

New coped the top of my kitchen-chimney, mended the tiling, & toached¶ the inside of the roofing to keep out the drifting snow.

Saturday 31.
29 8/10½; 31; N.
Frost, stormy, ice, sun,
severe wind.

Small snow on the hill.
Rain in October – 5 inch. 4 hund.

NOVEMBER 1789

Sunday 1.
29 8/10; 30, 41; N, W,
SW.
Frost, sun, pleasant.

Frost. Thick ice. Insects play in the air.
Timothy the tortoise is preparing his hybernaculum; but comes out when the sun shines warm.

Monday 2.
29 1/10; 47; S, SW;
21.
Rain, rain, sun, bright.
Full moon.

The severe wind of saturday has stripped the trees of their leaves, in great measure.

Tuesday 3.
28 7/10¾; 47, 50; S.
Vast dew, sun, clouds,
& gleams, mild.

Planted 150 cabbages to stand the winter; dunged the ground. Grapes all very bad.

Novem.ʳ 3. Two swallows were seen this morning at Newton vicarage house, hovering & settling on the roofs, & out-buildings. None have been observed at Selborne since Octob.ʳ 11. It is very remarkable that after the hirundines have disappeared for some weeks, a few are occasionally seen again some times, in the first week in Novem.ʳ & that only for one day. Do they not with draw, & slumber in some hiding place during the interval? for we cannot suppose that they had migrated to warmer climes, & so returned again for one day. Is it not more probable that they are awakened from sleep,¶ & like the bats are come forth to collect a little food? Bats appear at all seasons, thro' the autumn, & spring months, when the Thermom.ʳ is at 50, because then *phalaenae*, moths, are stirring. These swallows looked like young ones.

Wednesday 4.
28 8/10; 47½; S, SE;
29.
Sun, & showers.

Mild. The wind on Saturday last occasioned much damage among the shipping in the river, & on the E. coast.

Thursday 5.
28 8/10; 47; E, SW.
Showers, sun, warm,
showers.

Bro. & Sister Benj.ⁿ came to us from Newton.

Friday 6.
28 4/10; 42; SE, S,
SE.
Rain, snow, sun, rain,
snow.

The hermitage capped with snow.

Saturday 7.
28 6/10; 43; NW; 56.
Rain, rain, bright.

Sunday 8.
29; 43; NW.
Grey, sun, pleasant.

The tortoise retires into his hole at night, but comes out when the sun shines.

Monday 9.
29 3/10⅓; 42; NW.
Grey, sun, pleasant.

Men sow wheat.

Tuesday 10.
29 5/10; 29, 30; NW.
Frost, sun, sweet day,
frost.

Leaves fall. Gossamer abounds.
Men sow wheat.

Wednesday 11.
29 5/10; 30, 40; S.
Frost, sun, pleasant,
dark.

The tortoise is going under ground, but not quite buried: he is in motion, & pushing himself beneath the turf.

Thursday 12.
29 2/10¾; 46; S; 34.
Grey, sun, pleasant,
dark & mild.

Rain in the night with thunder.
Tortoise almost covered.
Bro.ʳ & Sister Benj.ⁿ left us, & went to Newton.

Friday 13.
29 1/10½; 49; S, W;
11.
Hazy, blowing, cold,
& wet.

Dew on the outsides of the windows; a sign that the air is warmer without than within.

Saturday 14.
29 2/10; 48; S, SW;
18.
Wet & blowing, fair.

Dew on the outsides of windows.

Sunday 15.
29; 49; SE, SW.
Rain, blowing, fair.

A flock of redwings.
Men have not finished their wheat-season: some low grounds too wet to be sown.

Monday 16.
29 2/10; 45; S; 46.
Showers, showers,
showers.

Few wood cocks; & few pheasants left.
Many hares have been found on our hill: the wetness of the
season, it is supposed, induces them to leave the vales, & to
retreat to the uplands.
Much lightening early in the morning.
Reb. & Hannah White came from Newton.

Tuesday 17.
29 1/10; 45; S; 33.
Hail & vast showers,
bright.

Dᵒ left us.
Flood at Gracious street.

Wednesday 18.
29 1/10⅓; SE; 80.
Grey, dark.

Heavy rain in the night.

Thursday 19.
29 3/10½; 43; E; 13.
Grey, sun, soft & still.

Rain in the night.
The tortoise is gone in out of sight.
Much lightening to the S.
Broʳ Benjⁿ & family left Hants, & returned to South Lambeth.

Friday 20.
29 5/10; 42; S.
Sun, grey & still.

Saturday 21.
29 5/10; 42; NW, N.
Cold & wet.

Sunday 22.
29 6/10½; 44; N.
Rain, rain, rain.

Monday 23.
29 8/10; 43; N; 26.
Grey, cold air, grey.

Rain in the night.

Tuesday 24.
29 9/10; 43; N.
Grey, sun, grey,
shower.

Still, & pleasant.
Men sow wheat.

Wednesday 25.
29 8/10¾; NW, N.
Grey, wet, grey.

Men sow wheat.

Thursday 26.

The miller supplies us with cold, damp flour, & says he can get no
other: he adds, that the best wheat is at the bottom of the mows,¶

30; 41; E.
Grey, sun, sleet,
bright, frost.

& will not come forth till the spring. The latter part of the wheat harvest was very wet.

Friday 27.
30 ½/10; 25, 30; NW.
Hard frost, sun, grey
& still.

Saturday 28.
30; 37; N, NE.
Deep fog, sun, grey.

Rime on the hanger.

Sunday 29.
29 9/10; 38; SE.
Grey, still, bright.

Housed 8 cords of beech billet,¶ which had taken all the rains of the late wet summer, & autumn; & is therefore of course in but indifferent order.

Monday 30.
29 6/10; 38; SE.
Frost, sun, mild.

Rain in Novem.ʳ – 3 inch. 67.

DECEMBER 1789

Tuesday 1.
29 3/10; 44; SE.
White frost, sun, mild,
wet, rain.

After the servants are gone to bed the kitchen-hearth swarms with minute crickets not so large as fleas, which must have been lately hatched. So that these domestic insects, cherished by the influence of a constant large fire, regard not the Season of the year; but produce their young at a time when their congeners are either dead, or laid up for the winter; to pass away the uncomfortable months in the profoundest slumbers, & a state of torpidity.

Wednesday 2.
29 4/10; 46; SE, S; 16.
Grey, sun, mild,
bright.
Full moon.

Finished the trimming & tacking of my vines, which produced a great crop, but no good fruit this year on account of the badness of the season: there is however much good, bearing wood trained-in for the following summer.

Thursday 3.
29 7/10½; 42; E.
Frost, sun, pleasant.
Moonshine.

Beautiful picturesque, partial fogs along the vales, representing rivers, islands, & arms of the sea! These fogs in London & some other parts were so deep that much mischief was occasioned by men falling into rivers, & being over-turned into ditches, &c.

Friday 4.
29 8/10¼; 46; S.
Wet, dark & wet.

Saturday 5.
29 9/10½; 49; SW,
W; 13.

Rain in the night. Paths very dirty.
Mrs Ben White brought to bed of a son, (Glyd) who makes my

Sun, wind, mild.

nephews & nieces 55 in number.

Sunday 6.
30 ¾/10; 49, 49; SW.
Grey, mild, grey &
still.

Hares abound on the hill.
Flies come forth, & crawl about.
Hares gnaw the pinks in my garden.

Monday 7.
30, 30 ¼; 46, 46; S.
Great dew, sun,
pleasant, & mild.

Paths steady.

Tuesday 8.
30 1/10½; 44; E, SE.
Fog, grey, gleams,
mild.

The Bramshot hounds kill a leash of hares¶ on the hill.
Pleasant, & spring-like.

Wednesday 9.
30 1/10¾; 41; S, SW.
Deep fog, deep fog.

The Emshot hounds kill a leash of hares¶ on the hill.

Thursday 10.
30 1/10¾; 39; NW.
Dark & still.

Friday 11.
30 1/10; 43; S.
Dark, mild, & still.

Saturday 12.
30 ½/10; 45; W.
Grey, sun, grey & still.

Soft, & spring-like.
Paths dry, & steady.

A bushel of American wheat, which Bro. Tho. sent last year to one of his tenants in the hundreds of Essex from Nore hill, produced this last harvest 40 bushels of seed; & is much admired in that district, because from the stifness of it's straw it does not lodge. Wheat is so apt to lodge in those parts, that they are often obliged to mow it down in the blade about May, lest it should fall flat on the ground. This process they call swonging.

One of my neighbours shot a ring-dove on an evening, just as it was returning from feed, & going to roost. When his wife had picked & drawn it, she found it's craw stuffed with the most nice & tender tops of turnips. These she washed & boiled, & so sate down to a choice & delicate plate of greens, culled & provided in this extraordinary manner.

Hence we may see, that granivorous birds, when grain fails, can subsist on the leaves of vegetables. There is reason to suppose that they would not long be healthy without: for turkies, tho' corn-fed,

delight in a variety of plants, such as cabbage, lettuce, endive, &c.
& poultry pick much grass; while geese live for months together on
commons by grazing along.
... "Naught is useless made" ...
.... "On the barren heath"
"The Shepherd tends his flock, that daily crop"
"Their verdant dinner from the mossy turf"
"Sufficient; after them the cackling Goose,"
"Close-grazer, finds where with to ease her want."
Philips's Cyder

Sunday 13.
29 8/10; 46; S.
Dark, soft & still.

Crocus's sprout.

Monday 14.
29 3/10½; 44; E, S;
27.
Fog & rain, rain, dark
& moist, rain.

Tuesday 15.
29 3/10; 45; W; 84.
Rain, sun, & sharp
wind.

Much rain, & wind in the night.

Wednesday 16.
28 8/10; 32; W; 10.
Frost, sun, bright,
clouds.

Snow on the ground.
Several claps of thunder! Showers about.

Thursday 17.
29 3/10; 42; NW.
Sun, & sharp wind,
cold shower.

Friday 18.
29 6/10½; 41; SW.
Frost, sun, pleasant,
clouds.

Walked down to short heath: the sands were very comfortable, &
agreeable to the feet; the grass grounds, & arable paths very wet,
& unpleasant.

Saturday 19.
29 3/10; 46; S, SW,
NW; 29.
Rain, rain, bright.

Sunday 20.
29 4/10¾; 45; S.
Grey, mild, sun, grey.

Monday 21.
29 3/10½; 46; S.
Dark, mild & wet.

Tuesday 22.
29 2/10; 51; S, SW.   Rain all night. Flies come forth.
Rain, & wind, rain.   Much water stands in drops on the walls of rooms where there is
                             no fire.

Wednesday 23.
29 3/10; 51; SW; 77.   Dark & dismal. Blowing.
Wet, wet, wet.   Mr Churton came from Oxford.

Thursday 24.
29; 47; SW.   Vast rain in the night.
Rain, rain, fair.

Friday 25.
29 2/10½; 42; SW;   Much rain in the night.
137.   Our rivulets were much flooded; & the water at Oakhanger ran
Grey, & mild.   over the bridge, which in old days was called tun-bridge.

Saturday 26.
29 6/10; 32; SW.
Frost, sun, bright.

Sunday 27.
29 4/10½; 46; SW.
Rain, wind, & rain.

Monday 28.
29 7/10; 47; SW, W;
30.
Sun, mild & pleasant.

Tuesday 29.
29 3/10½; 51; SW.
Wet & blowing.

Wednesday 30.
29 2/10; 50; SW.   The Hares still continue to eat my pinks, & cabbages.
Wet, & blowing.

Thursday 31.
29; 47; SW; 39.   Storm in the night, that blew down my rain-measurer.
Wet, & blowing.   The newspapers say, that there are floods on the Thames.

                            Rain in Decemr – 4 inch. 62 hund.
                            The whole rain in 1789 was 42 inch. 0 hund.

JANUARY   — 1790 —

Friday 1.
29 8/10; 32; SW.
Frost, ice, sun,
pleasant.
Full moon.

SELBORNE
The hounds found a leash of hares on the hill.
Moon-light.

Saturday 2.
29 9/10; 41; S.
Frost, grey & mild.

Sunday 3.
29 7/10½; 47; SW;
12.
Rain, wet, dark &
mild.

The spotted Bantam lays a second time.

Monday 4.
29 8/10¾; 44; E, S.
Dark, mild, & still.

Tuesday 5.
29 8/10½; 45½; SE.
Dark, mild, still.

Hepatica's, winter-aconites blow: crocus's, snow-drops bud for
bloom.
Flies come forth in windows.

Wednesday 6.
29 9/10; 44; SE, S.
Dark, still & mild.

Polyanths blow.

Thursday 7.
30 1/10; 45; N, NW,
S.
Cloudless, still, &
bright.

Mr Churton left us, & went to Waverley.
Sweet weather: gnats play in the air.
Paths dry.

Friday 8.
30 ½/10; 42; W.
Deep fog, fog, fog.

Wall-flowers, & stocks blow.
Boys play at taw on the plestor.

Saturday 9.
29 8/10½; 41; SE.
Fog, sun, pleasant.

Water-cresses come in.

Sunday 10.
29 8/10; 43; S.
Frost, deep fog, sun,
grey.

A ripe wood-straw-berry¶ on a bank, & several blossoms. Moist
& mild. Grass grows on the walks.

Monday 11.
29 7/10; SW.
Fog, wet, wet.

The white spotted Bantam hen lays.

Tuesday 12.
29 5/10½; 49; SW.
Rain, driving rain.

Snow-drops blow. We have in the window of the stair-case a flower-pot with seven sorts of flowers, very sweet & fragrant.

Wednesday 13.
29 5/10; 49, 49; SW.
Rain, rain, rain.

Driving rain all day.

Thursday 14.
29 5/10½; 49; E, N; 83.
Dark, moist, & mild, rain.

A large speckled diver or loon was sent to me from the Holt, where it was shot by one of Lord Stawell's servants as it was swimming & diving on a large lake or pond. These birds are seldom seen so far S. in mild winters.

Friday 15.
29 6/10⅓; 44; E, SW; 33.
Deep fog, sun, warm.

Saturday 16.
29 8/10½; 42; NW, W.
Sun & brisk air.

Turnip-greens come in.

Sunday 17.
30; 39; N.
Sun, pleasant.

Monday 18.
29 7/10; 37; E.
Sun, sharp wind.

Tuesday 19.
29 8/10; 28; E.
Hard frost, bright.

A trufle-hunter came with his dogs, & tryed my tall hedges, where, as he told us, he found only a few small bulbs, because the season was over: in the autumn, he supposes many large trufles might be met with. He says, trufles do not flourish in deep woods, but in hedge-rows, & the skirts of coppices within the influence of the sun & air.

Wednesday 20.
29 9/10⅓; 28; E.
Hard frost, sun, frost.

Thursday 21.
30; E.
Deep fog, partial fogs.

NEWTON

Friday 22.
29 9/10½.
Deep wet fog.

Saturday 23.   SELBORNE
29 9/10; 46.   Carryed in dung for the hot-bed.
Frost, deep fog.

Sunday 24.
29 8/10; 47; SW.
Dark, warm, & moist,
fog.

Monday 25.
29 9/10; 46; N; 47.   Some crocus's begin to open.
Hard rain, rain, grey,
sun.

Tuesday 26.
29 6/10½; 37; W, S.
White frost, grey &
mild, rain.

Wednesday 27.
29 2/10; 40; W.   Much rain & wind in the night.
Sun & wind, bright.

Thursday 28.
28 8/10½; SW.
Driving rain, wind,
showers, wind.

Friday 29.
28 9/10¾; 39; W; 11.
Frost, sun, sleet, wind,
bright.

Saturday 30.
29 4/10; 39; NW; 8.
Sun, bright.
Full moon.

Sunday 31.
29 3/10½; 45; NW; 5.   Rain in January – 1 inch. 99 hund.
Wet, sun & clouds.

FEBRUARY 1790

Monday 1.
29 8/10; 44; NW.
Grey, sun, pleasant.

A fine young hog salted & tubbed: weight 7 scores, & 18 pounds.

Tuesday 2.
29 9/10; 44; SW.
Grey, mild, & pleasant.

Wednesday 3.
30 1/10; 40; SW.
Grey, still, mild &
dark.

Wet mist; rain-bow.

Thursday 4.
30 3/10; 44; SW.
Dark, mild, & still.

Red breast, wren, & hedge-sparrow sing; the two former the
winter thro'.

Friday 5.
30 2/10; 45; SW.
Dark, still, & mild.

The missel-thrush, or storm-cock sings on the great oak in the
meadow.

Saturday 6.
30 1/10½; W.
Sun, summer-like.

The great titmouse, or sit ye down, sings.
One crocus is blown-out. Insects abound in the air: bees gather
much on the snow-drops, & winter-aconites. Gossamer is seen,
streaming from the boughs of trees.

Sunday 7.
30; 40, 40; SW.
Dark & still, dark &
cold.

Paths dry, & pleasant.

Monday 8.
29 8/10; 37; NW.
Dark, & still.

Made a seedling cucumber-bed.
Planted two rows of beans.

Tuesday 9.
29 7/10; 42; SW.
Grey, sun, grey.

Men dig their hop-gardens.

Wednesday 10.
29 9/10; 43; E.
Wet mist, dark & still.

Men work in their gardens.
Bull-finches pick the buds of damson-trees.

Thursday 11.
29 9/10; 45; W; 11.
Rain, sun, grey, bright.

Three gallons of best french brandy from London.
Crocus's blow.

Friday 12.
29 9/10; 48; W.
Sun, strong gale.

Sowed cucumber-seeds in the hot-bed; green prickly cucumbers, a good sort.

Saturday 13.
29 9/10½; 43; SW.
Fog, sun, dark.

Sunday 14.
29 7/10; 46; SW.
Dark & still.

Monday 15.
29 8/10; 31; SW.
Ice, sun, pleasant.

Tuesday 16.
29 7/10; S, W; 10.
Wet, rain, fair.

Wednesday 17.
30; 40; SW.
Frost, ice, sun, bright.

Thursday 18.
30 1/10; S.
Frost, sun, bright.

Potted the cucumber-plants, & sowed more seeds.

Friday 19.
30 ½/10; S, SE.
Frost, bright, red even.

The moon & Venus in the S.W. & Jupiter & Mars in the E. make nightly a charming appearance.

Saturday 20.
30 ½/10; 31, 35; E.
Frost, vast white dew,
hot sun, red even.

Brimstone buttery-fly, *papilio rhamni*, appears.

Sunday 21.
29 9/10½; 30; E.
Frost, ice, prodigious
white dew, bright, dew,
red even.

As the Surveyor of the Gosport turnpike was mending the road in Rumsdean bottom, he found several Roman coins, one of which was silver. Hence we may conclude that the remarkable entrenchments in that valley, whatever use may have been made of them since, were originally Roman. There is a tradition that they were frequently occupied during the grand rebellion in the time of Charles the first, a period in which many skirmishes happened in these parts, as at Cherriton, Alton, &c. These trenches must have been a post of consequence, because they are on a great road, & between large sloping woods. At the S:W. end of this valley, towards Filmer-hill, in a place called Feather-bed-lane, are three large contiguous barrows, which seem to indicate, that near the spot some considerable battle must have been fought in former times.

Monday 22.
29 7/10½; 31; E.
Frost, ice, sun, cloudy,
rain.

Viper appears.

Tuesday 23.
29 7/10½; 50; S, NW;
12. Soft, gleams,
spring-like.

Wednesday 24.
29 8/10; 49; SW.
Fog, mild, wet.

Sowed radishes, & some broad beans.
Dr Chandler came.

Thursday 25.
29 8/10½; 50; SW.
Warm, & showery.

Cabbage sprouts come in.
Both the pullets of last summer lay.

Friday 26.
29 8/10; SW, W; 16.
Blowing, but mild.

Crocus's begin to make a show.

Saturday 27.
29 9/10½; 39; W.
Sun, sharp wind.

Daffodils begin to open.
Dr Chandler left us.

Sunday 28.
29 9/10; SW.
Sun, dark & harsh.

Violets abound.
The rain in Feb: was – 0 inch. 49 hund.

MARCH 1790

Monday 1.
30; N, W.
Grey, mild, still.

Made a hand-glass celeri-bed, & sowed it in part with seed from
the parsonage-garden.
Men sow their fields.

Tuesday 2.
30; 51; N, W.
Sun, grey, & warm.

Carted-in five loads of hot dung for the cucumber-bed. Sowed the
meadow with ashes; of my own 22 bushels; bought 39: total 61.

Wednesday 3.
30; 50; N, W.
Sun, & clouds,
summer-like.

Cabbage-sprouts very fine. Apricot & peach blossoms begin to
open. Male yew-tree sheds its farina.
Sheep turned into the wheat.

Thursday 4.
29 9/10; N, NW.

Timothy the tortoise comes forth: he does not usually appear 'till

Cold dew, cloudless,
red even.

the middle of April.

Friday 5.
30; N, NE.
Fog, cloudless, red
even.

The tortoise does not appear.
The trufle-man still follows his occupation; when the season is
over, I know not.

Saturday 6.
30 ½/10; 29; NE, N.
Frost, ice, sun &
clouds, dark.

Ficaria verna.
A couple & an half of wood-cocks, & several pheasants were seen
in Hartley wood.

Sunday 7.
30 ½/10; 48; E.
Dark & harsh.

On the dark, still, dry, warm weather occasionally happening in
the winter-months.

Th'imprison'd winds slumber within their caves
Fast-bound: the fickle vane, emblem of change,
Wavers no more, long-settling to a point.
　　All nature nodding seems compos'd: thick steams
From land, from flood up drawn, dimming the day,
"Like a dark ceiling stand": slow thro' the air
Gossamer floats, or stretch'd from blade to blade
The wavy net-work whitens all the field.
　　Push'd by the weightier atmosphere, up springs
The ponderous Mercury, from scale to scale
Mounting, amidst the Torricillian tube.*¶
　　While high in air, & pois'd upon his wings
Unseen, the soft, enamour'd Wood-lark runs
Thro' all his maze of melody; — the brake
Loud with the black-bird's bolder note resounds.
　　Sooth'd by the genial warmth the cawing rook
Anticipates the spring, selects her mate,
Haunts her tall nest-trees, & with sedulous care
Repairs her wicker eyrie, tempest-torn.
　　The plough-man inly smiles to see up turn
His mellow glebe, best pledge of future crop:
With glee the gardener eyes his smoking beds:
E'en pining sickness feels a short relief.
　　The happy school-boy brings transported forth
His long-forgotten scourge, & giddy gig:
O'er the white paths he whirls the rolling hoop,
Or triumphs in the dusty fields of taw.
　　Not so the museful Sage: — abroad he walks
Contemplative, if haply he may find
What cause controls the tempest's rage, or whence
Amidst the savage season Winter smiles.

---

*The barometer.

> For days, for weeks prevails the placid calm.
>   At length some drops prelude a change: the sun
> With ray refracted bursts the parting gloom;
> When all the chequer'd sky is one bright glare.
>   Mutters the wind at eve: th'horison round
> With angry aspect scowls: down rush the showers,
> And float the delug'd paths, & miry fields.
>
>   For this subject see Derham's *Physico-theology*,
>   book 1ˢᵗ chap: 3ʳᵈ note 1ˢᵗ

Monday 8.
30; 44; E, SE.
Dark, sun, red even.

The wheat in the N. field looks well: there has been no good crop since the year 1780.
A N. *aurora*.

Tuesday 9.
29 7/10½; 46; SW.
Sun, wind, dark.

Apricot blows: the quantity of bloom will be small.

Wednesday 10.
29 6/10½; 47; W; 11.
Sun, blowing.

Shower in the night.
About this time Charles Etty sailed for Bengal direct, as second mate to the *Carl Fitzwilliam* Indiaman: Dundas captain.

Thursday 11.
29 9/10½; 47; SW.
White frost, sun, grey, rain.

Turned the hot-bed dung. Several hundreds of field-fares on the hill: they probably congregate in order to migrate together.

Friday 12.
30; 52; SW; 4.
Wet fog, gleams, fog.

Black snails come out.
Prim-roses blow.

Saturday 13.
30 1/10¼; 52; SW.
Grey & mild, gleams, dark, shower.

Planted curran-trees. The garden hoed, & cleaned.

Sunday 14.
30 1/10½; SW, NW; 9.
White frost, sun, pleasant.

About this time Ned White is to sail for Antegoa in the *Lady Jane Halliday*: Ross, Captain.

Monday 15.
30 2/10⅓; 36; N, NE.
Cold dew, sun, clouds, dry & harsh.

A vast snake¶ appears at the hot-beds.

Tuesday 16.
30 2/10; 31; NE.
Frost, ice, cloudless.

Dog's toothed violets blow.

Wednesday 17.
30 2/10¼; 30 ½/10;
NE.
White frost, ice,
cloudless, red even.

Timothy the tortoise lies very close in the hedge.

Thursday 18.
30 1/10½; 35; NE.
Frost, fog, harsh, red
even.

Turned the dung for the cucumber-bed a second time.

Friday 19.
30; 40; NE.
Dark & harsh, sun, red
even.

Finished weeding & cleaning the quarters & borders of the
garden.
Winter-aconites & snow-drops gone.

Saturday 20.
30; 35; NE.
Frost, cloudless, red
even.

Cucumber-plants thrive, & throw out side-wood.

That noise in the air of some thing passing¶ quick over our heads
after it becomes dark, & which we found last year proceeded from
the Stone-curlew, has now been heard for a week or more. Hence
it is plain that these birds, which undoubtedly leave us for the
winter, return in mild seasons very soon in the spring; & are the
earliest summer birds that we have noticed. They seem always to
go down from the uplands towards the brooks, & meads.
    The next early summer bird that we have remarked is the
smallest Willow-wren, or chif-chaf: it utters two sharp, piercing
notes, so loud in hollow woods as to occasion an echo, & is usually
first heard about the 20th of March.

Sunday 21.
30; NE.
Cold dew, cloudless,
sharp air, red even.

Bombylius medius, a hairy fly, with a long projecting snout,
appears: they are seen chiefly in Mar. & April.
"*Os rostro porrecto, setaceo, longissimo, bivalvi.*"¶ A dipterous
insect, which sucks it's aliment from blossoms.

On the 21st of March a single bank, or sand-martin was seen
hovering & playing round the sand-pit at short heath, where in the
summer they abound. I have often suspected that S. martins are
the most early among the hirundines.¶

Monday 22.
29 6/10; 30; NE, SE.
Frost, ice, sun, mare's
tails.

Made the bearing cucumber-bed: watered the dung, which was
very dry.
The well sinks very much.

Tuesday 23.
29 5/10½; 40; SE, S.
Dark, soft rain, wet &
warm.

Polyanths make a fine show.

Wednesday 24.
29 4/10¾; 53; S, SW;
18.
Dark & wet, sun.

The new-made cucumber-bed gets very warm.

Thursday 25.
29 7/10; 49, 52, @.
Fog, soft, sun, grey &
mild.

Chaffinches pull-off the flowers of the finest polyanths. The
cucumber-bed very hot.
The smallest willow-wren, or chif-chaf is heard.

Ned White sailed on this day.

Friday 26.
29 6/10½; 52; E.
Grey, sun, mild.

Hedge-sparrow has eggs. Began to mow the grass-walks: planted
out lettuces that have stood the winter, & seedling polyanths.

Saturday 27.
29 6/10; 42; E.
Fog, harsh, sun, harsh.

A heavy shower near Farnham.

Sunday 28.
29 6/10; E; 3.
Wet fog, sun & blue
mist, wind cold.

Small birds, Tanner says green finches, pull off my polyanth
blossoms by handfulls.

A neighbour complained to me that her house was over-run with a
kind of black beetle,¶ or as she expressed herself, with a kind of
black-bob, which swarmed in her kitchen when they get up in a
morning before day break.

Soon after this account I observed an unusual insect in one of
my dark chimney-closets; & find since, that in the night they
swarm also in my kitchen. On examination I soon ascertained the
Species to be the *Blatta Orientalis* of Linnaeus, & the *Blatta
molendinaria* of Mouffet. The male is winged, the female is not;
but shows some what like the rudiments of wings, as if in the pupa
state.

These insects belonged originally to the warmer parts of
America, & were conveyed from thence by shipping to the East
Indies; & by means of commerce begin to prevail in the more N.
parts of Europe, as Russia, Sweden, &c. How long they have
abounded in England I cannot say; but have never observed them
in my house till lately. They love warmth, & haunt chimney-
closets, & the backs of ovens. Poda says, that these, & house-
crickets will not associate together: but he is mistaken in that
assertion, as Linn. suspected he was. They are altogether night-
insects, *lucifugae*, never coming forth till the rooms are dark, &

still: & escaping away very nimbly at the approach of a candle. Their antennae are remarkably long, slender, & flexile.

When h. crickets are out, & running about in a room in the night, if surprized by a candle they give two or three shrill notes, as it were for a signal to their fellows, that they may escape to their crannier & lurking holes to avoid danger.

Monday 29.
29 6/10¼; 36; NE.
Fog, dark & still, haze.

Timothy still keeps close.
In open places the air is sharp.

Tuesday 30.
29 6/10¼; NE.
Fog, grey, sun, haze.
Full moon.

Took-off the cucumber-frames, & shaped the bed, & put-on the mould.
Two Swallows seen on the hill.

Wednesday 31.
29 5/10¾; 51; NE.
Bright, cloudless, red even.

Wall-cherry begins to blow.
Rain in March – 0 inch. 45 hund.

APRIL 1790

Thursday 1.
29 7/10¼; 34; NE.
Frost, cloudless, red even.

Sharp, & biting wind.
Some crude oranges were put in a hot cupboard in order that the heat might mellow them, & render them better flavoured: but the crickets got to them, & gnawing holes thro' the rind, sucked out all the juice, & devoured the pulp.

Friday 2.
29 9/10½; 31; NE.
Ice, sun, sharp, & cutting.

Saturday 3.
29 8/10½; NE.
Sharp frost, ice!!
cloudless.

Nightingale heard in honey-lane.

"The Nightingall, that chaunteth all the springe,
Whose warblinge notes throughout the wooddes are harde,
Being kepte in cage, she ceaseth for to singe,
And mourns, because her libertie is barde."
         Geffrey Whitney's *Emblemes*: ¶ 1586. p. 81

Sunday 4.
29 8/10½; 41; NE.
Sun, cloudless, red even.

Wry-neck pipes in my outlet.
Sharp, cutting wind! Heath-fire in the forest makes a great smoke.

Monday 5.
29 8/10½; NE.
Frost, sun & clouds, sharp wind.

ALTON
Transplanted the cucumber plants in to the bearing bed.

Tuesday 6.
NE.
Sun & sharp wind.

READING
Young goslings on commons.

Wednesday 7.
NE.
Harsh & very dusty.

OXFORD
Thames very full, & beautiful, after so much dry weather: wheat
looks well; meadows dry, & scorched. Roads very dusty.

Thursday 8.
E.
Sun, harsh.

Friday 9.
E, NE.
Dark & harsh, flights
of snow.

Much rain at Selborne, 92.

Saturday 10.
29 1/10, 29; NE; 92.
Black & cold.

Rain in the night. Rain.
Ground wet.

Sunday 11.
29; 34; NE.
Dark & harsh.

Deep snow at Selborne: five inches deep!

Monday 12.
Dark & wet.

READING
Great bloom of plums.
Swallows over Oakhanger ponds.

Tuesday 13.
NE.
Harsh, wet, much
snow.

ALTON

Wednesday 14.
29 5/10; NW, NE; 83,
31.
Clouds, hail, sun,
bright.

SELBORNE
Red start appears. Snow lies deep in the lanes. First swallow seen
at Fyfield.

Thursday 15.
29 1/10½; 31; E, SW,
N; 55, 11.
Heavy snow, rain, swift
thaw.

Snow covers the ground. Sharp air.

Friday 16.
29 5/10½; 45; N.
Grey, cold, gleams.

Snow lies under hedges.

Saturday 17.
29 6/10½; 34; N.
White frost, sun &
gleams.

Fly-catcher, & Black-cap appear.

Red starts, Fly-catchers, & Black-caps arrive. If these little delicate beings are birds of passage (as we have reason to suppose they are, because they are never seen in the winter) how could they, feeble as they seem, bear up against such storms of snow & rain, & make their way thro' such meteorous turbulencies, as one should suppose would embarrass & retard the most hardy & resolute of the winged nation? Yet they keep their appointed times & seasons, & in spite of frosts & winds return to their stations periodically as if they had met with nothing to obstruct them. The withdrawing & appearance of the short-winged summer-birds is a very puzzling circumstance in natural History!

Sunday 18.
29 6/10½; 34; E.
Frost, sun & clouds.

Cutting wind.

Monday 19.
29 6/10; 31½; E, N.
Frost, ice, sun &
clouds.

Sowed carrots, parsnips, onions, radishes, & lettuces: made an other celeri-bed for an hand-glass.

Tuesday 20.
29 9/10; 34; E, S.
Sun, & clouds, harsh.

Set the old Bantam speckled Hen with eleven eggs. My cook-maid desired there might be an odd egg for good luck:
. . . numero Deus impare gaudet.¶

Wednesday 21.
29 8/10; S, SE, S.
Grey, dark, wet.

Thursday 22.
29 4/10; 43; S, SW.
Sun, mild, dark.

Two swifts seen at Fyfield.
Some swallows about the village. Men pole hops.

Friday 23.
29 3/10½; 50; SW.
Wet, sun, clouds.

Two House martins appear. Planted 20 rows of potatoes. Spring-like.

A boy has taken three little young Squirrels in their nest, or drey as it is called in these parts. These small creatures he put under the care of a cat who had lately lost her kittens, & finds that she nurses & suckles them with the same assiduity, & affection as if they we[re] her own offspring. This circumstance again corroborates my suspicion, that the mention of deserted & exposed children being nurtured by female beasts of prey who had lost their young, may not be so improbable an incident as many have supposed: – & therefore may be a justification of those authors who have

gravely mentioned what some have deemed to be a wild &
improbable story.

For a leveret nursed by a cat see my *Nat: History* p. 214. I have
said, "that it is not one whit more marvellous that Romulus, &
Remus, in their infant & exposed state, should be nursed by a she
wolf, than that a poor little suckling leveret should be fostered &
cherished by a bloody grimalkin."

So many people went to see the little squirrels suckled by a cat,
that the foster mother became jealous of her charge, & in pain for
their safety; & therefore hid them over the ceiling, where one dyed.
This circumstance shews her affection for these foundlings, & that
she supposes the squirrels to be her own young. Thus hens, when
they have hatched ducklings, are equally attached to them as if
they were their own chickens.

Saturday 24.
29 2/10½; 44; SW;
39.
Sun, hail, thunder,
rain.

Planted potatoes & beans in the meadow-garden.
Much thunder & hail at Alton.
The *cuckoo* is heard in the hanger. The tortoise appears again.
Shell-snails come forth.

Sunday 25.
29 3/10; W.
Sun, showers, & hail,
sun.

Tortoise out.

Monday 26.
29 5/10; 52; N; 22.
Showers, gleams,
showers.

Sowed cucumber-seeds in the frames: the plants do not thrive.

Tuesday 27.
29 7/10; 52; N; 19.
Early shower, sun &
clouds, pleasant, red
even.

A nightingale is heard in my outlet.

Wednesday 28.
29 6/10¼; 36; E, S.
Sun & frost, clouds,
grey.
Full moon. Total
eclipse.

Thursday 29.
29 3/10; 52; SW, S;
12.
Rain, rain, dark &
moist.

Doctor Chandler, & Lady came to the parsonage house.¶

Friday 30.
29 3/10; 43; SW, S.
Sun, clouds, pleasant.

Rain & snow in April – 3 inch. 64 hund.

Laburnum tunnel.
WaRes

MAY 1790

Saturday 1.
29 1/10; 52; SE, E.
Dark & wet, rain.

Wall-fruit cut-off.

Sunday 2.
29 3/10½; 59; SW, S;
37.
Sun, pleasant, bright.

Rain in the night.
Much cherry, & pear-bloom.

Monday 3.
29 6/10; 59; N.
Sun, summer, red
even.

House-martins frequent their nests.
Swift appears. Fern-owl, or eve-jar chatters.

Tuesday 4.
29 6/10½; 59; SW.
Wh. frost, sun,
pleasant.

Sowed more cucumber-seeds in the frames.
Some cucumbers swell. Grass grows.
Timothy the tortoise begins to eat.
Some trees in the hanger begin to shew leaves.

Wednesday 5.
29 5/10¼; 53½; W,
NW.
Showers, showers,
clouds.

Thursday 6.
29 3/10½; 52; NW, NE; 36.
Showers, showers, clouds.

Rain in the night.
Mrs Chandler brought to bed of a daughter at the parsonage-house.

Friday 7.
29 4/10; 56; SE, SW; 16.
Grey, sun, warm.

Showers in the night. Planted-out Polyanths sown last year.
Wall-flowers very fine: marked the double ones.
Great showers to the N.E.
Marked the best polyanths for seed.

Saturday 8.
29 5/10; 54; NE, N.
Mist, sun, pleasant.

Began to mow the orchard for the horses.

Sunday 9.
29 6/10½; 60; N.
Fog, sun, showers.

Master Trimming is taken with the small-pox.
No swifts round the church yet: they are very late!
Timothy the tortoise eats dandelion leaves, & stalks: he swallows his food almost whole.

Monday 10.
29 6/10¾; N.
Mist, rain, gleams.

The Bantam hen hatches seven chickens.
Young red breasts.
Made some tarts with the stalks of the leaves of the garden, or Monks rhubarb.
Only three swifts: one was found dead in the church-yard.

Tuesday 11.
29 7/10½; N; 37.
Showers, mist, sun.

Opened & slipped-out the artichokes, & planted the places where they had failed. Made annual bed: lined cucumber-bed.

Wednesday 12.
29 8/10; 60; NE.
Sun, steady gale.

Cut a few asparagus: cut a brace of cucumbers.
The rhubarb-tart good, & well-flavoured.
Five swifts. Seven swifts.

Thursday 13.
29 7/10½; 59; NE.
Cloudless, stiff gale, red even.

Bro. Tho. came from London.

Friday 14.
29 7/10; 62; NE.
Cloudless, gale, red even.

Eleven swifts.

Saturday 15.
29 6/10; 57; NE, SW.
Vast dew, sun, summer.

Timothy the tortoise weighs 6 pd. 12 oz. 14 drs.

Sunday 16.
29 4/10¼; 65; SW.
Sun, hot, fine even.

Mʳˢ Edmund White brought to bed of a boy, who has encreased the number of my nephews & Nieces to 56.

Monday 17.
29 4/10½; 59; SW;
30.
Rain in the night,
showers, strong gales,
sun, & clouds.

One polyanth-stalk produced 47 pips or blossoms.

The bloom of apples is great: the white pippin, as usual, very full. It is a most useful tree, & always bears fruit. The dearling in the meadow is loaded with bloom: last year it produced only one peck of apples, the year before 14 bushels. This year it bore 10 bush. of small fruit.

The white pippin produced a good crop again this year: the apples of this tree come in for scalding, & pies in August.

Tuesday 18.
29 5/10; S.
Cold dew, sun &
clouds, cool air.

Cut three brace of cucumbers. Sowed the large three-light frame with sundry annuals.

Wednesday 19.
29 4/10; 57; S.
Sun, clouds, rain,
gleam.

Planted two rows of scarlet kidney-beans.
Made an hand-glass hot bed with two barrows of dung.

Thursday 20.
29 5/10¼; 56; SW;
20, 33.
Sun, showers & hail.

Friday 21.
29 6/10; SW.
Sun, shower, dark &
moist.

Saturday 22.
29 4/10¼; 56; S.
Sun, rain, rain, fog.

Sowed green & white cucumbers under a hand-glass. Monks rhubarb in full bloom.

Sunday 23.
29 5/10; 57; S.
Dark, sun, pleasant.

The dark & moist season turns the wheat yellow.

Monday 24.
29 4/10; 57; SE, S; 59.
Dark, sun, fog.

Thunder, & heavy rain. Much verdure: grass grows.

Tuesday 25.
29 5/10¼; 56; N, E;
27.
Rain, dark, moist,
close.

Sowed a specimen of some uncommon clover from farmer Street.
Sowed a pint of large kidney beans, white: also Savoys, Coss lettuces, & bore cole.

Wednesday 26.
29 7/10; 59; E; 13.
Rain in the night, dark, sun.

Sowed ferruginous fox-gloves. Cut several fine cucumbers, four brace.

Thursday 27.
29 6/10; 54; N, E; 12.
Dark, warm, frequent showers, gleam, warm.

House-martins now begin to build in earnest: there are many this year.
Thunder damage done in London.
Near 20 swifts.

Friday 28.
29 6/10; 67; E, S, NE; 16, 47.
Sun & clouds, vast clouds, thunder & rain.

Rain in the night.
Haw-thorn blows.
Heavy rain.

Saturday 29.
29 7/10; 62; S.
Dark, gleams.

Cut three brace of fine cucumbers.

Sunday 30.
29 6/10½; 60; S.
Dark, rain, wet, dark.

Serapias longifolia blossoms: a fine plant.

Monday 31.
29 7/10½; 55; N, NE; 55.
Showers, sun, showers.

Bottled-out the port-wine which came here in October, but did not get fine. Thunder.
Rain in May – 4 inch. 38 hund.

JUNE 1790

Tuesday 1.
29 7/10½; 57; S.
Fog, sun, pleasant.

House-martins wash.
Fiery lilies blow.
My horses begin to lie out.

John Carpenter brings home from the Plasket at Rotherfield some old chestnut trees which are very long. In several places the woodpeckers had began to bore them. The timber & bark of these trees are so very like oak, as might easily deceive an indifferent observer; but the wood is very shakey, & towards the heart cup-shakey, that is to say, apt to separate in serried pieces like cups, so that the inward parts are of no use. They were bought for the purpose of cooperage, but must make but ordinary barrels, buckets, &c. ¶ Chestnut sells for half the price of oak; but has some times been sent into the King's docks, & passed off instead of oak.

Wednesday 2.
29 8/10; N.
Great dew, sun, warm
& pleasant.

Made second hand-glass bed.

Thursday 3.
29 7/10; 63; W.
Sun, shower, sun.

Honey-suckles are beautiful, & fragrant.
Sowed cucumbers. Planted-out four rows of celeri, very fine.

Friday 4.
29 8/10; 60; NW.
Sun & clouds, gale,
sweet even.

Began to cut summer-cabbage.
Ophrys nidus avis, & *ophrys apifera* blossom.

After ewes & lambs are shorn, there is great confusion & bleating,

Saturday 5.
29 8/10; 54; W.
White frost, sun, &
gale.

neither the dams nor their young being able to distinguish each
other as before. This embarrassment seems to arise not so much
from the loss of the fleece, which doubtless does occasion an
alteration in their appearance, as from the defect of that *"notus
odor,"* that familiar & well-known smell, discriminating each

Sunday 6.
29 7/10; SW.
Sun & clouds, shower.

individual personally; which is also confounded by the strong scent
of the pitch & tar where with they have been newly marked. For
the brute creation recognize each other more from smell than sight,
& in matters of identity & diversity appeal more to their noses than
their eyes. Thus dogs smell to persons they meet, when they want
to be informed whether they are strangers or not.
      After sheep have been washed, there is the same confusion, for
the reason given above.

Monday 7.
SW.
Sun, & clouds.

LONDON
Went to London by Guildford, & Epsom.
Spring-corn, & grass look well. Hay making near town. Rain
15.

Tuesday 8.
SW.

Wednesday 9.
S.
Clouds, rain in the
night, & gale.

Thursday 10.
S, NW.
Sun, shower.

Heavy shower. Rain 21.

Friday 11.
NW.
Sun, sun & wind.

Saturday 12.
N.
Sun, sun.

SOUTH LAMBETH
Cauliflowers abound. Pease sold for ten pence the peck.

Sunday 13.
30 2/10½; N, NE.
Sun, cool air, chilly.

Artichokes, & chardons come into eating.
Cucumbers abound.

Monday 14.
30 2/10; S, SW.
Sun, gloomy & hot.

Sweet hay-making weather.
My Brother begins to make his rick.
Melons swell.

Tuesday 15.
30 2/10½; NE.
Gloomy & hot.

No wall-fruit, plums, cherries, or apples.

Wednesday 16.
30 2/10; E.
Wet, dark & still.

My Brother finishes a large rick of hay in very nice order.
Scarlet lychnis blows. Vines are backward.

Thursday 17.
30 2/10; E.
Dark, cool wind, dark,
rain.

Strawberries are cried about, but they have little or no flavour.
Thunder to the S. & S.E. rain 6.

Friday 18.
29 9/10; SW, S.
Sun, dark & louring,
gale.

Saturday 19.
30 ½/10; S.
Sun & clouds, gale.

Sunday 20.
30 2/10; 70; S.
Sun, summer, gale,
sweet even.

Muck laid on a gardener's field poisons my Brother's outlet.

A martin at Stockwell chapel has built it's nest against the window:
it seems to stick firmly to the glass, & has no other support. In
former summers I remember similar instances.

Monday 21.
30 3/10; 69; 75; SW,
SW.
Sun & clouds, sultry,
red even, sweet
moonshine.

The longest day . . .
"The longest daye in time resignes to nighte;
The greatest oke in time to duste doth turne;
The Raven dies; the Egle failes of flighte;
The Phoenix rare in time herselfe doth burne;

The princelie stagge at lengthe his race doth ronne;
And all must ende that ever was begonne."
Geffrey Whitney's *Emblemes*:¶
p. 230   1586.

Scarlet straw-berries good.
A small praecox melon.

Tuesday 22.
30 1/10½; 74, 80; E,
SE.
Sun, sultry! golden
even.

Thermometer at Mᵣ Alexander's – 87 on a N. wall: a S. wall
near. Fruit-walls in the sun are so hot that I cannot bear my hand
on them. Broᵗ Tho. thermᵣ was 89 on an E. wall in the afternoon.

**Much damage was done, & some persons killed by lightening on
this sultry day.**
   My Broᵗ Thoˢ's thermᵣ in Blackfriars road against an eastern wall
in the afternoon was 89. My thermᵣ after the sun got round upon it,
was 100: Thomas forgot to look in time.

Wednesday 23.
29 9/10, 7/10½; 76;
W.
Clouds & gleams,
louring, gale. Sweet
moonshine.

Vines blossom.

Rosa mundi growing
with feverfew. Wakes.

Thursday 24.
64; W.
Sun & gale, shower.

Long-pod
beans come in.

Friday 25.
64; SW.
Sun, gale, showers,
cool.

Elder blossoms.

Saturday 26.
29 8/10½; W, NW;
13.
Sun, showers.

Sunday 27.
29 9/10¾; NW.
Sun, showers, shower.

Roses make a beautiful show. Orange-lillies blossom. Sᵣ George
Wheeler's tutsan blows.

Monday 28.
30; SW.
Sun & clouds, fine
even.

Shower in the night. Rain at S. Lambeth – 22.
Began to cut my meadow-grass.

Tuesday 29.
29 9/10¾; 63; E.

LONDON
Scarabaeus solstitialis: Solstitial chafers begin to fly in my

Haze.

Wednesday 30.
S. Sun, rain, rain.

Brother's outlet.

Rain at Selborne in June – 0 inc. 13 hund.

JULY 1790

Thursday 1.
S; 25.
Sun, & clouds.

S. LAMBETH

Friday 2.
W; 27.
Sun, clouds, heavy
showers.

ALTON
Thunder. Two heavy showers at Guildford with thunder.

Saturday 3.
29 3/10; W.
Sun, & clouds.

SELBORNE
My hay made into small cocks.
Young swallows come out, & are fed on the wing.
Wood straw-berries ripen.

Sunday 4.
29 1/10½; 61; S.
Dark, wet, wet.

My vines are nicely trimmed, & tacked; the quantity of blooms
seems to be but small.

July 4. The woman who brought me two fern-owls eggs last year
on July 14 on this day produced me two more, one of which has
been laid this morning, as appears plainly, because there was only
one in the nest the evening before. They were found, as last July,
on the verge of the down above the hermitage under a beechen
shrub on the naked ground. Last year those eggs were full of
young, & just ready to be hatched.

These circumstances point out the exact time when these curious
nocturnal, migratory birds lay their eggs, & hatch their young.
Fern owls, like snipes, stone-curlews, & some few other birds,
make no nest: Birds that build on the ground do not make much of
nests.

In my natural History, p. 274 I have said, "that Philosophers
have defined Instinct to be that secret influence by which every
species is impelled naturally to pursue, at all times, the same way
or track without any teaching or example; whereas Reason,
without instruction, would often vary, & do that by many
methods, which Instinct effects by one alone."

"Now this maxim must be taken in a qualifyed sense: for there
are instances in which instinct does vary, & conform to the
circumstances of place & convenience."¶

"thus the regular nest of the house-martin is hemispheric: but
where a rafter, or a joist, or a cornice may happen to obstruct, &

stand in the way, the nest is so contrived as to conform to the obstruction, & becomes flat, or oval, or compressed."

In confirmation of what has been advanced above, there are now two new martin's nests at Tim Turner's, which are tunnel-shaped, & nine or ten inches long, in conformity to the ledge of the wall of the eaves under which they are built.

Monday 5.
29, 29 1/10; 60; SW, N; 22, 51.
Showers, showers, heavy showers.

Priced out savoys, & borecole; sowed celeri.
Young martins peep out of their nests: there are many nests in the village.

Tuesday 6.
29 6/10½; 60; N.
Rain, wind, rain, cold wind.

Artichokes come in.
Turned the cocks of hay.

Wednesday 7.
29 8/10¼; 60; N.
Sun, sweet day, vast dew.

Grass-hopper lark whispers in my outlet.
Put my hay in large cock.

Thursday 8.
29 8/10; 63; W.
Sun, clouds, dark.

Ricked five jobs of hay.
Hops throw-out side shoots.

Friday 9.
29 5/10, 29 6/10; 62; SW, NW; 35, 7.
Rain, rain, sun & wind.

Gathered our first beans, long pods.
Planted-out annuals.

Runner beans

Saturday 10.
29 3/10½; SW.
Louring, gleams, clouds, rain.

Turned-out the cucumbers from under the hand-glasses; & took away the frames from the old beds, where there are young plants. Carted-in the two last jobs of hay, & finished the rick.

Sunday 11.
29 4/10; 59, 59; W.
Shower, heavy shower, shower.

Now the meadow is cleared the brood-swallows sweep the face of the ground all day long; & from over that smooth surface collect a variety of insects for the support of their young.

Monday 12.
29 3/10¼; 55; W; 29.
Showers & cold wind.

Planted-out more annuals.
Stopped some of the vine-shoots.

Tuesday 13.
29 1/10½; 59; S.

Wall-cherries are well flavoured: wood-strawberries do not ripen:

Sun, heavy showers, cold showers.

rasps begin to turn colour.

Wednesday 14.
29 3/10; 53; W; 9.
Sun, showers, cold wind.

Planted-out annuals; & many ten-weeks stocks.
Tempest, & much thunder to the N.W.

Neither cucumbers, nor kidney-beans, nor annuals thrive on account of the cold, blowing season. Timothy the tortoise is very dull, & spends most of his time under the shade of the vast, expanded leaves of the monk's rhubarb.

Thursday 15.
29 5/10¾; 55; W, SW.
Dark & cold, chill air.

Continual gales all thro' this month, which interrupt the cutting of my tall hedges.

Friday 16.
29 7/10½; 63; W.
Sun, summer weather.

Many young swallows out, & perching on the wall-nut tree.
A fly-catcher has a nest in my vines.
Young swallows settle on the grass-plots to catch insects.

Saturday 17.
29 8/10; 67; W.
Wet mist, grey & warm.

Scarlet lychnis's make a fine show.
Mʳ Churton came. Finishing cutting my hedges. White & orange lillies blow. A nightingale continues to sing; but his notes are short & interrupted, & attended with a chur.
Grass-hopper lark whispers.

Sunday 18.
29 7/10; 65; SW.
Dark, & warm.

Mʳˢ Clement & daughters came.

Monday 19.
29 7/10; 66; S.
Sun, warm, dark.

Finished stopping the vines. Several broods of house-martins are out: some grapes are set.

Tuesday 20.
29 4/10; SW, W; 26.
Wet & windy, gleams.

Rasps come in.
My flowers are much broken by the wind.

Wednesday 21.
29 6/10½; SW, W.
Wet & blowing, cold wind.

Annuals look as if they would die: cucumbers are hurt, & do not bear. Many hop-poles are blown down.

Thursday 22.
29 7/10; 61; SW.
Sun, dark & warm.

Dug some ground for celeri, & spinage.
A man brought me a young cuckoo, found in the nest of a water-wagtail among the rocks of the hollow lane leading to Rood. This bird was almost fledge.

Friday 23.
29 6/10½; 62; SW;
17.
Rain, sun, dark.

Some wheat is much lodged by the wind & rain.

There is reason to fear from the coldness & wetness of the season that the crop will not be good. Windy, wet, cold solstices are never favourable to wheat, because they interrupt the bloom, & shake it off before it has performed it's function.

Saturday 24.
29 7/10¼; 66; W.
Summer weather, sweet
even.

Trenched four rows of celeri, good streight plants.
Lime-trees in full bloom.
Large honey-dews on my great oak, that attract the bees, which swarm upon it.
The women & children bring quantities of strawberries from the high wood, & hanger. They do not ripen very well for want of sun.

Sunday 25.
29 8/10; 64; SW.
Dark & soft, gleam,
deep fog on the hanger.

*Lime trees are fragrant: the golden tassels are beautiful.

*Dr. Chandler tells us that in the south of France in infusion of the blossoms of the lime tree,¶ *tilia,* is in much esteem as a remedy for coughs, hoarsenesses, fevers, &c: & that at Nismes he saw an avenue of limes that was quite ravaged & torn to pieces by people greedily gathering the bloom, which they dryed & kept for their purposes.
   Upon the strength of this information we made some tea of lime-blossoms, & found it a very soft, well-flavoured, pleasant saccharine julep, in taste much resembling the juice of liquorice.

Monday 26.
29 7/10¾; 64; SW, S.
Dark, gleams.
Full moon.

Earthed-up the old cucumber-beds, which begin to bear again.
Rasps, goose-berries, currans, & wood-straw-berries abound.
Wheat begins to be reaped near Alresford.

Tuesday 27.
29 8/10; 69; W.
Grey, summer weather,
sweet even.

Honey-dews,¶ which make the planters in pain for their hops.
Several swifts course round, as if their young were out.
Hops are infested with aphides; look badly.

Wednesday 28.
29 7/10, 5/10; 72; E,
S.
Deep fog, sun, turbid
sunset.

Swallows repair their nests with a view to a second brood.
Children gather strawberries every morning from the hanger where the tall beeches were felled in winter 1788.

Thursday 29.
29 2/10½; 62; N,
NW.
Dark & cool, louring.

Some mushrooms, & funguses appear on the down.
Young house martins begin to hover round the tower.
Heavy showers around.
Mrs J. White made Rasp, & strawberry jam & red curran jelly, & preserved some cherries.

Friday 30.
29 3/10; 61; SW.
Sun, clouds, shower,
louring, shower, rain
all night.

Much hay housed.

Saturday 31.
29 3/10½; 62; SW,
W; 76.
Rain, sun, fine even.

Trenched-out three long rows of celeri in the melon ground:
planted out two rows of Savoys in the same place.
Rain in July – 3 inch. 24 hund.

Mr Marsham of Stratton near Norwich informs me by letter thus: –
"I became a planter early: so that an oak which I planted in 1720
is become now at one foot from the earth 12 ft. 6 inch. 0 in
circumference; & at 14 feet (the half of the timber length) is 8 ft.
2 inch. 0. So if the bark was to be measured as timber, the tree
gives 116 ½ F. buyer's measure. Perhaps you never heard of a
larger oak while the planter was living. I flatter myself that I
increased the growth by washing the stem, & digging a circle as far
as I supposed the roots to extend, & by spreading saw dust, &c. as
related in the *Phil. Trans*:¶ I wish I had begun with Beeches (my
favourite trees as well as your's) I might then have seen very large
trees of my own raising. But I did not begin with beech till 1741, &
then by seed: so that my largest is now at five feet from the ground
6 f. 3 inch.0 in girth, & with it's head spreads a circle of 20 yards
diameter. This tree was also dug round, washed, &c."
                                "Stratton: July 24. 1790."
    The circumference of trees in my outlet planted by myself, at
one foot from the ground.

	f.	inch.
Oak by alcove in 1730	4.	5
Ash by D^o in 1730	4	6½
Great fir, bakershill . 1751	5	0
Greatest beech . . 1751	4.	0
Elm 1750	5	3
Lime over at Mr Hale's		
planted by me in 1756	5	5
My single great oak in the		
meadow, age unknown	10	6½

The diameter of it's boughs three
ways is 24 yards, or 72 feet:
circumference of it's boughs 72 yards.
    Mr White's great single oak at Newton measures at one foot
above the ground 12 feet 6 inch: the exact dimension of that
belonging to, & planted by Mr Marsham. A vast tree must that be
at Stratton to have been planted by a person now living!!

AUGUST 1790

Sunday 1.
29 7/10; 61; W.
Sun, pleasant, cool.

Three swifts only seen.

Monday 2.
29 4/10½; 60; SW.
Rain, rain, rain.

Potatoes come in: codlins come.
No swifts.

Tuesday 3.
29 4/10; 60; SW; 28.
Showers, showers,
chilly.

Sowed a pint of prickly spinage seed to stand the winter on a rich
well-dunged cucumber-ridge.
Sowed brown lettuce to stand the winter.
No swifts. Mr Churton left us.

Wednesday 4.
29 6/10; 59; SW.
Sun, chilly & windy.

The wheat does not ripen.

Thursday 5.
29 6/10½; 60; SW.
Cold, dark & louring.

Hops blow. One swift.
Piled & housed all the cleft wood of 8 cords of beech: the
proportion of blocks was large.

Friday 6.
29 6/10; SW; 12.
Dark, wet, cold, &
blowing.

No swift. The fern-owl churs still; grass-hopper lark has been
silent some days.

Saturday 7.
29 6/10½; 61, 67;
SW.
Hot, sun, close.

Strawberries from the woods are over: the crop has been
prodigious.
Four swifts about the church: probably the last pair, & their
young. Eight or ten swifts were seen round the church.
Ants swarm from under the stairs.

On July 22. the decanter, into which the wine from a cool cellar
was poured, became clouded over with a thick condensation
standing in drops. This appearance, which is never to be seen but
in warm weather, is a curious phaenomenon, & exhibits matter for
speculation to the modern philosopher. A friend of mine enquires
whether the "*rorantia pocula*" of Tully in his "*de senectute*" had
any reference to such appearances. But there is great reason to
suppose that the ancients were not accurate philosophers enough to
pay much regard to such occurrences. They knew little of
pneumatics, or the laws whereby air is condensed, & rarifyed; &
much less that water is dissolved in air, & reducible therefrom by
cold. If they saw such dews on their statues, or metal utensils, they

looked on them as ominous, & were awed with a superstitious horror. Thus Virgil makes his weeping statues, & sweating brazen vessels prognostic of the violent death of Julius Caesar:

... *"maestum illacrymat templis ebur, aeraq sudant."*

Georgic 1st¶

The phaenomenon in question is finely explained by the following quotation. "If a bottle of wine be fetched out of a cool cellar in the hottest & driest weather in summer, it's surface will presently be covered with a thick vapour, which when tasted appears to be pure water. This watery vapour cannot proceed from any exudation of the wine thro' the pores of the bottle; for glass is impervious to water, & the bottle remains full, & when wiped dry is found to weigh as much as when taken out of the cellar. The same appearance is observable on the outside of a silver, or other vessel in which iced water is put in summer time; & it is certain, that the water which is condensed on the surface of the vessel does not proceed merely from the moisture exhaled by the breathing of the people in the room where this appearance is most generally noticed, because the same effect will take place, if the vessel be put in the open air."

Watson's chemical essays,
Vol. 3rd p. 92.

Sunday 8.
29 6/10; 65; S.
Gleams, clouds, gleams.

The fields of corn begin to turn colour.
Fern-owl chatters.

Monday 9.
29 7/10; NW.
Sun, gales, red even.

Men hack pease.
Apricots begin to ripen: we have not a dozen.

Tuesday 10.
29 7/10½; NW.
Sun, summer.

A labourer has mown out in the precincts of Hartley-wood, during the course of this summer, as many pheasants nests as contained 60 eggs!
Bro. Thomas White came.

Wednesday 11.
29 7/10¾; 69; E, S.
Sun, great dew, summer.

The winter spinage comes up well.
Scarlet martagons blow. Ants swarm on the stairs.

Thursday 12.
29 7/10; 72; SE.
Sun, dark & hot.

Wheat-harvest begins in several parts of the parish.
Young martins congregate on trees.
Sister Barker, & Nieces Mary, & Eliz: came.

Friday 13.
29 7/10; NW, SE.

Men house pease.

Bright, grey & warm.   Cucumbers begin to bear.

Saturday 14.
29 7/10; NW, NE.   Young hirundines cluster on trees.
Cloudless, sweet harvest   Harvest-bugs bite the ladies.¶
weather.

Sunday 15.
29 5/10½; 60, 69; SE.   The last gathering of wood-straw-berries.
Sun, clouds, louring.   Bullfinches & redbreasts eat the berries of honeysuckles.

Monday 16.
29 6/10; 72; SW.   Cut 43 cucumbers.
Wet, dark & warm.   Wheat is binding.

Blackstonia perfoliata, yellow centory, blossoms, on the right
hand bank up the North field hill. The *Gentiana perfoliata
Linnaei*. It is to be found in the marl-dell half way along the N.
field lane on the left; on the dry bank of a narrow field between the
N. field hill, & the Fore down; & on the banks of the Foredown.

Tuesday 17.
29 7/10; 66; NW.   Women glean.
Sun, dark & louring,
sprinkling.

Wednesday 18.
29 7/10½; 66; NW, S.   Scarlet kidney-
Sun, sweet harvest.   beans come in.

Blackstonia perfoliata.
Nore Hill.

Thursday 19.
29 7/10; 66; SW.   Wheat housed.
Grey, louring, wet.

M⁼ˢ Barker, & her daughters Mary & Elizabeth, & M⁼ˢ Chandler, &
her infant daughter, & nurse maid, went all in a cart to see the
great oak in the Holt, which is deemed by M⁼ Marsham of Stratton
in Norfolk to be the biggest in this Island. Bro. Tho. & D⁼ Chandler
rode on horse-back. They all dined under the shade of this tree. At
7 feet from the ground it measures in circumference 34 feet: has in
old times lost several boughs, & is tending towards decay. M⁼

Marsham computes that at 14 feet length this oak contains 1000 feet of timber.

Friday 20.
29 6/10½; 66, 69; SE, S.
Close & hot, sun, sultry, sweet even, partial fogs.

Some swifts seen at Lyndon in the county of Rutland.

Aug: 20. On this day farmer Spencer built a large wheat-rick near his house, the contents of which all came from a field near West-croft barn at the full distance of a mile. Five waggons were going all day.

Saturday 21.
29 4/10, 5/10; 72; S, W.
Sun, & gale, warm.

Hops grow white. Pease & wheat housed.
Showers about.

Sunday 22.
29 7/10¼; 55, 65; W, S.
Sun, cool gale, cool.

There is a covey of partridges in the North field, seventeen in number.

Monday 23.
29 7/10; S, W; 8.
Blowing & wet, bright & cool.

Cut sixty cucumbers. John Hale made a large wheat-rick on a staddle.¶
Hops improve & begin to whiten. Dew on windows.

Tuesday 24.
29 6/10½; 60; W.
Grey & cool, cloudless, chill air.
Full moon.

Colchicum autumnale begins to blossom.

Wednesday 25.
29 2/10¾; SE, E; 156.
Rain, rain, rain.

Steady, still rain.

Thursday 26.
29 5/10; 63; SW, N.
Dark & moist, dark, moist.

Planted out a row of borecole, & three long rows of curled endive.
Bat comes out before the swallows are gone to roost.

Friday 27.
29 5/10; 60; NE.
Fog, dark, rain, rain.

Cold & comfortless weather.

Saturday 28.
29 6/10½; 53; NW; 23.
Cold dew, sun, pleasant, chill.

Wool Lane.
13 August.

Sunday 29.
29 7/10; 58; W.
Grey, louring, chill.

Mich: daisies begin to blow.

Monday 30.
29 8/10; 59; SW.
Sun, clouds, dark.

Cut 152 cucumbers.
A fine harvest day: much wheat bound, & much gleaning gathered.

Tuesday 31.
29 7/10; 63; SW.
Wet, gleams, dark.

Farmer Spencer's wheat-rick, when it was near finished parted & fell down.
Charles, & Bessy White came from Fyfield.
Rain in Augst – 2 inch 30 h.

SEPTEMBER 1790

Wednesday 1.
29 6/10; 64; SW.
Clouds, showers, bright.

Kidney-beans, & cucumbers abound. Several farmers finish wheat-harvest.
Ophrys spiralis, ladies traces, begin to blow.

Thursday 2.
SW.
Dark, blowing & wet.

Friday 3.
29 1/10½; 3/10; 58; W.
Strong gales, gleams, showers.

Some hop-poles blown down.
Two swifts seen at Lyndon!
Mr Prowting of Chawton begins to pick hops.

Saturday 4.
29 3/10; 54; W, NW.
White frost, sun, showers, bright, & chill.

Nep. John White came from Sarum.
One swift at Lyndon.

There is a fine thriving oak near the path as you go to Combwood, just before you arrive at the pond, round which, at about the distance of the extremities of the boughs, may be seen a sort of circle in the grass, in which the herbage appears dry & withered, as if a fairy-ring was beginning. I remember some what of the same appearance at the same place in former years.

Sunday 5.
29 5/10; 52; W, N.
Cold dew, sun, louring, shower.

Boiled a mess of the autumnal spinage, sown Aug: 3rd
Nep. J. White left us, & returned to Sarum.

Monday 6.
29 6/10½; N.
White dew, cold, sun,
chill & bright.

Several men begin to pick hops.
Hardly here & there a wasp to be seen.

Tuesday 7.
29 7/10; 42; N.
Cold dew, sun, bright
& chill.

Hops small.

Fly-catchers seem to have withdrawn themselves for some days.
House martins continue to hatch broods, & to throw out the shells.
Hirundines cluster on the tower, & on roofs.

Wednesday 8.
29 8/10; 52; N.
Cold dew, sun &
clouds, bright & cold.

One fly-catcher appears.

Thursday 9.
29 7/10; 49; SW.
Grey & mild, dark,
rain.

Mushrooms abound below Hartley wood.
Two stone-curlews in a fallow near Southington.
A fern-owl flies over my House.

Friday 10.
29 7/10; 52; W; 11.
Driving mist, sun,
warm, gale, red even.

Cut 140 cucumbers. Hops light, & not very good.
Sister Barker & Molly & Betsy left us, & went to London:
Charles White also, & Bessy returned to Fyfield.

Saturday 11.
29 8/10; NW.
Sun, gale, gale.

Annuals very backward: China asters not blown.
Several martins nests contain unfledged young.
Began to light fires in the parlor.
Kidney-beans, & cucumbers injured by the cold winds.
Grapes do not come on.
Hops are light & do not prove well.

Sunday 12.
29 7/10½; 58; SW.
Sun, dark & mild.

Some few grapes begin to turn colour.
Hirundines swarm along the side of the hanger.

Monday 13.
29 6/10; SW.
Sun, sweet day.

Cut 158 cucumbers.
Nep. Ben White, & wife, & little Ben & Glyd came from
Fyfield.

Tuesday 14.
29 4/10½; 62; S.
Grey, sun, dark &
mild.

Onions rot. Barley round the village very fine.

The Wakes.
September 12.
Chimney Bellflower.

Wednesday 15.
29 5/10½; 60; S, NW.
Fog, sun, pleasant,
shower, bright.

The hanger just begins to be tinged a little on the tops of the trees.

The boys brought me their first wasps nest from Kimbers; it was near as big as a gallon. When there is no fruit, as is remarkably the case this year, wasps eat flies, & suck the honey from flowers, from ivy blossoms, & umbellated plants: they carry-off also flesh from butchers shambles.

Thursday 16.
29 8/10¾; 56; NW.
Sun, warm.

Cut 100 cucumbers.
Sweet autumnal weather.

Friday 17.
29 8/10½; 53; SE.
Vast dew, cloudless,
moonlight.

Sweet autumnal weather.
Martins congregate on the weather-cock & vane of the may-pole.

Saturday 18.
29 6/10¾; 69; SE, S.
Vast dew, cloudless,
sweet night!

Boys bring a large wasps nest.

My tall beech in Sparrow's hanger, which measures 50 feet to the first fork, & 24 afterwards, is just 6 feet in girth at 2 feet above the ground.
   At the back of Burhant house, in an abrupt field which inclines towards nightingale-lane, stand four noble beech trees on the edge of a steep ravin or water-gully, the largest of which measures 9 f.

Selborne High Wood.
September.

5 in. at about a yard from the ground.

This ravin runs with a strong torrent in winter from nightingale-lane, but is dry in the summer. The beeches above are now the finest remaining in this neighbourhood, & carry fine heads. There is a romantic, perennial spring in this gully, that might be rendered very ornamental, was it situated in a gentleman's outlet.

Sunday 19.
29 3/10; 70, 60; S.
Grey, sun, sultry, wet,
grey.

Young martins continue still to come out: they are become very numerous.

Septr 19. On this day Lord Stawell sent me a rare & curious water-fowl, taken alive a few days before by a boy at Basing near Basingstoke, & sent to the Duke of Bolton at Hackwood park, where it was put into the bason before the house, in which it soon dyed. This bird proved to be the *Procellaria Puffinus* of Linnaeus, the Manks puffin, or Shear-water¶ of Ray. Shear-waters breed in the Gulf of Man, & as Ray supposes, in the Scilly Isles, & also in the Orknies: but quit our rocks & shores about the latter end of August; & from accounts lately given by navigators, are dispersed over the whole Atlantic. By what chance or accident this bird was impelled to visit Hānts is a question that can not easily be answered.

Timothy the tortoise forsakes the fruit-wall, & retires to the laurel-hedge, where he will lay himself up here after.

Monday 20.
29 4/10; 63; SW; 28.
Sun, & strong gale.

Rain & wind in the night.

Tuesday 21.
29 7/10½; SW, NW.
Sprinkling, sun &
strong gale, cold air.

Mrs Clement, & six of her children, four of which are to be inoculated,¶ & Mrs Chandler, & her two children, the youngest of which is also to undergo the same operation, are retired to Harteley great house. Servants & all, some of which are to be inoculated also, they make 14 in family.

Wednesday 22.
29 7/10¾; 40; SE, S.
White dew, sun,
louring.

Gathered-in the white pippins: the crop has been very great!

Thursday 23.
29 7/10; 68; SW, NW;
27.
Warm, showers.
Full moon.

Rain in the night. Coss-lettuce finely loaved, & bleached! Nep. B. White left us, & went to London.

Friday 24.
30 ½/10; N, NW.
Grey, sun, sweet even.

Thomas cut 130 cucumbers.

Saturday 25.
30; 55; NW.
Grey, sun, pleasant,
sweet moonshine.

A vast flock of lapwings, which has forsaken the moors & bogs,
now frequents the uplands.
Some ring-ouzels were seen round Nore hill.

. . . "there the Snake throws her enamel'd skin."
    Shakespear, *Mids. night's dream.*
About the middle of this month we found in a field near a hedge
the slough of a large snake, which seemed to have been newly cast.
From circumstances it appeared as turned wrong side outward, &
as drawn off backward, like a stocking, or woman's glove. Not
only the whole skin, but scales from the very eyes are peeled off, &
appear in the head of the slough like a pair of spectacles. The
reptile, at the time of changing his coat, had intangled himself
intricately in the grass, & weeds, so that the friction of the stalks &
blades might promote this curious shifting of his *exuviae.*
. . . "*lubrica serpens*"
"*Exuit in spinis vestem*" . . Lucret:¶
    It would be a most entertaining sight could a person be an eye-
witness to such a feat, & see the snake in the act of changing his
garment. As the convexity of the scales of the eyes in the slough
are/is now inward, that circumstance alone is a proof that the skin
has been turned: not to mention that now the present inside is
much darker than the outer. If you look thro' the scales of the
snake's eyes from the concave side, viz: as the reptile used them,
they lessen objects much. Thus it appears, from what has been
said, that snakes crawl out of the mouth of their own sloughs, &
quit the tail part last; just as eels are skinned by a cookmaid. While
the scales of the eyes are growing loose, & a new skin is forming,
the creature, in appearance, must be blind, & feel itself in an
awkward, uneasy situation.

Sunday 26.
30 ½/10; 54; N, NE.
Dark, still, & warm.

Tho' several hirundines appear still, yet the major part of the h.
martins seem at present to have withdrawn.

Monday 27.
29 9/10; 54; E.
Grey, sun, bright.

The ground is very dry: turnips want rain.
A larger flock of martins is seen this evening.
The inoculated at Harteley sicken.

Tuesday 28.
29 7/10½; 50; E,
NW.
Vast dew, hot sun, sweet
even.

China asters blow. Ivy begins to blow.

Wednesday 29.
29 9/10; 54; E.
Grey, great dew, sun,
grey & mild.

Several hirundines: about half the whole number seems to be left.

Thursday 30.
29 8/10¼; 50; E.
Dew, sun & gale, sweet
afternoon.

Cut 81 cucumbers.
Rain in Septem.ʳ 0 inch. 66 h.

Sept.ʳ 30ᵗʰ On this day M.ʳˢ Brown¶ was brought to bed at Stamford of twins, making my nephews & nieces 58 in number. The night following, this poor, dear woman dyed, leaving behind her nine young children!

OCTOBER 1790

Friday 1.
29 5/10; 53; E.
White frost, sun, sweet
day.

Many hirundines. Dug up the potatoes in the upper garden: a fine sort.

Saturday 2.
29 4/10; 59; E, NE.
Dew, warm sun, sweet
afternoon.

Bro. Thomas, & his daughter M.ʳˢ Ben White left us, & went to London.

Lord Stawell sent me from the great Lodge in the Holt a curious bird¶ for my inspection. It was found by the spaniels of one of his keepers in a coppice, & shot on the wing. The shape, & air, & habit of the bird, & the scarlet ring round the eyes agreed well with the appearance of a cock pheasant: but then the head, & neck, & breast, & belly were of a glossy black: & tho' it weighed 3 pd 3½ oun. the full weight of a large full-grown cock pheasant:* yet there were no signs of any spurs on the legs, as is usual with all grown cock pheasants, who have long ones. The legs & feet were naked of feathers; & therefore it could be nothing of the Grous kind. In the tail were no long bending feathers, such as cock pheasants usually have, & are characteristic of the sex. The tail was much shorter than the tail of an hen pheasant, & blunt & square at the end. The back wing-feathers, & tail were all of a pale russet curiously streaked, some what like the upper parts of an hen partridge.

I returned it to the noble sender with my verdict, that it was probably a spurious, or hybrid hen bird, bred between a cock-pheasant, & some domestic fowl. When I came to talk with the keeper who brought it, he told me, that some Pea-hens had been known last summer to haunt the coppices, & coverts where this mule was found.

My advice was that his Lordship would employ Elmer of Farnham, the famous game-painter, to take an exact copy of this curious bird. His Lordship did employ Elmer, & sent me as a present a good painting of that rare bird.

---

*Hen pheasants usually weigh only 2 pd. 1 oun.

Sunday 3.
29 5/10¾; 66; SE, S.
Deep fog, sun, sweet &
soft.

The row of ten weeks stocks under the fruit-wall makes a
beautiful show. The foliage of the vines & Virginia creepers
begins to turn red. Gossamer.

Mr Edm^d White, while he was at South Lambeth this summer,
kept for a time a regular journal of his Father's barometer, which,
when compared with a journal of my own for the same space,
proves that the mercury at S. Lambeth at an average stands full
three tenths of an inch higher than at Selborne. Now as we have
remarked that the barometer at Newton Valence is invariably three
tenth lower than my own at Selborne, it plainly appears that the
mercury at S. Lambeth exceeds in height at an average the
mercury at Newton by six tenths at least. Hence it follows,
according to some calculations, that Newton vicarage house is 600
feet higher than the hamlet of S. Lambeth,¶ which, as may be seen
by the tide coming-up the creek before some of the houses, stands
but a few feet above high water mark. It is much to be wished that
all persons who attend to barometers would take care to use none
but pure distilled Mercury in their tubes: because Mercury
adulterated with lead, as it often is, loses much of it's true gravity,
& must often stand in tubes above it's proper pitch on account of
the diminution of it's specific weight by lead, which is lighter than
mercury. The remarks above show the futility of marking the
plates of barometers with the words – fair, changeable, &c.
instead of inches, & tenths; since by means of different elevations
they are very poor directions, & have but little reference to the
weather.

Monday 4.
29 6/10½; 55; 59; SE;
32.
Deep fog, rain, warm
& dark.

Three martin's nests at Mr Burbey's are now full of young!

Tuesday 5.
29 6/10; 52; SE.
Grey, hot sun, sweet
even, red.

Cut 3 bunches of grapes: they were just eatable.
Distant lightening. Rain in the night.
Thunder.

Wednesday 6.
29 5/10; S; 2, 29.
Grey, sun & showers,
warm.

Tyed up endive; & planted 100 of cabbages to stand the winter.
Men load their waggons with hops which are to be sent to Wey
hill.
49 cucumbers.

Thursday 7.
29 4/10¼; 60, 64; S,
SW.
Sun, hot, summer like.

Martins still in their nests. Hirundines abound under the
hanger.
Planted out tufts of pinks. Moved the variegated Colchicums into

the garden.

Timothy the tortoise came out into the walk, & grazed.

Friday 8.
29 6/10; 55; W, NW.
Sun, sweet day.

My hedges beautifully variegated.

One martin's nest has young still.

After the servants are gone to bed, the kitchen-hearth swarms with young crickets, & young *Blattae molendinariae* of all sizes from the most minute growth to their full proportions. They sem to live in a friendly manner together, & not prey the one on the other.

Saturday 9.
29 6/10¼; 14.
Mist, sun, sweet day,
red even:

Earthed-up celeri, which thrives well.

Rain in the night.

Sunday 10.
29 7/10; 34; N, NE.
Hard frost, bright &
sharp.

The cucumbers are all cut down.

No hirundines since thursday.

Monday 11.
29 7/10; 34; SE, S.
White frost, sun,
pleasant.

Gathered the Cadillac pears, a bushel; the knobbed russets 2 bushels; the kitchen, ruddy apple at the end of the fruit-wall, near a bushel.

Tuesday 12.
29 2/10; 50; SW.
Blowing, wet, driving
rain.

Gathered in near 4 bushels of dearling apples from the meadow tree: the crop is great, but the fruit is small.

No hirundines.

Mushrooms abound in the pastures near Honey-lane.

Wednesday 13.
29 5/10; NW; 27.
Sun & strong gales.

Gathered in a bushel more of dearlings. Mrs Chandler returns home from the Harteley inoculation.

Four or five house-martins, & about the same number of swallows now appear again round the Plestor. These proved to be last hirundines seen by me this autumn.

Thursday 14.
29 4/10; W.
Rain, grey, shower.

Gathered in more dearlings: the fruit is small, but the crop on that single tree amounts to nine bushels, & upwards.

Friday 15.
29 7/10½; W; 12.
Sun, pleasant.

Gathered in the royal russets, & the nonpareils, a few of each. Earthed up the celeri, which is fine. Gathered the berberries.

Saturday 16.
30; 44; E.
Sun, most sweet day.

Red-wings return, & are seen on Selborne down.
There are no haws this year for the redwings, & field fares.
A most beautiful mackarel sky!

Sunday 17.
29 6/10; SE, S.
Vast dew, sun, pleasant.

Gracious street stream is dry from James Knight's ponds, where
it rises, to the foot bridge at the bottom of the church litton closes.
Near that bridge, in the corner, the spring is perennial, & runs
to Dorton, where it joins the Well-head stream.

Monday 18.
29 7/10, 45; W; 24.
Dark, rain, bright.

Gathered a plate of grapes; they are just eatable.

Tuesday 19.
29 8/10; SE.
White frost, sweet day,
yellow even.

Timothy the tortoise still lies out.
The air abounds with insects.
My well is very low, & the water foul.
D.ʳ Chandler saw a Woodcock in the high wood.

Wednesday 20.
29 5/10; 40; SE.
Dark & mild, showers,
fog.

Spring-keepers¶ come up in the well-bucket.
How they get down there does not appear:
they are called by M.ʳ Derham *squillae aquaticae*.

Thursday 21.
29 4/10½; 52, 60; SE.
Fog, sun, warm, sweet
even.

A large flock of redwings on the down.

I conclude that the Holiburne trufler finds encouragement in our
woods, & hangers, as he frequently passes along the village: He is a
surly fellow, & not communicative. He is attended by two little
cur-dogs, which he leads in a string.

Friday 22.
29 3/10½; 58; SE.
Dark & mild,
sprinkling, mild.

The beechen hangers turn colour very fast.
Leaves fall.
Total esclipse of the moon.

Saturday 23.
29 3/10; E; 41.
Fog, rain, rain.

Planted out two rows of winter-lettuce under the fruit wall: the
border was well dunged.
The leaves fall in showers.

Sunday 24.
29 3/10½; E.
Sun, soft, & mild,
heavy clouds, deep fog.

The tortoise comes out. Flesh-flies abound.

D.ʳ Chandler buys of the Holiburne trufle-man one pound of
trufles; price 2s. 6d.

Monday 25.
29 4/10½; E, SE.

A flock of 46 ravens over the hanger.

Sun, pleasant.

Slipped-out pinks, & fraxinels; planted-out dames violets from cuttings.

Tuesday 26.
29 5/10½; 40; E.
Deep fog, sun,
pleasant.

My well very low, & the water foul.
This morning Rear Admiral Cornish, with six ships of the line, & two smaller ships of war, sailed from Saint Hellen's.

Wednesday 27.
29 4/10; E.
Sun, strong gale, wet.

Grapes better.

Thursday 28.
29 3/10; E; 29.
Dark, rain, rain.

Wet & uncomfortable.

Friday 29.
29 4/10½; E, NE.
Dark, sun, grey.

Dug & cleansed the border in the orchard, & planted it with polyanths slipped out.

Saturday 30.
29 4/10½; NE.

Large fieldfares, a great flock, seen on the hill.
Ravens on the down.
Wild wood-pigeons, or stock doves are seen at my wood at Holtham.

Sunday 31.
29 6/10; N.
Sun, pleasant, sharp.

Leaves fall.
Rain in October – 2 inc. 10 h.

NOVEMBER 1790

Monday 1.
29; SW.
Rain, rain, much rain
with wind.

Bro.ʳ Benj.ⁿ & his wife came to us.
Celeri comes in; large & fine.
Lightening. Much thunder at Portsmouth.

Tuesday 2.
29 1/10½, SW; 117.
Sun & wind.

Wednesday 3.
29 3/10; 41; SW.
Sun, pleasant, rain.

Grapes good.

Thursday 4.
29 4/10; 48; W; 36.
Sun, showers.

Green wheat comes up well.
Stewed some trufles: the flavour of their juice very fine, but the

roots hard, & gritty. They were boiled in water, then sliced, & stewed in gravy.

Friday 5.
29 5/10; 52; SW, S.
Grey, sun, mild.

Saturday 6.
29 3/10; S.
Rain, rain, windy, rain.

Very rough weather at Portsmouth: boats overset, & people drowned in coming from Spithead.

Sunday 7.
29 3/10½; 37; E; 91.
Dark & cold.

Monday 8.
29 5/10; E.
Vast dew, sun, pleasant.

A wood-cock seen in the high wood.

Tuesday 9.
29 7/10½; NE.
Grey, & cold, dark.

Dug, & cleansed the rest of the border in the orchard, & filled it with polyanths slipped out.

Wednesday 10.
29 6/10; NE.
Sun, sharp, wet.

Paths dry.
Primrose blows.

Thursday 11.
29 6/10½; 46; NE.
Mild, dark & still.

Two or three wood-cocks seen in the high wood; one was killed.
Fyfield¶ improves, & promises to make a good cock-dog.

Friday 12.
29 7/10½; 45; NE.
Fog, dark & still.

Parted-out, & planted more polyanths.

Saturday 13.
29 8/10; 43; NE.
Dark, sun, cloudless,
red even.

Bro.ʳ & Sister Benj.ⁿ left us.
Pleasant. Insects abound.
Planted out more polyanths.

Sunday 14.
29 8/10½; 44; NE.
Dark & harsh.

March-like weather.

Monday 15.
29 8/10, 45; E.
Sun, sweet, cool day,
cloudless.

Timothy the tortoise gone under ground in the laurel-hedge.
Paths very dry: boys play at taw on the Plestor.

Tuesday 16.
29 6/10½; 31; NE.

Some wood-cocks are found in the coverts.

Wh. frost, ice,
cloudless, sharp air.

Paths greazy from the frost. Raked, & swept up the leaves in my outlet. The hanger naked.

Wednesday 17.
29 5/10; 37; E.
Grey & still, sun,
bright & cold.

Thursday 18.
29 1/10; 42; E, SE.
Deep fog, grey, wet.

Finished sweeping-up the fallen leaves in the field-walks.

Friday 19.
28 7/10½, 8/10; S,
SW; 77.
Much rain in the night,
gleam, showers.

Saturday 20.
29; 45; SW.
Much rain in the night,
showers, & wind.

The parish church of Calstock in Cornwall destroyed by lightening. The tempest was of vast extent, & in many places mischievous, & awful! This village lies up the Tamar above Saltash.

Sunday 21.
28 8/10; 45; SW; 113.
Much rain in the night
with strong gusts,
shower, gust,
hail, thunder.
Full moon.

A vast tempest at Sarūm, & an house beat down. The mast of a man of war was struck at Spit-head by the lightening.

Monday 22.
29 1/10; SW; 109.
Much rain in the night
with thunder, rain,
rain, rain.

Flood at Gracious pond.

Tuesday 23.
29 4/10; W, NW; 50.
Deep fog, dark & wet.

Wednesday 24.
29 4/10½; S.
Great dew, sun, mild.

Thursday 25.
29 1/10; 49; S; 102.
Wet & blowing, rain,

The water in my well is risen three or four rounds of the winch viz: five or six feet: the spring that runs in may be seen, & heard. The water is now clear. Thus will three or four inches of rain replenish my well, deep as it is, after it has been very low, & foul, & almost dry for several months. I have made the same remark in former Years. Our stream has been so low for many weeks that the miller at Kingsley could not grind; but was obliged to send his corn to Headleigh, where the Blackdown stream never fails. At Headleigh park-corner the Black-down stream joins the Selborne rivulet: & at Tilford bridge they are met by the much rain, rain.

Friday 26.
29 6/10; 47; W, NW.
Grey, bright.

Saturday 27.
29 9/10½; 32; NW,
N.
Frost, ice, bright.

Sunday 28.
29 9/10; 40; N.
Dew, frost, grey &
still, pleasant.

Monday 29.
29 5/10; 31, 29, 31; E.
Hard frost, sharp, &
dark.

Tuesday 30.
29 3/10; 27, 33; E.
Frost, dark, still &
cold.

Farnham river, where together they form so considerable a body
of water as within a few miles to become navigable, viz. at the
town of Godalming; & there take the name of Wey.

Rain in Novem.ʳ – 6 inch. 95 h.

DECEMBER 1790

Wednesday 1.
28 8/10½; 37, 33; SE,
S.
Dark & cold, snow,
rain & thaw.

Snow deep on the ground.
Wind very strong.

Thursday 2.
29 5/10½; NW; 86.
Showers in the night
with wind &
lightening, blowing,
bright.

Friday 3.
29 2/10, 45; W.
Rain with wind, rain,
blowing, rain.

Walls sweat, & the dew stands on the outsides of windows.

Saturday 4.
29 7/10; W; 46.

Dark, still & mild.

Sunday 5.
29 7/10; 38, 41; NW,
N.
Grey, still & mild.

Some wood-cocks are found in Hartley wood.

Monday 6.
30 ½/10; N.
Frost, sun, still, &
pleasant.

Mr Richardson came.

Tuesday 7.
29 8/10; 41; NW.
Dark & mild, wet, wet.

Wednesday 8.
29 8/10; 49; NW.
Wet, wet.

Thursday 9.
29 8/10; 48; W; 16.
Dark & mild.

Mr Richardson left us.
Water-cresses come in.

Friday 10.
29 8/10; 47; W.
Dark, mild & still.

Saturday 11.
29 6/10; 51, W.
Grey & mild, wet,
mild.

Sunday 12.
29 8/10; 40.
White frost, sun, bright
moon.

Monday 13.
29 1/10½; SW.
Rain, rain, rain.

Blowing, rough day.

Tuesday 14.
29 5/10½; 44; W, SW;
106.
Sun & wind, louring.

Wednesday 15.
29 3/10; SW; 33.

Rain with strong wind in the night.

Blowing, strong wind
all day.

The water in the well rises very much.

Thursday 16.
29 3/10½; 44; S.
Dark, wet, windy.

Thatch torn by the wind.

Friday 17.
28 6/10; 44; SE, 19.
Dark & still, wet.

Saturday 18.
29 1/10; NW; 41.
Rain with wind in the
night, driving snow,
rain, wind.

Sunday 19.
29 2/10½; SE; 82.
Snow, driving snow.

Snow covers the ground.

Monday 20.
29 8/10; 32, 34; NW.
Sun, still & bright.

Snow on the ground.

Tuesday 21.
29 5/10; 50; SW.
Foggy, & wet, rain,
moon & clouds.
Full moon.

Wednesday 22.
29 8/10; 36, 42; SW;
36.
Sun, wind.

Thursday 23.
29 7/10; 40; W, NW;
48, 10.
Thunder, lightening,
wind, rain, snow! sun
& wind.

A severe tempest. Much damage done in & about London.
Damage to some ships at Portsmouth.
Harry & Ben Woods come.
Vast damage in various parts!

Two men were struck dead in a wind-mill near Rooks-hill on the
Sussex Downs: & on Hind-head one of the bodies on the gibbet
was beaten down to the ground.

Friday 24.
29 7/10; SW.
Foggy & wet.

Saturday 25.
29 8/10; NW, N.
Shower, sun, pleasant.

H. & Ben Woods left us.

Sunday 26.
29 8/10; 31, 40, 28;
W, NW.
Frost, bright, frost.

Monday 27.
29 4/10; 31; S, SE.
Frost, thaw, dark &
still.

Tuesday 28.
29 7/10½; 31; N.
Frost, rain in the night,
bright, frost.

Wednesday 29.
29 8/10; 28; NE.
Hard frost, sun, frost,
thaw.

On this day M.rs Clement was delivered of a boy, who makes my
nephews & nieces again 57 in number. By the death of M.rs
Brown & one twin they were reduced to 56.

Thursday 30.
29 4/10; S.
Thaw, dark & wet,
rain.

Friday 31.
29 7/10; 39; N, NE;
71.
Dark, still & mild.

Rain in Decem.r – 5 inch 94 hund.
Total of rain in 1790. – 32 inch 27 h.

JANUARY

— 1791 —

Saturday 1.
29 4/10; 33; S.
Dark, still, & mild.

SELBORNE

Sunday 2.
28 8/10; S.
White frost, dark, rain.

Monday 3.
29; 30; S; 42.
Frost, ice, sun, frost.

Many horse-beans sprang up in my field-walks in the autumn, &
are now grown to a considerable height. As the Ewel was in beans
last summer, it is most likely that these seeds came from thence:
but then the distance is too considerable for them to have been
conveyed by mice. It is most probable therefore that they were
brought by birds, & in particular by jays, & pies, who seem to
have hid them among the grass, & moss, & then to have forgotten
where they had stowed them. Some pease also are growing in the
same situation, & probably under the same circumstances.

Mr Derham recorded that mice hide acorns one by one in

pastures in the autumn; & that he has observed them to be hunted-out by swine, who discovered them by their smell.

Tuesday 4.
29; S.
Dark, wind, & driving
rain.

Hepatica blows.

Horse beans.
July.

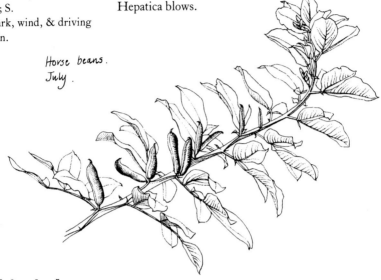

Wednesday 5.
29; 33, 35; SW, SE;
42.
Sun, snow, snow.

Thursday 6.
29 1/10; 37; W.
Frost, sun, pleasant.

The great oak in Harteley avenue, just as you enter the pasture field, measures in girth 14 feet. It is a noble tree, & if sound worth many pounds. Why it was left at the general sale does not appear. The girth was taken at four feet above the ground. N. aurora's, pale but extensive.

Friday 7.
28 7/10; 49; SW; 45.
Grey, gleams, hail,
rain, wind.

Snow gone.
Lightening & wind in the night.

Saturday 8.
29; SW; 10.
Strong sun, gales.

Sunday 9.
28 6/10, 29 1/10½;
SW, NW.
Sun, pleasant, bright
stars.

Monday 10.
29 3/10½; S; 47.

Snow-drop blows.

Rain, rain, mild.

Stormy with heavy showers.

Tuesday 11.
29 5/10½; 39; W; 67.
Grey, sun, red clouds.

Ten weeks stocks blow. Crocus's sprout, & swell.

Wednesday 12.
29 2/10; S.
Red, wet, windy.

Mr Churton left us.
Winter aconite blows.

Thursday 13.
29 1/10½; SW; 40.
Stormy with showers.

The earth is glutted with water: rills break out at the foot of every little hill; my well is near half full.
The wind in the night blew down the rain-measurer.

Friday 14.
29 3/10½; 47; SW.
Rain, rain.

Ivy-berries swell, & grow: there have been no frosts to check them.
Tubbed, & pickled a good young fat hog: weight – 12 scores, & 4 pounds.

Saturday 15.
29 4/10½; 38; SW;
42.
Hoar frost, sun, rain.

Sunday 16.
29 4/10; 47; SW.
Grey, wet, wet.

A disorder prevails among the horses; but has not reached this village yet.

Monday 17.
29 3/10; SW; 21.
Grey, sun, mild,
bright.

Wall-flower blows. Finished trimming & tacking the vines. The new wood looks well.
Sam & Ned White came from Fyfield.

Tuesday 18.
28 4/10¾; SE.
Rain, rain, rain, vast
rain.

Wednesday 19.
28 3/10, 5/10; SW;
157.
Hail, wind, rain.

This morning the Barom.^r at Newton was only 28!!
Furze in bloom.

Thursday 20.
28!! 4/10½; 45; SW;
67. Sun, pleasant,
moonshine, rain.
Full moon.

Rain & wind in the night. Thomas says, that when he got up the Barom.^r was down at 27–8!!

Friday 21.
29 2/10; 41; NW; 21.   Sam & Ned White left us.
Sun, cold wind, bright.   Late in the evening the planet Jupiter¶ shines in the E.

Saturday 22.
29 4/10; S.
Dark, wet, wet.

Sunday 23.
29 8/10¾; 44; NW.   Rain & gusts in the night.
Rain, wet, grey, bright.

Monday 24.
30 1/10½; SW; 42.
Frost, sun, grey.

Tuesday 25.
29 8/10½; W.
Grey, drying wind,
pleasant.

Wednesday 26.
29 7/10; 48; SW.
Grey, gleams, mild, &
still.

Thursday 27.
29 4/10; 42; SW, NW.   One of the Bantam hens begins to lay.
Wet, rain, rain,   Mice devour the crocus's.
starlight.

Friday 28.
29 8/10; 31, 39; N; 19.   Cast hot dung, & housed earth for seedling cucumbers.
Frost, sun, sharp wind,
starlight, frost.

Saturday 29.
29 4/10½; 41; W; 11.   Three gallons of brandy from London.
Thaw, rain, rain,
stormy.

Sunday 30.
29 5/10; 44; W.
Dark, & harsh.

Monday 31.
29 6/10½; 50; W.   Paths dry.
Dark, cold, wind.   Rain in January – 6 inch. 73 hund.

FEBRUARY 1791

Tuesday 1.
29 3/10½; W.
Wind, driving rain,
windy.

My apricot-trees were never stripped of their buds before; &
therefore seem to have suffered from a casual flight of gross-
beaks,¶ that came into these parts.

Wednesday 2.
29 8/10½; 31; NW,
N.
Sun, flights of snow,
sharp, frost.

Made the seedling cucumber-bed with two good cart-loads of hot
dung.
Prodigious high tide at London, & in it's environs! it did much
damage in various parts.

Thursday 3.
29 9/10; 28, 29; N.
Hard frost, sun, sharp.

NEWTON
Covered the asparagus beds, & the artichokes with muckle; these
were grown out very tall.

Friday 4.
29 7/10; 39; N.
Frost, sun, pleasant.

Benham finished mending the hedges.

Saturday 5.
29 7/10, 30; N.
Thaw, sun, grey.

SELBORNE
Hot-bed heats.

Sunday 6.
30; 35; NW.
Frost, thaw, dark &
mild.

Some crocus buds begin to open.

Monday 7.
30; 41, 44; NW.
Grey, mild, wet.

Bull-finches made sad havock among the buds of my cherry, &
apricot trees; they also destroy the buds of of the goose-berries, &
honey-suckles! Green-finches seem also to be concerned in the
damage done: many neighbouring gardens have suffered. These

Tuesday 8.
30; 47; NW.
Grey, gleams, still,
wet.

birds were not observed at the time, nor do they seem to abound.

It appeared afterward, that this damage was done by a flight of
gross-beaks.

Wednesday 9.
29 8/10½; 42, 44;
SW.
Grey, sun, pleasant,
dark.

Sowed cucumber-seeds in pots plunged in the hot-bed: bed heats
well.

Thursday 10.
29 7/10; 45; SW.
Wet, wet, wet.

Brewed strong beer.

Friday 11.
29 5/10½; 38; SW.
Rain, rain, rain,
bright.

Saturday 12.
29 8/10½; 33; W; 56.
Frost, sun, grey.

Cucumber-seeds come up well in the pots: sowed more seeds.

Sunday 13.
29 5/10; 45; SW.
Rain, rain, rain.

As there has been little frost, the *antirrhinum cymb*: flourishes, &
blossoms thro' the winter.

Monday 14.
29 5/10; SW; 58.
Dark & moist, wet,
mild, rain in the night.

The Hazels blossom, & their catkins open.
Potted cucumbers: bed warm.

Tuesday 15.
29 4/10; 42; SW; 27.
Dark, sun, wind, &
shower.

Crocus's blow.

Wednesday 16.
29 8/10; W, NW, W;
22.
Rain, fair, & windy.

Snow-drops make a fine show.

Thursday 17.
29 4/10; 39; SW.
Frost, rain, rain.

Storms & rain in the night.

Friday 18.
28; 9/10; 38, 32; SW.
Frost, sun & flights of
snow, bright.
Full moon.

Saturday 19.
29 4/10; 35; NE; 28,
24.
Snow, thaw, snow.

Snow melted.

Sunday 20.
29; 9/10; NE.
Dark & harsh, wet.

Monday 21.
29 2/10; 43; SE; 9.

Chaffinches destroy the buds of the honey-suckles.

Wet, dark & still.

Tuesday 22.
29 4/10; 35; S, SW.
Frost, sun, pleasant.

Crocus's blow-out, & open.
Men dig in hop-gardens.

Wednesday 23.
29 2/10; 49; SE, SW,
89.
Rain, rain, gleams,
hail.

The farmers are very much behind in their plowings for a spring
crop thro' the wetness of the season.

Thursday 24.
29 7/10; 35; SW.
Frost, sun.

Friday 25.
29 4/10; SE.
Rain, rain, snow, snow.

M.r Edm.d White took down my Barometer, & cleaned tube, &
frame. It had not been meddled with for just 18 years, when my
Bro.r John also took it down.

Saturday 26.
29 5/10, 36; N; 151.
Snow, gleams.

Deep snow, which damaged & broke my plum-trees, & hedges.
This is much the greatest snow that we have seen this year. Some
of the deep lanes are hardly passable.

Sunday 27.
29 7/10; 36; NW.
Sun, thaw, sleet.

Snow covers the ground. A large bough broken from the yew-
tree in the church yard by the snow.

Monday 28.
29 8/10½; 33; N.
Frost, sun.

Snow covers the ground.
Rain in February – 4 inch. 64 hund.

MARCH 1791

Tuesday 1.
29 8/10½; 28; N.
Hard frost, sun, frost.

Snow on the ground.
Crocus's blow out.

Wednesday 2.
30; 30; N.
Frost, sun, frost.

Seven cart-loads of hot dung carried in for the cucumber-bed: 5
loads from Hale, 1 from Parsons, & 1 of my own.

Thursday 3.
30 2/10; 25; SW.
Hard frost, sun, grey.

Sent me by Lord Stawell a Sea mall. or Gull, & a *Coccothraustes*,
or Gross beak:¶ the latter is seldom seen in England, & only in

the winter.
Lined the cucumber-bed. Bees appears.

Friday 4.
30 1/10; W.
Grey, sun, gale, dark &
wet.

Saturday 5.
30; 44; W, SW.
Dark & mild.

Boys play at hop-scotch, & cricket.
Some snow under hedges.
The wry-neck returns, & pipes.

Sunday 6.
29 8/10½; 51; W,
NW.
Grey & pleasant.

Crocus's in full beauty.
Violets.

Monday 7.
30; 1/10; N.
Frost, sun, & clouds.

Coltsfoot blows. Stopped cucumbers.
Sowed dwarf lark-spurs. Turned the dung.

Tuesday 8.
30 2/10½; 33, 33; N,
NW.
Hard frost, sun, frost.

Snow under the hedges.
Flies come-out. Made a celeri bed for one hand-glass.

Wednesday 9.
3/10, 30 2/10½; 33;
W.
Hard frost, sun, frost.

Tapped the new hay-rick: the hay but moderate.
Sowed celeri seed.

Thursday 10.
30 1/10½; 34; NW.
Frost, sun, sharp.

Cucumbers grow.

Friday 11.
30; 36, 45; SW.
Wh. frost, grey, still.

Sowed radishes, & parsley. Weeded the garden, & dug some
ground.

Saturday 12.
29 8/10½; 41; SW.
Cloudless, no frost,
summer-like.

Planted four rows of broad beans in the orchard.
Some snow still under hedges.

Sunday 13.
29 8/10; 39; SW, SE.
Grey, sun, summer-
like.

Crocus's in high glory. *Helleborus viridis* blows. Snow-drops
fade.
Some snow under hedges.

Vast halo round the moon.

D.ʳ Chandler's labourer, in digging down the bank in the midst of the parsonage garden called the grotto, found human bones among the rocks. As these lay distant from the bounds of the church-yard, it is possible that they might have been deposited there before there was any church, or yard. So again in 1728, when a saw-pit was sunk on the Plestor under the wall of the court-yard, many human bones were dug-up at a considerable distance from the church-yard.

Monday 14.
29 9/10; 45; SW.
Grey & mild, fog.

Daffodil blows. Timothy the tortoise heaves-up the earth.
Turned the dung.

Tuesday 15.
30 ½/10; 46; SW.
Fog, sun, grey.

Made the bearing cucumber-bed.
Sweet weather. Mackerel.

Wednesday 16.
30 ½/10; 45; SW.
Sun, summer-like, frost.

Timothy the tortoise comes half-out.
Sweet weather. Put on the cucumber-frames.

Thursday 17.
29 9/10½; 47; SW.
Deep fog, sun, fog.

Planted ½ hundred of cabbages. Timothy comes out.
Earthed the lights of the cucumber-bed.
Bat comes out; & Timothy comes forth.
The yew-tree in the church-yard sends forth clouds of farina.
The Stone-curlew is returned again; & was heard this evening passing over the village from the uplands down to the meadows, & brooks.

Friday 18.
29; 9/10; 37; W.
Sun, summer-like.

Snow lies deep in Newton-lane, & under hedges in the uplands.
The hounds find no hare on all Selborne hill.
Men turn their sheep into the green wheat.

Saturday 19.
29 6/10; 34; SW.
White frost, sun, dark & harsh.

Sowed my own ashes on the great meadow.
Timothy hides himself again.
The hunters killed a female hare, which gave suck: so there are young leverets already.

Sunday 20.
28; 9/10½; SW.
Rain, rain, rain.

M.ʳ Burbey shot a cock Gross-beak,¶ which he had observed to haunt his garden for more than a fortnight: D.ʳ Chandler had also seen it in his garden. I began to accuse this bird of having made sad havock among the buds of the cherries, goose-berries, & wall-fruit of all the neighbouring orchards. Upon opening it's crop or craw no buds were to be seen; but a mass of kernels of the stones of fruits. Mʳ B. observed that this bird frequented the spots where plum-trees grow: & that he had seen it with some what hard in it's mouth, which it broke with difficulty; these were the stones of damasons. The latin Ornithologists call this bird *Coccothraustes*, i.e. berry-breaker, because with it's large, horny beak it cracks & breaks the shells of stone-fruits for the sake of the seed or kernel. Birds of this sort are rarely seen in England, & only in the winter. About 50 years ago I discovered three of these gross-beaks in my outlet, one of which I shot.

Monday 21.
29 2/10; 38; W; 112.
Sun, & wind, sleet, cold air.

Stormy in the night with heavy showers.
A hen gross-beak was found almost dead in my outlet: it had nothing in it's craw.

Tuesday 22.
29 7/10½; W.
Sun, & clouds.

Dog-tooth violets blow.
Turned-out a pot of cucumbers into each hill.

Wednesday 23.
30; 49; W, NW.
Sun & clouds, bright.

Apricots, peaches, & nectarines blow.
Soft wind. The wood-pecker laughs.

Thursday 24.
30 1/10; 48; NE.
White frost, sun, hot sun, bright.

My nephew John White of Salisbury sent me a fine pike, or jack; it was in high season, full of soft roe, & weighed five pounds, & six ounces. The length from eye to fork two feet. It was baked, & much admired when it came on the table.

Friday 25.
29 8/10; 40; S.
Frost, sun & clouds.

Sowed onions, radishes, & lettuce: the ground harsh, & cloddy.
Crocus's make a show still. Timothy comes out.

Saturday 26.
29 5/10, 43; S, NW; 38.
Rain, rain, cold wind.

Cucumber-plants show bloom: but the bed is too hot, & draws the plants. We sow our seeds too soon, so that the plants want to be turned out of the pots before the great bed can be got to due temperament.

Sunday 27.
29 7/10½; 36; N.
Frost, sun, bright.

Monday 28.
29 7/10½; 46; SW.
Dark & still, & mild.

Sowed a large plot of parsnips, & radishes in the orchard.

Tuesday 29.
29 6/10½; 50; SE.

Crocus's fade, & go off. Sowed also Coss lettuce with the

Dark & mild, hail, dark & moist, wet, rain.

parsnips.

Wednesday 30.
29 7/10; SE; 9.
Sun, warm, heavy clouds.

Sowed a bed of carrots. Some rooks have built several nests in the high wood.

The building of rooks in the High wood is an uncommon incident, & never remembered but once before. The Rooks usually carry on the business of breeding in groves, & clumps of trees near houses, & in villages, & towns.
    Timothy weighs 6 pd 11 ou.
    A gross-beak seen at Newton parsonage-house. Grass grows in the fields.

Thursday 31.
29 7/10; 45, 44; N, SE, S.
Grey, mild & still.

Made two hand-glass beds for celeri.
Crocus's gone. Daffodils make a show.
Nightingale returns, & sings.
Rain in March – 1 inch. 59 h.

Looking down on the village. Selborne High Wood. April.

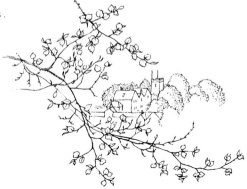

APRIL 1791

Friday 1.
29 5/10; 45; S, SE.
Sun, grey, & gleams.

The bearing cucumber-bed becomes milder & more mellow; & the plants shoot, & blow well.
Planted potatoes in the meadow-garden, ten rows.

Saturday 2.
29 3/10; 39, 41; SE, E.
Bright, with brisk gale.

Crown imperials begin to blow. Pronged the asparagus beds.
Wheat looks well.
Mrs B. White & Hannah White¶ come from London.

Sunday 3.
29 5/10; E.
Cold dew, bright, & calm.

The chif-chaf, the smallest uncrested wren, is heard in the Hangar, & long Lythe. They are usually heard about the 21 of March. These birds, no bigger than a man's thumb, fetch an echo out of the hanger at every note.

Monday 4.
29 4/10½; NE.
Bright, red even, cold
air.

Mary White came from Newton.

Tuesday 5.
29 1/10½; NE.
Dark, rain, rain, wet.

Wednesday 6.
29 2/10½; W.
Rain, rain, rain.

The apricots have no blossoms: they lost all their buds by birds.
The cuckoo arrives, & is seen, & heard.
Red start returns, & appears on the grass-plot.

Thursday 7.
29 5/10½; 59; W, SE;
77.
Sun, summer.

Fritillaria's blow. Hyacinths blow:
polyanths make a fine show.
Swallow returns, & is seen over the village.

Friday 8.
29 6/10; S.
Sun, gleams, sweet
even.

Mary White left us.

Saturday 9.
29 6/10; 57; W, SW.
Fog, sun, sweet
weather.

Sowed polyanth-seed, some in a box, & some in the ground.
Heavy clouds to the W. & NW.

Sunday 10.
29 6/10; E, S.
Vast dew, sun, grey.

The early beech in the long Lythe shows leaves fully expanded.

Monday 11.
29 6/10; 42; SW.
Shower, shady, &
mild.

Wall-cherries begin to blow.
Began to mow the walks: grass grows.
Timothy the tortoise marches forth on the grass-plot, & grazes.

Tuesday 12.
29 6/10½; 60; NE.
Dew, sweet summer
weather.

Ivy-berries ripen, & are eaten by birds.
Mountain snow-drops blow. Black thorns blossom.
Hannah White¶ walks up to the alcove before breakfast.

Wednesday 13.
29 5/10½; 48; E, SE.
Fog, dark, rain.

Polyanths, & hyacinths make a fine show.
Swift appears.

Swift & house-martin are seen: the former comes unusually early,
encouraged by the warmth of the season.

Timothy the tortoise is become very alert, & marches about the walks.

Thursday 14.
29 7/10; 53; W, SW; 24.
Fog, sun, grey, bright.

Bombylius medius appears in the walks.

A man brought me half a dozen good mushrooms from a pasture field! a great rarity at this season of the year!

Friday 15.
29 7/10; 61; SE.
Cold dew, summer.

A nightingale sings in my outlet.
Sowed sweet peas, candy-tuft, sweet alyssum, &c.
Several beeches in the hanger show a tinge of green.

Saturday 16.
29 7/10; 45, 60; E.
Cold dew, summer weather.

Men pole their hops.
Vines shoot a little.

Sunday 17.
29 5/10; SE, S.
Great dew, sun, grey.

Monday 18.
29 4/10; SW.
Fog, sun, grey, cool.
Full moon.

Pear-trees, & the wild merise (cherry) blow.
Mr Ben White came from London.

Tuesday 19.
29 2/10; SW, S.
Grey, gleams, dark, rain, blowing.

Mrs Chandler & son went away on a visit.
Began to use the winter lettuce.

Tho' a swallow or two were seen in the village as long ago as the 7th yet have they absconded for some time past. The house-martin is also withdrawn: no Swift has yet appeared at Selborne; what was seen was at Bentley.

Wednesday 20.
29 1/10½; SW.
Dark & cool, rain.

Finished weeding, & dressing all the flower-borders.
Several nightingales between the village, & comb-wood pond.
Comb-wood coppice was cut last winter.

Thursday 21.
28 9/10½; SW.
Grey, fine.

A swallow or two, & a h. martin or two.
One swift.

Friday 22.
28 8/10; 57; SW, W.
Sun, fine.

The merise, or wild cherries in vast bloom.
Vast, heavy clouds about. Grass grows, & clover looks very fine.
Mr & Mrs B. White, & Hannah left us, & went to Newton.

Saturday 23.
28 9/10; W.
Gleams, showers, &
hail.

Made an annual bed for the great three-light frame.

Sunday 24.
29 2/10½; W.
Shower, sun, cold air.

Monday 25.
29 5/10; 41; W.
Cold air, sun & clouds.

ALTON
Cut a brace of cucumbers; but the plants are weak, & not in good condition.
Mowed some coarse grass in the orchard for the horses.

Tuesday 26.
E.
Grey, warm.

OXFORD
Some of the oaks, planted on the commons between Odiham & Reading about the time that I first knew that road, begin to be felled. Swallows, Goslings.

Wednesday 27.
E.
Harsh, & dark, dark.

Cherries, apples, & pears in beautiful bloom along the road: grass forward, & corn looks well.

Thursday 28.
N.
Dark, rain.

Friday 29.
N.
Rain.

Saturday 30.
N; 12.
Harsh & wet.

Rain in April – 1 inc. 13 hund.

MAY 1791

Sunday 1.
42; N; 15.
Harsh, rain.

A prodigious bloom on the apple-trees along the road.

Monday 2.
N; 21.
Cold & wet.

ALTON
Swifts, & house-martins over the Thames at Pangbourn.

Tuesday 3.
29 6/10½; NE.
Dark & harsh, wet

SELBORNE

Wednesday 4.
29 6/10; 48; NE, N.
Dark & harsh.

Planted some tricolor violets, & some red cabbages sent from South Lambeth.

Thursday 5.
29 6/10; 52; N, NE.
Sun, & clouds, gleam.

The bloom of my white apple is again very great.
Many house-martins over Dorton.
Set the middle Bantam hen with eleven eggs: the cook desired there might be an odd one.

Friday 6.
29 8/10; 52; NE; 4.
Shower, harsh wind,
sun & clouds, gleam.

Sowed hardy annuals on borders: cut five cucumbers. Hanger in full leaf & very beautiful.
The nightingales sing in my outlet.
Cut the stalks of garden rhubarb to make tarts: the plants are very strong.

Saturday 7.
30; 39; N.
White frost, sun, &
sharp air.

Vast bloom on my nonpareils.
The orchard is mown for the horses.

Sunday 8.
29 9/10; 56; N, NW.
Frost, sun, summer.

Mrs Clement & four children, & a nurse-maid came.
Horses lie out.

Monday 9.
29 7/10½; 58; SW,
W.
No dew, grey, gleam.

Swallows begins to build.

Tuesday 10.
29 7/10½; 57; SW,
NW; 11.
Rain, rain, gleams.

The shoots of the vines in some places are injured by the late frosts.

Wednesday 11.
29 5/10½; 57; S.
Frost, dark, wet, rain.

Planted seven rows of garden-beans in the meadow plot.

The down of willows floats in the air, conveying, & spreading about their seeds, & affording some birds a soft lining for their nests.

Thursday 12.
29 2/¾; 57; S; 12.
Dark & mild, shower.

Sowed more basons of annuals.
Apples show vast bloom. Shower in the night.

Friday 13.
29 4/10; S; 21.

Martins begin to build.

Sun & clouds, shower, bright.

Ashen shoots injured by the late frosts, & kidney-beans & potatoe sprouts killed.

Saturday 14.
29 8/10; 59; S, NW.
Fog, sun & clouds, red even.

Sowed one row of large kidney-beans, white.

Sunday 15.
29 7/10½; SW.
Sun, & clouds.

Flesh flies get to be troublesome: hung out the meat-safe.
Mrs Clement &c. left us.

Monday 16.
29 7/10¼; 59; W.
No dew, harsh, dark & cool.

Slipped-out the artichokes, & dressed the beds.
Saw a flie-catcher at the vicarage, I think.

Tuesday 17.
29 5/10; 56; W; 11.
Strong gales, showers, strong gales.

Made two hand-glass beds for cucumbers.
Sowed one row of scarlet kidney-beans.

Fly-catcher returns.
    The fern-owl, or eve-jar, returns, & is heard in the hanger.
These birds are the latest summer-birds of passage: when they appear we hope the summer will soon be established.

Wednesday 18.
29 6/10; 56; NW, W.
Strong gales, sun, clear.
Full moon.

Cut 4 brace & an half of cucumbers: earthed-out the cucumber-bed: three of the lights have weak plants.

Thursday 19.
29 2/10, 5/10; 51; W; 19.
Strong wind, blowing, sharp & windy.

Showers in the night.
The apple-bloom appears to be much injured, & blown away.
In such windy weather the swifts, & other Hirundines are hardly seen.

Friday 20.
29 6/10¾; 50; W.
Gale, sun, cool.

Sowed two hand-glass beds with cucumber-seeds.

Saturday 21.
29 6/10¼; 44, 57, SW.
Cool, gale, dark.

Haw-thorn blows.

These strong gales shake-off the bloom of the apples, & litter the walks with scraps, & leaves.
    The weather has been so harsh, that the swallows, & martins are not disposed to build.
    Found a hen redstart dead in the walks.

Sunday 22.
29 7/10; 57; SW.
Sun & clouds, cold
wind.

Wheat loses it's colour, & grass does not grow.
Gardens are bound up, & want rain.

Monday 23.
29 4/10; S; 19.
Dark & cold, rain,
cold.

Brother Thomas White came.

Tuesday 24.
29 7/10; 57; SW.
Sun, bright & pleasant.

Ophrys nidus avis blows in Comb-wood.
Rain is wanted. Wheat looks yellow.

Wednesday 25.
29 9/10; 57; NE.
Bright, & fine.

Mole cricket jars.

An old hunting mare, which ran on the common, being taken very
ill, came down into the village as it were to implore the help of
men, & dyed the night following in the street.

Thursday 26.
29 9/10¾; 39, 60;
NE. White frost, sun,
cool wind, red even.

Finished sowing kidney-beans, having used one quart, which
makes five rows, half white & half scarlet.

Friday 27.
29 9/10¾; 63; NE, E.
Dew, bright, dew,
sweet even.

Garden red valerian blows: where it sows itself it soon becomes
white.
Many swifts.
Some house-martins have just made a beginning of some new
nests under Mr Burbey's eaves.

Saturday 28.
29 9/10¼; 63; NE.
Cloudless, brisk gale,
red even.

Bantam hen brings-out four chickens.

Sunday 29.
29 8/10½; 63; NE.
Wh. frost, bright, fine
even.

Cut nine cucumbers.

The race of field-crickets, which burrowed in the short Lythe, &
used to make such an agreeable shrilling noise the summer long,
seems to be extinct. The boys, I believe, found the method of
probing their holes with the stalks of grasses, & so fetched them
out, & destroyed them.

Monday 30.
29 8/10; 64; NE.
Dark, no dew, sun, &
sharp wind, red even.

Cinamon-roses blow.

Tuesday 31.
29 7/10¼; 66; E, S.
Haze, no dew, sun,
heavy clouds.

Gardens suffer from want of rain.
Flowers smell well this evening: some dew.
Rain in May – 1 inch 33 h.

JUNE 1791

Wednesday 1.
29 7/10; 70; SW.
Hot sun, clouds, sultry.

Grass-walks burn.
Fern-owl, & chur-worm jar.¶

Ophrys nidus avis blows in the hanger.
Early orange lillies, & fiery begin to blow.
     Men wash their fatting sheep; & bay the stream¶ to catch trouts.

Thursday 2.
29 7/10¼; 63, 73; E,
S.
Some dew, hot sun,
sultry, heavy clouds.

Watered the garden. Kidney-beans begin to sprout.
Trouts come-up our shallow streams almost to the spring-heads to
lay their spawn.

Friday 3.
29 7/10¾; 73; E, SE.
Cloudless, sultry, red
even, dew.

Cleaned away the earth behind the hermitage, & alcove.
We draw much water for the garden, so that the well sinks.
Flowers are hurried out of bloom by the heat; spring corn &
gardens suffer.

Myriads of tadpoles traverse Comb-wood pond in shoales: when
rain comes they will emigrate to land, & will cover the paths &
fields.
     Fyfield sprung a fern-owl on the zig-zag, which seemed
confounded by the glare of the sun, & dropped again immediately.

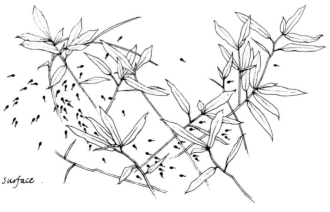

Tadpoles crowd near the surface.
Newton Valence pond.
Mid May.

Saturday 4.
29 7/10¼; 63, 73; SE, S.
Haze, sun, sultry, red even.

Transplanted out some cucumber-plants from an hand-glass in three of the lights. The distant hills look very blue in the evenings.

Mr Bridger sends me a fine present of trouts caught in the stream down at Oakhanger.

Saint foin blows, & the S^t foin fly, *Sphinx filipendula*, appears.

Rain at Emsworth.

Nightingale sings.

Sunday 5.
29 7/10½; 63, 76; SE, S, NW.
Sun, sultry, heavy clouds, red even.

Elder, & corn-flags begin to blow already.

Thunder to the SE, NE & NW.

Gardens, & fields suffer.

Wheat begins to come into ear: wheat, which was very yellow from the cold winds, by means of the heat has recovered it's colour without the assistance of rain.

   Male glow-worms, attracted by the light of the candles, come into the parlor.

Monday 6.
29 8/10¼; 74; NE.
Dew, cloudless, sultry, red even, dead calm.

Made seven hand-glass beds for ridge-cucumbers.

We draw much water for the garden.

The distant hills look very blue.

Tuesday 7.
29 8/10½; 66, 74; NE, SE, S.
Dew, cloudless, sultry, clouds, red even.

Hops grow prodigiously, yet are infested with some aphides.

Early cabbages turn hard, but boil well.

Watered kidney-beans, which come-up well.

The lettuces, which stood under the fruit-wall thro' the winter, are just over. They have been of great service at the table now for many weeks.

There was rain on Sunday on many sides of us, to the S. the SE. & the NW. at Alton & Odiham a fine shower, & at Emsworth, & at Newbury: & as near us as Kingsley.

Wednesday 8.
29 8/10; 66; N.
Shady, no dew, & cool.

Planted out the cucumbers raised under hand-glasses; & put four or five under each glass of which there are nine. The plants are some what drawn, but look fresh, & well.

Lime-trees show their bracteal leaves, & the rudiments of bloom.

Thursday 9.
29 6/10½; 66; N.
Shady & cool, sun, red even, dew.

Summer-cabbages, & lettuce come in.

Roses red & white blow.

No rain since May 23: gardens & fields much parched. ¶

No May chafers this year with us.

Path at foot of Hanger.
6 June.

Friday 10.
29 4/10; 63; NE, N.
Sun, drying air, clouds
about.

Grass burns.
The well sinks much.

Saturday 11.
29 3/10½; 50, 60; N.
Cloudy, & cold,
gleams, sharp wind.

Began to tack the vines Thomas finds more rudiments of bloom
than he expected.

Sunday 12.
29 4/10½; 50, 56;
NW.
Clouds, hail, shower,
gleams.

Pinks blow.
Sharp air, & fire in the parlor. Showers about. Garden-crops
much retarded, & nothing can be planted out.

Farmer Bridger sends me three real snipe's eggs: they are in shape,
& colour exactly like those of the lapwing, only one half less. The
colour of the eggs is a dull yellow, spotted with chocolate: they are
blunt at the great end, & taper much till they become sharp at the
smaller. The eggs, sent me for snipe's last year, seem to have been
those of a fern-owl.

Monday 13.
29 4/10½; 41, 56; N,
@, NE.
Ice! sharp air, hail,
showers, thunder,
gleams.

Serapias longilia, blows in the hanger.
Farmer Spencer mows his cow-grass.

Tuesday 14.
29 4/10¾; 40, 50; N,
SW.
White frost, dark &
cold.

Covered the kidney-beans with straw last night.

My annuals, which were left open, much injured by the frost: the
balsams, which touches the glass of the light, scorched. Kidney-
beans injured, & in some gardens killed. Cucumbers secured by
the hand-glasses; but they do not grow.
     The cold weather interrupts the house-martins in their building,
& makes them leave their nests unfinished.

Covered the kidney-beans with straw.

Wednesday 15.
29 5/10; NE, N.
Dark & cold, sharp.
Full moon.

Finished tacking vines: some few blossoms begin to open.
The kidney-beans at Newton-house not touched by the late frost.
Bro: Thomas left us.

Thursday 16.
29 1/10½; 40; N; 26.
Wet, stormy, cold rain,
wet, wet.

Snails come out of hedges after their long confinement from the
drought.
A swallow in Tanner's chimney has hatched.

I have no martins at the end of my brew-house, as usual.

The fern on the forest killed; but hardly touched by the frost on Selborne down, which is 400 feet higher than Wolmer.

Friday 17.
29; 4/10; 51, 58; E; 22.
Clouds, showers, heavy showers.

Planted out many annuals from Dan. Wheeler.
Pricked-out some celeri, good plants.
My crop of spinnage is just over: the produce from a pint of seed, sowed the first week in August, was prodigious.

Saturday 18.
29 4/10; 51, 58; NE.
Fog, soft showers, moist & warm.

Pricked out more celeri in my garden, & Mr Burbey's. Planted some cabbages from Dr Chandler's.
Hardly any hirundines to be seen.
Timothy hides himself during this wintry weather. The dry weather lasted just 3 weeks & three days; part of which was very sultry, & part very cold.

Sunday 19.
29 4/10; 62; E.
Sun, bright, cold wind.

A flock of ravens about the hanger for many days.

Monday 20.
29 4/10; E, N.
Grey, & cool, still.

BRAMSHOT PLACE
Went round by Petersfield.
Foxgloves blow.
By going round by Petersfield we made our journey to Bramshot 23 miles. After we had been driven 20 miles we found ourselves not a mile from Wever's down, a vast hill in Wolmer forest, & in the parish of Selborne. Bramshot in a direct line is only seven miles from Selborne.

Tuesday 21.
29 6/10; SW; 22.
Sun rises bright, grey, cool, rain, hard shower.

Mr Richardson's straw-berries dry, & tasteless.

Wednesday 22.
NW.
Fair, summer weather.

Thursday 23.
NW.
Fair, summer like.

GODALMING
Went to visit Mr Edmund Woods Senr
Swifts abound at Godalming.
Went to see the village of Compton, where my father lived more than sixty years ago, & where seven of his children were born. The people of the village remember nothing of our family. Mr Fullham's conservatory richly furnished; & the grounds behind his house engaging, & elegant.

Friday 24.
SW.
Summer like.

Meadows not cut.
Nymphaa lutea in bloom in a watry ditch.

The romantic grounds, & paddock at the west end of Godalming town are very bold & striking. The hanging woods very solemn, & grand; & many of the trees of great age & dimensions. This place was for many years inhabited by General Oglethorpe. The house is now under a general repair being with it's grounds the property of Mr Godbold a quack Doctor.

The vale & hanging woods round Godalming are very beautiful: the Wey a sweet river, & becomes navigable at this town. One branch of the Wey rises at Selburne.¶

Saturday 25.
SW.
Dark, bright & sultry.

SOUTH LAMBETH
Gardens & fields suffer from want of rain.
My brother's straw-berries well-flavoured.
The vines here in bloom, & smell very sweet.

Sunday 26.
29 9/10; SW.
Sun, sultry.

Fifteen Whites dined this day at my Bro. B. White's table as did also a Mr Wells, a great great great grandson of the Revd John Longworth, in old times vicar of Selburne, who dyed about the year 1678.
Dr & Mrs Chandler returned to Selburne.

At the entrance to the avenue leading to Bramshot-place are three great hollow oaks, the largest of which measures 21 feet in girth. We measured this tree at about 5 feet from the ground, & could not come at it lower on account of a dry stone-wall in which it stands. We measured also the largest Sycamore in the front of the house, & found the girth to be 13. They are very tall, & are deemed to be 80 feet in height: but I should suppose they do not exceed 74 feet. I hear much of trees 80 or 90 feet high; but have never measured any that exceed the supposed height of the Sycamores above.

Monday 27.
30; SW.
Sun, hot, clouds & a gale.

The bloom of the vine smells very fragrant.
Timothy Turner cuts my grass for himself, a small crop.
Scarabaeus solstitialis first appears in my brother's outlet: they were very punctual in their coming-out every year. They are a small species, about half the size of the May-chafer, & are known in some parts by the name of fern-chafer.

Tuesday 28.
30; 69; SW; 21.
Sun, bright, gales.

When the Baromr is 30 at S. Lambeth, it is 29.7 at Selborne, & 29.4 at Newton.
My brother cut a good Romagna melon.

Wednesday 29.
29 9/10; 7/10; 68, 75,
84; SE.
Sun, gales, sultry!

Hot sun, & drying wind. The gardens & fields suffer greatly.
No crops of celeri or cabbages can be pricked out. Annuals wither
& dye.
Thundrous clouds, lightening very distant.
Some swallows in this district, & only two pairs of swifts, & no
martins. No wonder then that they are over run with flies, which
swarm in the summer months, & destroy their grapes.

Thursday 30.
6½/10; 73; SE.
Dark, gale, rain,
gleams.

The Passion-flower buds for bloom: double flowering
Pomegranade has had bloom.
Rain in June – 91 hund.

Burnet moth on sanicle
Edge of the Hanger.
July .

JULY 1791

Friday 1.
30; 66; W; 15.
Dark, gale, hot.

Roses are now in high bloom, & very beautiful.

Large American straw-berries are hawked about which the sellers
call pine strawberries. But these are oblong, & of a pale red; where
as the true pine, or Drayton straw-berries are flat, & green: yet the
flavour is very quick, & truly delicate.
    The American new sorts of strawberries prevail so much, that
the old scarlet, & hautboys are laid aside & out of use.

Saturday 2.
29 8/10½; SW.
Fine rain, dark.

Four swifts.
The rain here was – 33.

Sunday 3.
29 6/10½; 62; SW;
49.
Clouds, hot, showers
about, wind, & rain.

M.ʳ M. black cluster-grapes in his pine-house seem to be well
ripened.

Monday 4.
29 5/10; 66; SW.
Wind & clouds,
showers, wind.

Rain here – 24. Rain 4.
The strong gales of July prevail: that month is usually blowing.

My brother's cow, when there is no extraordinary call for cream,
produces three pounds of butter each week. The footman churns
the butter overnight, & puts it in water; in the morning one of my
nieces beats it, & makes it up, & prints it.

Tuesday 5.
29 7/10; SW; 54.
Wind & clouds,
showers.

LONDON
Rasps come in.
Many Martins in the green park.

Wednesday 6.
W, SW.
Sun, showers, fine
even.

Rain here – 17.
Many martins in Lincolns inn fields.
Orange & white lilies make a fine show.
In a fruit-shop near St James were set out to sale black cluster-grapes, pine apples, peaches, nectarines, & Orleans plums.

Thursday 7.
30; SW; 18.
Fine, showers, clouds.

S. LAMBETH

Friday 8.
30, 30; 75; W, N.
Warm, hot gleams, red
even.

Cut chardon-heads for boiling: artichokes dry, & not well flavoured.
Roses in high beauty.
My nieces make Rasp jam. Goose-berries not finely flavoured.

Saturday 9.
30; 62; W.
Dark & chill.

A cuckoo cries in my Bro$^{r's}$ garden: some birds of that sort have frequented this place all the summer.
Scarlet kidney-beans blow. Young swallows at Stockwell.
Passion-flower begins to blow in the open air.
Double-flowering pomgranade¶ blows.
Cucumbers are scarce, & sell for 2½d. a piece.
Crops of pease go off. Some celeri trenched out from the seedling-bed.

In Mr Malcolm's gardens there is a bed of small silver firs, the tops of which are all killed by the frosts in June. The hothouses of this Gent: afford a most noble appearance; & his plantations are grand, & splendid.

Sunday 10.
29 7/10; SW; 97.
Louring, rain, rain.

Grapes swell. New potatoes.

Chardons are usually blanched, & stewed like celeri: but my Brother boils the heads of his, which are very sweet, & in flavour like artichokes; the chief objection is, that they are very small, & afford little substance in their bottoms. The heads of chardons are sold in the markets, & are thought to be a delicate morsel.
Chardons are strong, vigorous plants, & grow six & seven feet high, & have strong sharp prickles like thistles.

Monday 11.
57; N.
Dark & wet, blowing.

Rain in the night, 54.
Cuckoo sings. Rain – 5.

Tuesday 12.
29 8/10½; 59; NW.
Dark, sun, sweet
moonshine.

Young swallows come out.
Hollyhocks blow.

July 12. On this day my Bro. Benj. White began to rebuild his
house in Fleetstreet which he had entirely pulled to the ground. His
grandson Ben White laid the first brick of the new foundation, &
then presented the workmen with five shillings for drink. Ben, who
is five years old, may probably remember this circumstance
hereafter, & may be able to recite to his grandchildren the
occurrences of the day.

Wednesday 13.
30; W.
Dark & moist, sweet
gleam.

My brother's passion-flower blows: jasmines begin to blow.
My brother gathered a sieve of mushrooms: they come up in the
flower-borders, which have been manured with dung from the
old hot beds.

Thursday 14.
68; NW.
Fair.

A bat of the largest sort¶ comes forth every evening, & flits about in
the front of my brother's house. This is a very rare species, &
seldom seen. See my history of Selburne.

Friday 15.
30 2/10; 70; NW.
Sun, gale, sweet
moonshine, dew.
Full moon.

    The University of Oxford has just presented the Rev.ᵈ Samuel
Pegge to an honorary Doctor's degree. This venerable person is
arrived at the very advanced age of 87 years; & has been a writer
in the Gent: Mag: for more that[n] 60 years, by means of which
he has been the promoter of a great variety of knowledge, &
particularly in matters of Antiquity. He is Rector of Whittington in
the county of Derby.

Saturday 16.
30 1/10½; 68; NW.
Great dew, sun, gale,
cold, fog.

Ripening weather.
Perennial sun-flower blows.

Sunday 17.
29 9/10¾; 77; E; 39.
Fog, sun, hot, thunder,
small shower.

Heavy rain at Clapham, & Battersea.

On this day Mrˢ Edm.ᵈ White was brought to bed of a daughter,
who encreases my nephews, & nieces to the number of 58.

Monday 18.
29 8/10; 76, 81; E.
Dark, & hot, shower.

Beans & pease are gone, & their ground is filled up by several
sorts of cabbages to stand the winter.
Rain about.

Tuesday 19.
SW, W.
Sun, clouds, fine even.

ALTON
Kidney-beans come in, but most of the forward crop was killed
by the frosts.

Wednesday 20.
29 6/10; 61; SW; 19.

SELBORNE
Mrˢ Budd's annuals very fine.

Clouds, rain, gleam.

Ground well moistened: after-grass grows.
Rye cut, & bound at Clapham. Wheat looks well, & turns colour. Hay making at Farnham: pease are hacking near that town; Hops distempered.

Thursday 21.
29 7/10½; 60; W.
Grey, sun, warm.

Lime-trees in full bloom, & smell finely.
My broad beans are but just come in.

Friday 22.
29 7/10; 65; W.
Sun, warm, dark cloud.

Children bring wood-strawberries in great plenty. Made straw-berry jam.
Gathered currans, & rasps for jam: my rasps are fair & fine.
The farmers at Selborne had not half a crop of hay. Hops thrive at this place.

Saturday 23.
29 5/10; 64; SW; 21.
Rain, sun & gale, wet.

My celeri is trenched-out: it is strong & well grown.
Merise, wild cherries, over at the vicarage ripen.

Sunday 24.
29 4/10; 63; SW.
Dark, rain, rain.

The foreign Arum in the vicarage court, called by my Grandmother Dragons, & by Linnaeus *Arum dracunculus*, has lately blown. It is an Italian plant, & yet has subsisted there thro' all the severe frosts of 80, or 90 years; & has escaped all the diggings, & alterations that have befallen the borders of that garden. It thrives best under a N. wall, but how it is progagated does not appear.
The spatha, & spadix were very long.

Monday 25.
29 4/10; 62; SW; 73.
Heavy shower, wind & clouds, cold wind.

Preserved more rasps, strawberries, & currans, & some cherries.

Tuesday 26.
29 3/10¾; 62; SW; 29.
Showers, dark, rain, rain.

Mrs Henry White, & Lucy came from Fyfield.

Wednesday 27.
29 4/10½; 64; SW; 117, 6.
Vast rain in the night, sun & clouds, gleam.

Some straw-berries.

Thursday 28.
29 6/10; 62; W, S.
Dew, sun, pleasant.

Many swifts; probably the young are out.
Hops thrive at Selborne, & throw-out side shoots, & begin to shew bloom.

Friday 29.
29 3/10¾; 65; SW.
Shower, sun, louring,
wet.

A basket of mushrooms from Honey-lane.
Gathered wall-nuts for pickling.

Saturday 30.
29 6/10¾; 63; SW;
19.
Grey, mild, pleasant.

Made black curran-jelly.
Finished cutting the tall hedges.
Gathered some lavender.

Lavender in the herb garden.
Wakes.

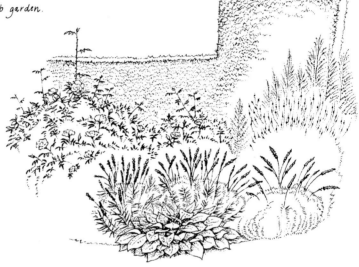

Sunday 31.
29 5/10; 65; SE, SW.
Grey, gale, louring.

Scarlet martagon blows. Some swifts.
Rain in July – 5 inch 56 h. 10, or 12 swifts.

"On the last of this month my Fathʳ Mʳ Ben. Wh. shot in his own
garden at S. Lambeth, a *Loxia curvirostra*, or Cross bill, as it was
feeding on the cones of his Scotch firs. There were six, four cocks,
& two hens: what he shot was a cock, which was beautifully
variegated with brown, & green, & a great deal of red: it answered
very accurately to Willughby's description; & weighed rather more
than 1 ounce & an half. In the evening the five remaining birds
were seen to fly over the garden, making a chearful note." Thus
far Mʳˢ Ben White. To which we add, that flights of Cross bills used
to frequent Mʳˢ Snooke's Scotch firs in the month of July only. Mʳ
Ray says "*per autumnum interdum sed rarius in Angliam venit,
non autem apud nos perennat aut nidificat.*"¶
Synopsis. avium.

AUGUST 1791

Monday 1.
29 6/10¾; 65; SW,

8 swifts.

W; 19.
Rain, rain, sun &
clouds.

The young plants on the old cucumber-bed bear a few: the hand-glass plants have no fruit set yet. Kidney-beans blow, but have no pods.
Gathered our whole crop of apricots, being one large fine fruit.

Tuesday 2.
29 8/10¾; 62; NW.
Sun, mild, sweet
afternoon.

2 swifts.
Sowed white turnip radishes.
Some wood straw-berries are brought still.
Planted-out Savoys, & other winter cabbages.

Wednesday 3.
29 9/10½; 59, 64;
NW, S.
Sun, sweet day.

Some what of a chilly feel begins to prevail in the mornings & evenings. Wood straw-berries.
5 swifts.
Sowed a pint of London prickly spinage-seed to stand the winter. The same quantity last year produced an incredible crop. Trod & rolled in the seed.

Thursday 4.
29 9/10; 65; NW, W.
Sun, sweet day.

Farmer Tull begins to reap wheat.
Bullfinches, & red-breasts eat the berries of honey-suckles.

In Mr Hale's hop-garden near Dell are several hills containing male plants, which now shed their farina: the female plants begin to blow. Men hoe turnips, & hack pease.
Men house hay as black as old thatch.

Friday 5.
29 8/10; 69; SW.
Fog, hot sun, sweet
weather.

Mrs H. White & Lucy left us.
Cut one cucumber from the hand-glass plants.
Two dobchicks in Combwood pond. Two swifts.
Young martins, & swallows cluster on the tower, & on trees, for the first time. A pleasing circumstance mixed with some degree of regret for the decline of summer'.

Saturday 6.
29 7/10½; 66; 69; N,
S.
Dark & hot, warm.

Boys bring wasp's nest.
Codlings, & stewed cucumber come in.
Housed, & piled 8 cords of beechen billet in fine order.
Watered the cucumbers; well very low.

Sunday 7.
6/10½; 29 7/10; 65,
71; S, NW.
Partial fogs, sun,
ripening weather.

The first broods of swallows, & house-martins, which congregate on roofs, & trees, are very numerous: & yet I have not this year one nest about my buildings.
Received from Farnham, well packed in a box, a picture of a mule pheasant,¶ painted by Mr Elmer, & given me by Lord Stawell. I have fixed it in a gilt, burnished frame, & hung it in my great parlor, where it makes an elegant piece of furniture.

Monday 8.
29 7/10½; 56, 68;
NE.
Sun, hot ripening
gleams, dark &
louring.

M.ʳ Hale begins wheat harvest. 1 swift.
Boys bring a wasp's nest. Cut 22 cucumbers.

Goose-berries, rasps, currans, & straw-berries are gone, & over.
Some young broods of fly-catchers play about.

Tuesday 9.
29 7/10; 65; NE, E.
Sun, cool wind, haze.

Wheat-harvest becomes general.
Boys bring two wasps nests.

Wednesday 10.
29 5/10½; 67; E.
Sun, brisk gale, still.

Watered cucumbers.

Thursday 11.
29 5/10; 67; E, S.
Dark, no dew, sun, hot,
sweet moon-light.

Half hogshead of portwine from Southampton.
Gleaners come home with corn.
One swift.

Friday 12.
29 6/10; 68; SE, S.
Wet fog, sultry gleams,
louring.

Men bind their wheat all day. The harvesters complain of heat.
The hand-glass cucumbers begin to bear well: red kidney-beans
begin to pod.
Showers about.

Saturday 13.
29 8/10; 68; W.
Shower, sun, louring.
Full moon.

Farmer Tull makes a wheat-rick at Wick-hill.

Sunday 14.
29 7/10; 71; SE, S.
Sun, sultry, soft even.

Hirundines enjoy the warm season.
Bright gleam to the W. Lightening to the S.
Shower.
Farmer Spencer's char-coal making in his orchard almost
suffocated us: the poisonous smoke penetrated into our parlor, &
bed-chambers, & was very offensive in the night.

Aug.ˢᵗ 14. Late this evening a storm of thunder arose in the S.
which, as usual, divided into two parts, one going to the S. W. &
W. & the greater portion to the SE. & E. so round to the N.E.
From this latter division proceeded strong & vivid lightening till
late in the night. At Headleigh there was a very heavy shower, &
some hail at E. Tisted. The lightening, & hail did much damage
about the kingdom.

Monday 15.
29 6/10; 72; SE; 9.

Distant thunder.

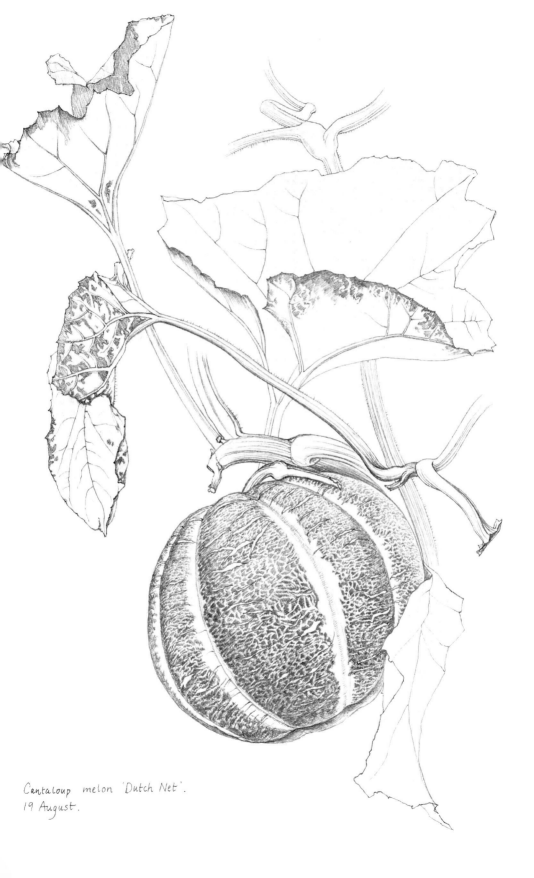

Cantaloup melon 'Dutch Net'.
19 August.

Shower, hot gleams,
louring, & sultry.

Wheat ricked, & housed all the day.
Lightening every moment in the W. & N.W.
Cut 114 cucumbers.
Harvesters complain of violent heat.

Tuesday 16.
29 5/10½; 70, 70; W;
8.
Dark, & moist,
shower, rain, steady
shower.

Some pease, & wheat housed.
Colchicums, or naked boys appear.

Wednesday 17.
29 8/10; 66; SW, W;
51.
Showers, showers, red
even.

Holt White, & Harry Woods came from Fyfield.

Thursday 18.
29 9/10¼; 30; 62; NE.
Bright, sun, great dew,
hot, chill.

Timothy grazes.
John White came from Salisbury.
Farmer Spencer, & Farmer Knight make each a noble wheat-
rick: the crop very good, & in fine order.
Cut 133 more cucumbers.
Much damage was done by lightening, & hail about the country.
Michaelmass daiseys begin to blow.

Friday 19.
30 1/10; 65; NE.
Dew, sun, sweet day,
golden even.

The young men left us, & went to Funtington.
Corn housed.
Red horizon. Some what of an autumnal feel.
A second crop of beans, long pods, come in.

Saturday 20.
30 1/10; 65; E.
Dew, sun, sweet day,
cool.

John White called in his way from Funtinton to Salisbury.
The whole country is one rich prospect of harvest scenery!!
Fern-owl glances along over my hedges.

Sunday 21.
29 8/10½; 62; E, SE.
Dark & cool, sun, cool.

Scarlet kidney-beans come in.

Many creatures are endowed with a ready discernment to see what
will turn to their own advantage & emolument; & often discover
more sagacity than could be expected. Thus Benham's poultry
watch for waggons loaded with wheat, & running after them pick
up a number of grains which are shaken from the sheaves by the
agitation of the carriages. Thus when my brother used to take
down his gun to shoot sparrows, his cats would run out before him
to be ready to catch up the birds as they fell.

Monday 22.
29 7/10; 62; SE.
Fog, dark, gleams.

Showers about.
Cut 60 cucumbers.

Tuesday 23.
29 6/10½; 75; SE, S.
Vast dew, cloudless, not
sun.

Sowed brown Dutch lettuce to stand the winter.

Wednesday 24.
29 6/10; 66; SW; 8.
Dark, gale, wet,
gleams, yellow evening.

Gathered kidney-beans, scarlet.
Cut 80 cucumbers.

Thursday 25.
29 6/10; W.
Sun, gale, dark.

Several men finish wheat-harvest.
Holt White came back from Shopwick.
Ophrys spiralis blows.
Peaches & nectarines well-flavoured.

Friday 26.
29 6/10¾; 63; W.
Sun, gale, mild.

Distant thunder in the night.
Cut 30 cucumbers.
My potatoes come in, & are good.

Saturday 27.
29 5/10; 62; SW; 28.
Rain, showers.

Cut 179 cucumbers: in all this week – 349.
A large sea-gull went over my house.

Sunday 28.
29 3/10½; 63; SW.
Sun, gale, gleam,
shower.

White kidney-beans come in.

Monday 29.
29 6/10; 60, 62; NW.
Sun & clouds, red
even.

Hop-picking begins in Hartley-gardens.
Cut 96 cucumbers.
Fern-owl appears. Autumnal feel.

Tuesday 30.
29 7/10; 59, 55; NW.
Sun & clouds, cool
even.

Mr Hale begins his hops near the Poundfield.
Farmer Hoar says, that during this blowing weather his well was
raised some rounds of the rope.

Wednesday 31.
29 3/10½; 58; SE, 50.
Rain, rain, rain.

Cut 31 cucumbers.
Rain in August – 1 inc; 73 hund.
Fly-catcher still appears.

SEPTEMBER 1791

Thursday 1.
29 8/10; 58, 61; N; 25.
Blowing night, &
morning, calm
sunshine, red even.

Much damage done to the hops.
Earthed celeri, & planted cabbages.
Chill air.

Friday 2.
29 6/10; 62; SW.
Grey, dark, moist.

Some few grapes begin to turn colour.
Cut 62 cucumbers.
Holt White left us, & went to Newton.

Saturday 3.
29 3/10¼; 62; SW.
Rain, dark, rain, rain.

Bad weather for the hops, & pickers.
Blowing.

When the boys bring me wasps nests, my Bantam fowls fare
deliciously; & when the combs are pulled to pieces, devour the
young wasps in their maggot-state with the highest glee, & delight.
Any insect-eating bird would do the same; & therefore I have often
wondered that the accurate Mr Ray should call one species of
buzzard *Buteo apivoros, sive vespivorus,* or the Honey Buzzard,
because some combs of wasps happened to be found in one of their
nests. The combs were conveyed thither doubtless for the sake of
the maggots or nymphs, & not for their honey; since none is to be
found in the combs of wasps. Birds of prey occasionally feed on
insects: thus have I seen a tame kite picking up the female ants,
full of eggs, with much satisfaction.

Sunday 4.
29 4/10; 62; W; 128.
Sun, showers, bright
even.

Vast rain in the night, with lightening.

Monday 5.
29 7/10; 63; W.
Sun, fine day.

Cut 107 cucumbers.
Nectarines are finely flavoured, but eaten by bees, & wasps.
Churn-owl is seen over the village: fly-catchers seem to be gone.

Tuesday 6.
29 6/10; 63; SW.
Rain, warm, & wet.

Tyed up about 30 endives.
A swift still hovers¶ about the brew house at Fyfield. About a
week ago one young swift, not half fledged, was found under the
eaves of that building! The dam no doubt is detained to this very
late period by her attendance on this late-hatched callow young!
The roof of my nephew's brew-house abounds with swifts all the
summer.

Wednesday 7.
29 8/10, 67; SW.
Wet, & warm, wet,
gleam.

Cut 125 cucumbers.

Young martins, several hundreds, congregate on the tower, church, & yew-tree. Hence I conclude that most of the second broods are flown. Such an assemblage is very beautiful, & amusing, did it not bring with it an association of ideas tending to make us reflect that winter is approaching; & that these little birds are consulting how they may avoid it.

House martins gather.
Selborne High Street.

Thursday 8.
29 8/10½; 66; NE; 20.
Dark & warm, sun,
hot, moist, & dark.

Fine nectarines abound, but are much eaten by wasps, & flies.

Friday 9.
29 7/10; 70; E.
Fog, hot sun, red even.

Gathered in the white apples, a very fine crop of large fine fruit, consisting of many bushels.
Grapes turn.

Saturday 10.
29; 7/10½; 73; SE.
Fog, cloudless, sultry,
red even.

Young broods of swallows come out.
Cut 171 cucumbers: in all 424 this week.
Sweet moon light!

Sunday 11.
29 8/10; 73; SE.
Vast dew, cloudless,
sultry, red even, sweet
moon.

Grey crow returns, & is seen near Andover.
Some nightly thief stole a dozen of my finest nectarines.
Broods of swallows & martins continue to come out.

Monday 12.
29 8/10; 72; E.
Deep fog, sun,
cloudless, sultry, sweet
moon-light.
Full moon.

Cut 108 cucumbers.
Ivy begins to blow.
Farmer Spencer finished his harvest.

The congregating flocks of hirundines on the church & tower are very beautiful, & amusing! When they fly-off altogether from the Roof, on any alarm, they quite swarm in the air. But they soon settle in heaps, & preening their feathers, & lifting up their wings to admit the sun, seem highly to enjoy the warm situation. Thus they spend the heat of the day, preparing for their emigration, & as it

were consulting when & where they are to go. The flight about the
church seems to consist chiefly of house-martins, about 400 in
number:but there are other places of rendezvous about the village
frequented at the same time. The swallows seems to delight more
in holding their assemblies on trees.

"When Autumn scatters his departing gleams,
Warn'd of approaching winter gathered play
The Swallow people; & toss'd wide around
O'er the calm sky in convolution swift,
The feather'd eddy floats: rejoicing once
Ere to their wintry slumbers they retire,
In clusters clung beneath the mouldring bank,
And where, unpierced by frost, the cavern sweats.
Or rather into warmer climes convey'd,
With other kindred birds of season, there
They twitter chearful, till the vernal months
Invite them welcome back:— for thronging now
In numerous wings are in commotion all."¶

Tuesday 13.
29 8/10½; 63, 70; E.
Deep fog, cloudless,
sultry, sweet even.

My well is very low, & the water foul!
Timothy eats voraciously.
Winged female ants migrate from their nests, & fill the air.
These afford a dainty feast for the hirundines, all save the swifts;
they being gone before these emigrations, which never take place
till sultry weather in August, & September.

Wednesday 14.
29 9/10; 72; NE.
Cloudless, hot sun, red
even.

Hop-picking goes on without the least interruption.
Stone-curlews cry late in the evenings.

Thursday 15.
29 9/10½; 69; N, NE.
Cloudless, hot sun, &
cool air.

The hops ripen very fast, & turn brown.
The springs are very low: the water fails at Webb's bridge.

Friday 16.
29 8/10½; 69; NW,
W.
Cloudless, brisk air,
red even, still.

Cluster-grapes begin to ripen.
Cut 25 cucumbers.

Saturday 17.
29 8/10; 63; N.
Cloudy, cool, sun.

Several young martins still in their nests.

Sunday 18.
29 5/10; 59, 60; W,
NW.

Very few hirundines are seen.

Dark, cold air, small
shower, gleams, chill
air.

Monday 19.
29 7/10½; 55; NW.
Sun, cold air, sun, red
even.

Few swallows: no flocks congregating.
Cut 59 cucumbers. Cut artichokes.

Tuesday 20.
29 7/10¼; 55; N.
White dew, sun, cool
air.

Few swallows. Timothy eats voraciously.
Several neighbours finish their hops.
Began to light a fire in the parlor.

Wednesday 21.
29 7/10½; 57; W.
Dark, & calm.

Several hirundines again. Some young martins in their nests.

The whole air of the village of an evening is perfumed by effluvia
from the hops drying in the kilns.

Thursday 22.
29 7/10; 59; N.
Grey, sun, sweet
afternoon.

The tops of the beeches begin to be tinged.
The frost of tuesday has cut the cucumber-leaves.

Friday 23.
29 7/10; 59; NW.
Grey, gleams, cool.

Very few hirundines.

Saturday 24.
29 8/10; 59; N.
Dark, sun, sweet even.

Young martins, & swallows come-out, & are fed flying.
Endive well blanched comes in.
Bottled-off half hogsh: of port wine. The port ran eleven doz. &
7 bottles.
Nep. Ben White, & wife, & little Ben came.

Sunday 25.
29 9/10; NE, E.
Grey, sun, sweet day,
red even.

Some hirundines.

Several wells in the village are dry; my well is very low; Burbey's,
Turner's, & Dan. Loe's hold out very well.

Monday 26.
29 8/10¾; 55; E.
White dew, sun &
clouds.

Gathered in the pear-mains, golden rennets, & golden pippins.

Tuesday 27.
29 8/10¾; E.
Sun, blue mist, red
even, still.

Strong cold gale.

Wednesday 28.
29 9/10; 53; E.
Sun, white dew, brisk
air, red even.

Linnets congregate in great flocks.
This sweet autumnal weather has lasted three weeks, from
Sept.ʳ 8.ᵗʰ

Thursday 29.
29 9/10; 59; NE.
White frost, sun, red
even.

A gale rises every morning at ten o'the clock, & falls at sunset.
Grapes very fine.

Friday 30.
29 8/10, 59; E.
Fog, sun, warm sun,
bright.

Rain in Septem.ʳ – 1 inch 73.

OCTOBER 1791

Saturday 1.
29 6/10½; 59; SW,
SW.
Sun, frost, mild, warm
sun, grey.

Nep. B. White left us, & went to London.
It was with difficulty that we procured water enough for a
brewing from my well.

Sunday 2.
29 7/10; 56; NE, W,
NW.
Sun, clouds,
sprinkling, grey, &
mild.

Gathered one fine nectarine, the last.
My double-bearing raspberries produce a good crop. Grapes
very fine. Endive good.

Monday 3.
29 7/10; 60; S, SE.
Fog, wet, dark, soft.

Tuesday 4.
29 5/10; 61; S.
Rain, dark, & wet.

Some few hirundines.

Wednesday 5.
29 5/10; 63; S, SE; 38.
Sun, mild, cloudless,
sweet day.

Swallows, & martins, that seemed almost to have left us, now
abound round the church, & tower. Some swallows just out.

Oct.ʳ 5.ᵗʰ Arrived off the isle of Wight the *Earl Fitzwilliams* Capt.ⁿ
Dundas from Madras. Charles Etty sailed in this India man as
second mate about the 10.ᵗʰ of March 1790.
     Poor Charles Etty did not come home in the *Earl Fitzwilliams*,
having unfortunately broke his leg at Madras the evening before
the ship sailed for Europe.

Thursday 6.
29 4/10¾; 61; S, SW;
19. Rain, rain, grey &
mild.

Received a bag of hops from M.ʳ Hale, weight 61 pounds.

Friday 7.
29 4/10½; 56; SW.
Grey, sun, dark, mild,
even yellow.

Some hirundines. Endive & Coss lettuce very fine.
Beeches in my fields shed their mast: their foliage turns very fast.
Gathered in Chaumontel, swans-eggs, & Virgoleuse pears: the
latter rot before they ripen. Gathered also the kitchen apples at
the end of the fruit-wall, & the knobbed russetings: of both there
is a great crop. Gathered the Cadillac pears, a small crop.

Saturday 8.
29 4/10¾; W, SW.
Sun, pleasant day.

Earthed up the celeri, which is very gross, & large.
Some martins.

Sunday 9.
28 9/10; 57; SE.
Rain, rain, rain, mild,
& still.

It has been observed that divers flies, besides their sharp, hooked
nails, have also skinny palms or flaps to their feet, whereby they
are enabled to stick on glass, & other smooth bodies, & to walk on
ceilings with their backs downward by means of the pressure of the
atmosphere, on those flaps; the weight of which they easily
overcome in warm weather, when they are brisk & alert. But in the
decline of the year, this resistance becomes too mighty for their
diminished strength; & we see flies labouring along, & lugging
their feet in windows as if they stuck fast to the glass: & it is with
the utmost difficulty they can draw one foot after an other, &
disengage their hollow caps from the slippery surface.

Upon the same principle that flies stick, & support themselves,
do boys, by way of play, carry heavy weights, by only a piece of
wet leather at the end of a string clapped close on the surface of a
stone.

Monday 10.
28 9/10; SE, 77.
Showers, sun, heavy
showers, lightening,
thunder.

Gathered a plate of fine raspberries.
Some swallows, & martins.

Some of my neighbours had so many hops, that they went twice to
Wey-hill with their waggons. The whole growth of the parish of
Selborne this year is estimated at near 30 tons. Hops sold well at
the fair.

Tho' the Virgoleuse pears always rot before they ripen, & are
eatable; yet when baked dry on a tin, they become an excellent
sweetmeat.

Tuesday 11.
29 2/10½; W; 58.
Sun, fair & pleasant,
sweet moonlight.
Full moon.

Some hirundines.
Cucumber haulm decays.
One of my Apricot-trees withers, & looks as if it would die.

Wednesday 12.
29 5/10; 41; 52; E, N.
White frost, fine, red
even.

Gathered cucumbers for picklers. Fine rasps.
Much gossamer on the down. One martin.
My beeches in the field shed ripe mast.
Some of the Bantams sicken.
Mrs Ben White left us, & took Tom with her, leaving Ben
behind.
Hunter's moon rises early.

Thursday 13.
29 2/10; 52; SE, S.
White dew, sun, heavy
clouds to the E.

Gathered in royal russets & nonpariels.
Several hirundines.

Friday 14.
29; 53; S; 31.
Rain, rain, fair.

One or two swallows.
Aurora.

Saturday 15.
29 ½/10; 53; E.
White frost, sun, &
wind.

Several hirundines.
Bro. Ben, & wife, Hannah came.
Wood-cock, & red wings return, & are seen.

Sunday 16.
29 2/10½; NW, N.
Fog, sun, cool.

Monday 17.
29 2/10; 45; SE.
Sun, white frost,
pleasant, wet.

Saw a wood-cock on the down among the fern:
Fyfield flushed it.

Tuesday 18.
29 1/10¾; 55; W.
Sun, strong wind, rain.

Celeri comes in, & is very large.

Wednesday 19.
29 1/10; 55; S, W, 68.
Rain, rain, sun, dark.

Three or four martins.

Thursday 20.
28 6/10; 56; SW; 121.
Vast showers with hail,
warm air.

Much rain in the night. Thunder & lightening.
A few hirundines.
Lightening.

Friday 21.
28 8/10; 55; 56; SW;
48.
Showers, & wind.

Rain in the night.
One swallow.

Saturday 22.
29 2/10; W; 11.
Sun, fair & cool.

One young martin in one of Burbey's nests, which the dams continue to feed.
Gracious stream now runs a little.

Sunday 23.
29 5/10½; N.
Frost, sun & sharp air.

Monday 24.
29 6/10½; 31; N.
Hard frost, ice, sun,
bright & still, frost.

The dams continue to feed the poor little martin in the nest at Burbey's with great assiduity!

Tuesday 25.
29 5/10; 2/10½; SE.
Sun, thaw, heavy
showers, hail & rain.

There are two young martins in the nest.

Wednesday 26.
29 4/10; 42; N; 112.
Rain, rain, rain.

No young martins to be seen in the nest, nor old ones round it.

Thursday 27.
29 8/10½; 41; NE; 51.
Sun, bright, &
pleasant.

Young martins, & their dams again.
Wood-cock on the down.
Bro. Ben, & wife, & Hannah left us, & went to Newton.
Shower.

Friday 28.
30 ½/10; 45; NE; 15.
Bright, & sharp.

There are now apparently three young martins in the nest nearly fledged.
Fieldfares in great flocks.

Saturday 29.
30; 44; NE.
Frost, ice, sun, & sharp
air.

The young martins remain.

Sunday 30.
29 7/10½; 44; E.
Sun, cutting wind.

The young martins still in their nests; at least some of them. Dr Chandler saw four hawking round the pleastor.

Monday 31.
29 5/10½; 43; E.
Sun, cutting wind.

The young martins not seen in their nest: dams about.
Rain in October – 6 in 49 hund.

NOVEMBER 1791

Tuesday 1.
29 5/10; 43; E.
Frost, cutting wind.

The young martins are out: one was found dead this morning in the parsonage garden.

Wednesday 2.
29 3/10; N.
Sharp air, snow, snow.

NEWTON
The late rains have not had any influence yet on my well-water, which is very low, & foul.
Snow on the Sussex downs.
Snow covers the ground.

Thursday 3.
29 3/10; N.
Thaw, rain, dark & wet.

Snow melts very fast.

Friday 4.
29 3/10; 38; NW; 41.
Grey, gleams.

SELBORNE
Snow gone.

Saturday 5.
29 5/10½; N.
Grey, sun, sharp wind, moonshine.

Sunday 6.
29 8/10½; 28; N.
Frost, bright & sharp, frost.

Monday 7.
29 8/10½; 22! 30; NE.
Severe frost, bright, & sharp.

Planted two rows of brown Dutch lettuce under the fruit-wall to stand the winter. Dug up carrots. Dunged the fruit-border under the wall.

Tuesday 8.
29 7/10; 42; SE, S.
Frost, sun, still, & bright.

Planted one doz. of red hairy goose-berries, & one doz. of smooth amber, from Armstrong, in the quarters of the garden. Gathered-in the grapes: decaying.
Two rills run now into my well, the water of which begins to get clear.

Wednesday 9.
29 7/10; 40; SW.
Vast dew, warm, heavy rain.

Dew on the *outside* of the windows.
Planted a row of Hyacinths on the verge of the fruit-border; & tulips along the broad walk. Planted winter-cabbages. Potatoes dug up.

Thursday 10.
29 7/10½; 50; SW;
77.
Dark & mild, rain.

Timothy comes out.

Friday 11.
29 5/10; 49; SE, S; 46.
Grey, moonshine.

Saturday 12.
29 2/10; SW.
Mild, & moist.

Timothy appears.

Sunday 13.
29; 48; SE; 19.
Dark & mild.

Thunder in the night.
Thomas heard the Portsmouth evening gun.

Monday 14.
28 7/10; 47; SE, NW;
40.
Wet, dark & dismal.

Tuesday 15.
28 8/10; SW, S; 46.
Bright, wet, rain.

Timothy out.
Stormy with much rain.

Wednesday 16.
28 6/10; 46; SW; 109.
Showers, blowing, fair.

Thunder in the night.

Thursday 17.
28 5/10½; 43; SE.
Dark & mild, heavy
rain.

Friday 18.
28 5/10; W, SW; 100.
Grey, gleam, rain.

Much rain in the night.

Saturday 19.
28 6/10; E, SE; 146,
50.
Dark & wet, rain.

Much rain in the night. Thunder.

Sunday 20.
29 2/10; 47; E.
Rain, rain, rain,
bright.

Monday 21.
29 5/10; SW; 48.
Mild & moist, grey,
bright.

Tuesday 22.
29 6/10; 47; SW.   Timothy comes out.
Grey, sun, pleasant.   Finished dressing & tacking my vines: the wood of last summer
                          is well ripened.

Wednesday 23.
29 5/10; SE.
Grey & mild.

Thursday 24.
29 5/10; 50; SE.
Grey & mild, rain.

Friday 25.
29 6/10; 48; SW; 58.   Well rises very fast.
Sun, sun, shower.

Saturday 26.
30; NW.   Timothy comes-out, & eats. Insects swarm in the air.
Bright, pleasant.   3 gallons of brandy from London.

Sunday 27.
29 8/10; W.
Grey, windy.

Monday 28.
29 1/10; W.   M^r & Mrs Edm^d White came.
Wet, & windy, hard
rain.

Tuesday 29.
29; W; 36.   Put a large white cross on the hermitage.
Sun, blowing.   A trufle-hunter tryed my tall hedges, & found some bulbs of
                          those peculiar plants, which have neither roots, nor branches, nor
                          stems.

Wednesday 30.
29 1/10; 41; W.   Rain in Nov^r – 8 inch 16 h.
Sun, mild, rain.   Lightening.

DECEMBER 1791

Thursday 1.
29 2/10; SW; 28.   M^r & Mrs White left us.

Grey, wet, dark.

Friday 2.
29; W; 38.
Showers, showers.
Moonshine.

The Hermitage, new capped with a coat of thatch, & embellished with a large cross, makes a very picturesq object on the hanger, & takes the eye agreeably.

Saturday 3.
29; 34; E.
Dark, & sharp, snow.

Snow covers the ground. Snow shoe deep.

Sunday 4.
29 2/10½; 31; NW;
128.
Dark, gleams,
moonshine.

Snow gone except on the hill: much rain in night. The snow of last night was very deep in many parts of the kingdom.

Monday 5.
29 3/10½; 24; E.
Hard frost, sun.

Cut down, & covered the artichokes: covered the rhubarb plants; & the lettuces under the fruit-wall, & the spinage lightly with straw.

Tuesday 6.
29 3/10½; 30; SE, S.
Hard frost, swift thaw,
rain, frost.

Wednesday 7.
29 1/10; SW; 37.
Sun, rain, fair.

Ground very wet.
Farmer Tull plants Butt-close with hops.

Thursday 8.
29 1/10½; 32; W.
Frost, sun, sharp wind,
frost.

Timothy has laid himself up under the hedge against Benham's yard in a very comfortable, snug manner: a thick tuft of grass shelters his back, & he will have the warmth of the winter sun.

Friday 9.
29 1/10¼; 31; W.
Frost, sleet, sun, frost.

Some little snow.

Saturday 10.
29 1/10; 29; W.
Hard frost, sun, cutting
wind, small snow,
frost.
Full moon.

Sunday 11.
29 4/10; 25; NW.

Snow covers the ground.

Hard frost, still, sun,
snow.

Monday 12.
29; 23; S.   Ice within doors.
Hard frost, dark, thaw,
rain & wind.

Tuesday 13.
28 8/10; SW; 53.
Rain, sun, clouds,
moonshine & frost.

Wednesday 14.
29; SE, E.
Shower, sun, mild,
rain.

Thursday 15.
29 6/10½.
Grey, still, bright.

Friday 16.
29 9/10; 26, 27; N.   Swept-up the leaves in the walks.
Hard frost, sun, frost.

Saturday 17.
30; 21, 29; NW, S.   Very white. Boys slide.
Hard frost, sun, still.   Snipes come up from the forest along the meads by the sides of
                                    the stream.
                                    Hardly here & there a wood-cock to be seen.

Sunday 18.
29 7/10½; 28, 40; SE,
S.
Frost, very white,
thaw, wet, rain.

Monday 19.
29 7/10; 34; N; 16.   Paths very dirty.
Grey, thaw, frost.

Tuesday 20.
29 7/10½; 32; N.   Saw lately a white, & a yellow wagtail¶ about the Well-head
Frost, sun, sharp, small   rivulet. No farther north than Rutland wagtails withdraw, & are
snow.   never seen in the winter.

Wednesday 21.   NEWTON
29 7/10; 32; N.
Dark & cold, frost.

Thursday 22.
28; S.
Frost, sun, pleasant,
rain, stormy, & much
rain.

Boys slide.

Friday 23.
28 5/10; 40; SW; 62.
Rain, gleams, rain,
frost.

SELBORNE
M.ʳ Churton came from Oxford.

Saturday 24.
29 3/10; 31; W.
Frost, sharp wind,
ground covered with
sleet.

Sunday 25.
29; SW.
Wet, rain, rain.

Aurora bor.

Monday 26.
29 4/10; SW.
Grey.

Tuesday 27.
28 9/10; 36.
Dark, & wet, rain.

Wednesday 28.
29 5/10; 45; W, 15.
Bright, sun.

Thursday 29.
29 9/10; 31; W.
Frost, sun.

Friday 30.
29 6/10; 35; SW.
Frost, sun, rain.

Saturday 31.
29 1/10½; SW; 80.
Rain, rain.

Rain in December – 4 in. 93 h.

Rain in 1791
Jan.	673
Feb.	464
Mar.	159
Apr.	113

May	133
June	91
July	556
Aug.	173
Sep.ʳ	173
Oct.ʳ	649
Nov.ʳ	816
Dec.ʳ	493
	44.93

JANUARY   — 1792 —

Sunday 1.
29 3/10½; SE.   Rain in the night.
Mild, & still.

Monday 2.
29 7/10½; 44; N; 32.
Rain, fog, grey.

Tuesday 3.
29 9/10; N.
Grey & still.

Wednesday 4.
30 ½/10; 44; N.
Grey, wet, mild.

Thursday 5.
30 ½/10; NE.
Dark & still.

Friday 6.
29 9/10½; NE.   Snow-drops, & crocus's shoot.
Still, moist, & dark.

Saturday 7.
29 6/10½; N.
Dark, mild & still.

Sunday 8.
29 8/10; N.   Sleet on the ground.
Frost, sun, moonshine.   Mʳ Churton left us, & returned to Oxford.

Monday 9.
29 1/10; 29; W.
Driving snow, rain &
wind. Full moon.

Honey Lane.
9 January

Tuesday 10.
29; 32; W; 24.
Grey, mild & still.

Wednesday 11.
28 9/10; 24, 21; NE.
Hard frost, sun, hard
frost.

Thursday 12.
29 1/10; 16½; NW.
Severe frost, bright,
frost.

Friday 13.
29 4/10; 16½, 21,   Vast frost-work on the windows.
15½; NW.
Severe frost, bright,
frost.

Saturday 14.
28 9/10; 25; SE, SE.   Lord Stawell sends me a cock & an hen brambling.
Red morn, grey &
windy, sharp, snow,
thaw.

Sunday 15.
28 7/10; 44; SE; 45.   Snow, which covered the ground, gone.
Dark, & wet.   Vast condensations on walls.

Monday 16.
28 8/10; 43; SE.   Vast condensations.
Rain, rain, rain.

Tuesday 17.
29 4/10; 43; SE, N;
53.
Warm & wet, rain.   The *Antirrhinum Cymb.*¶ which flourished, & blossomed thro' all
                           last winter, & the summer & autumn following, now killed by
Wednesday 18.   the frost. Hence it is probable that in milder regions it is at least a
29 5/10½; NE.   biennial, if not perrenial. Before, it has always dyed every winter
Dark & moist.   as soon as the hard frosts began to prevail.

Thursday 19.
29 6/10¼; 31; E.   Winter-aconites blow: snow drops bud.
Snow, snow, snow.   The wood-men begin to fell the beeches on the hanger.

Friday 20.
29 5/10; 32; E.   Snow on the ground.

Dark, & sharp.

Saturday 21.
29 5/10; 30; E.   Hepaticas blow.
Thaw with deep fog.

Sunday 22.
29 2/10; E.
Fog, dark & moist.

Monday 23.
29 3/10; NW; 61.   Rain & snow in the night.
Grey, thaw, snow gone.   Water-cresses come in.

Tuesday 24.
28 9/10; 43; S; 27.   Rain in the night.
Dark & mild, great   Condensations on the outsides of the windows.
rain.

Wednesday 25.
29 ½/10; SW; 91.
Grey & mild, gleams,
mild.

Thursday 26.
29; SW; 114.   Much rain in the night.
Rain, wet, & blowing
all day.

Friday 27.
29 3/10; SW.   *The Swallow*, Lord Cornwallis's advice sloop, arriv'd at Bristol
Mild, gleams.   from Madras, which it left on the 21ˢᵗ of Septemʳ The weather
                      was so rough, that it could not get up the British channel.

Saturday 28.
S; 74.
Rain.

Sunday 29.
29 2/10½; 47; S, SE. Snow drops blow.
Soft, grey, rain.

Monday 30.
29 2/10½; S; 33.
Rain, mild, wind &
rain.

Tuesday 31.
29 2/10½; 47; S; 53. Hasel-catkins open; crocus's swell; hasels blow.

Grey, mild.   Rain in Jan. – 6 inch 7 h.

FEBRUARY 1792

Wednesday 1.
29 6/10; SW.   Turner's heifers feed down the dead gra.. in my great mead.
Grey & mild, gleams,
wet.

Thursday 2.
29 4/10; SW.   Grass-walks are very verdurous.
Grey & mild, windy,
blowing, wet.

Friday 3.
29 8/10; 40; W; 11.
Dew, sun, gale,
moonshine.

Saturday 4.
33, 31; NW, W.   Spring like. Crocus blows: goassamer floats:¶ *musca tenax* comes
White frost, sweet day.   forth: blackbird whistles.

Sunday 5.
29 7/10; 33; S.
Frost, sweet day, vast
hoar frost.

Monday 6.
29 5/10; S.   Fairey-rings encrease on my grass-plot.
Thaw, fog, wet, rain.

Tuesday 7.
29 2/10½; 49; S.   Crocus's blow.
Rain, dark & wet, rain,
rain in the night.

Wednesday 8.
29 6/10½; 47; NW;   The hasels in my hedges are illuminated by numbers of catkins.
77.   Bantam lays.
Clouds, gleams,
moonshine.
Full moon.

Thursday 9.
30 ¼; 43; NE, SE.   Tubbed, & pickled a fat porker: weight nine scores,¶ & eleven
Sun, sweet day.   pounds: price 8ˢ & 4ᵈ from farmer Hoar.

Friday 10.
29 9/10½; S.
Dark, & still.

Wood-cock killed in the shrubs above the Hermitage.

Saturday 11.
29 8/10; W.
Grey, mild & still.

The meadow measures 2 acres & 19 rods, besides the dug ground.

Sunday 12.
29 8/10½; 50; W.
Grey, sun, sweet day.

Bees gather on the flowers, & flies come out.

Monday 13.
29 8/10¾; N.
White frost, sweet weather.

Sowed the ashes of my own making in the great mead where the grass is finest.
Finished tacking the fruit-wall trees.
Gossamer streams from the boughs of trees.
Brimstone butterfly, *Papilio rhamni*.

Tuesday 14.
29 8/10; 34; W, N.
White frost, cloudless.

Wheeled dung to the meadow-garden, & the orchard plot.
Many crocus's blow. Yew-trees shed their farina, or male dust.

Wednesday 15.
29 6/10½; NE, SE.
Fog, sun, sweet weather.

Crown imperials sprout.

Thursday 16.
29 8/10½; E.
Dark, & harsh.

Friday 17.
29 8/10½; 27; NE.
Hard frost, flights of snow.

Saturday 18.
29 5/10; 21; NE.
Severe frost, cutting wind, with flights of snow.

Snow in the night.

Sunday 19.
29 2/10; 28; N.
Snow, snow, deep snow.

Frost comes within doors.

Monday 20.
29 3/10; 17½, 17½;
N.
Severe frost, bright
sun.

Snow about four inches deep.
3 Bantam hens lay.

Tuesday 21.
29 3/10½; 12, 30; W,
SW.
Severe frost, bright
sun, snow.

Yellow wagtail appears.

Wednesday 22.
29 4/10; 31, 33; NW.
Frost, bright sun.

Snow covers the ground.

Thursday 23.
29 5/10¼; 31; SE.
Frost, sun & clouds.

Began to drink tea by day light.

Friday 24.
29 4/10; 37; SE; 30.
Frost, thaw, rain.

Bumble bee
Nore Hill.

Saturday 25.
29 3/10½; SE.
Fog, thaw, rain.

Snow gone.

Sunday 26.
29 4/10; SE; 50.
Dark, & moist.

Rain in the night. Humble bee.
Worms come out on grass plots: a great snail.

Monday 27.
29 6/10½; 52; SW.
Grey, sun, pleasant.

Mr Littleton Etty called.
Long tailed titmouse.
Crocus's blow very much. Winter-aconites fade.

Tuesday 28.
29 6/10¾; 50; SE.
Grey, mild, sun,
spring-like.

Planted two rows of broad beans: sowed radishes.
Carted in a load of dung for the hot-bed.

Wednesday 29.
29 6/10; SE.
Fog, dark, & wet, deep
fog.

Made a seedling cucumber-bed; & an hand-glass celeri bed:
sowed the celeri seed. Rain in Feb. 1 in. 68 h.

MARCH 1792

Thursday 1.
29 2/10; E.
Grey, gleams, heavy
clouds, rain.

The laurustines, & the young shoots of the honey-suckles are not hurt by the late frosts.

Friday 2.
29 1/10½; SE, SW.
Wet & warm, rain,
rain.

Saturday 3.
29 2/10; S; 20.
Dark & mild, rain.

Sowed early green cucumbers in the hot bed.
Crocus's make a very splendid appearance.

Sunday 4.
28 8/10; SW.
Vast rain in the night,
rain, rain, much rain!

Monday 5.
29 3/10; 40, W; 223.
Shower, sun, bright.

Tuesday 6.
28 8/10; S.
Shower, bright, heavy
shower.

Wednesday 7.
29 1/10; 37; W; 38.
Grey, rain, sleet.

Sowed more cucumber-seed.

Thursday 8.
29 5/10; 32; NW, NE;
38.
Frost, ice, icicles, sun,
sharp air, sleet.

Potted some cucumber-plants.

Friday 9.
29 6/10½; 25, 29;
NE.
Severe frost, cutting
wind.

Most sharp March weather. Flights of snow; freezing all day.

Saturday 10.
29 8/10½; 24½, 31;
NE. Hard frost, sun.

Bro.ʳ Benjamin, & wife, & Rebecca dined with us. White water-wagtail.

Sunday 11.
30; 26; NE.
Hard frost, bright,
sharp.

Monday 12.
30; 24; E.
Hard frost, bright sun,
sharp.

Carted in 6 loads of hot dung for the cucumber-bed; 1 of my
own, & 5 from Kimbers.

Tuesday 13.
29 4/10; 32; SE.
Frost, thaw, dark, rain.

Wednesday 14.
29; 40; SW; 18.
Bright, wind, rain.

Thursday 15.
29 1/10; SW; 46, 29.
Dark & moist, great
rain.

Snow-drops are out of bloom.
Rain-bow.

Friday 16.
29 6/10; SW.
Sun, pleasant.

Daffodil blows . . . "it takes the winds of March"
"Before the Swallow dares" . . .
Apricot blows.

Saturday 17.
29 4/10½; SW.
Dark & moist, wet.

Dog's toothed violets bud.

March 17. Lord Stawell¶ made me a visit on this day, & brought
me a white wood-cock: it's head, neck, belly, sides were milk-
white, as were the under sides of the wings. On the back, & upper
parts of the wings were a few spots of the natural colour. From the
shortness of the bill I should suppose it to have been a male bird. It
was plump, & in good condition.

Sunday 18.
29 6/10; SW.
Shower, hail, thunder.

Dog's toothed violets blow.

Monday 19.
29 9/10; 46; W; 21.
Hoar frost, sun,
spring-like.

Apricots, peaches, & nectarines blow.
Violets blossom.

Tuesday 20.
29 7/10; S.
Sun, pleasant, dark,
rain.

The Chif chaf, the first spring bird of passage, is heard in
Burhant hangers: it is the smallest willow-wren.

Wednesday 21.
29 8/10; W; 35.
Grey, rain in the night,
sun, pleasant.

Thursday 22.
29 7/10; NW.
Bright, summer like.

Turned the dung, & made two heaps.
Celeri, & radishes come-up well.

Friday 23.
29 5/10¼; SW.
Rain, bright, sun.

Timothy the Tortoise comes out.
Crown imperials bud for bloom, & stink much.¶

Saturday 24.
29 3/10½; S.
Wet, rain, rain, rain.

Sunday 25.
29 3/10; SW.
Rain, rain in the night,
grey, with wind.

M.rs Clement came with her three daughters.

Monday 26.
29 4/10; SW; 76.
Showers with hail.

Crocus's go off.

The Kingsley miller assures me, that he saw a Swallow skimming over the meadow near the mill. Hirundines are often seen early near mill-ponds, & other waters.

Tuesday 27.
29 2/10; SW; 42.
Rain, rain in the night,
sun & wind.

The ground in a sad wet condition, so that men cannot plow, nor sow their spring-corn. A wet March is very unkind for this district.

Wednesday 28.
29 4/10½; SW.
Sun & clouds.

Crown imperial begins to blow.
Tortoise continues to come out. Primroses.

Thursday 29.
29 1/10½; SE.
Sun, sun, shower.

Made a four-light cucumber bed: the dung has been well turned, & seems mild: made a second celeri hand-glass bed; & a bed for 10 weeks stocks.

Friday 30.
29 4/10½; S, SW; 38.
Sun, clouds, rain, rain.

Sowed celeri, & ten weeks stocks.

Saturday 31.
29 5/10½; S; 8
Frost, rain in the night,

Rain in March – 6 inch. 70 hund.

sun, wind & rain.   Mrs Chandler was brought to bed of a daughter.

APRIL 1792

Sunday 1.
29 3/10; SW.   Stormy, wet night.
Dark, & wet, windy.   Mrs Clement, & daughters left us.

                        Berriman's field measured contains 1 acre 3 qu. 25 rds.
Monday 2.
29 3/10½; W; 120.   Much rain in the night.
Sun, much hail with   Earthed the cucumber-bed.
thunder.

Tuesday 3.
29 1/10¾; SW.   Turned-out a pot of Cucumbers into each hill.
Sun, dark, rain, rain, Some players came hither from Alton.
much rain.   A hand-glass of early celeri entirely eaten-up by the *Chrysomela
                        oleracea saltatoria*, vulgarly called the turnip fly. Sowed more.

Wednesday 4.
29; SW; 83.   Grass grows, & meadows begin to look green.
Gleam, rain, wind,   Pear-trees bud for bloom.
rain, stormy.

Thursday 5.
29 4/10; W, NW; 34.   Stormy night. Wind damages the hedges.
Hail, windy, strong   Some thatch torn by the wind.
gale.   Mr White's tank at Newton runs over & Capt. Dumaresque's is
                        near full.

Friday 6.
29 9/10; 41; NW.   Players left us.
Small shower, sun,
pleasant, red even.

Saturday 7.
29 9/10; 54; S.   The cucumbers shoot out fibres down their hills: earthed them a
White frost, sun, dark. little.
Full moon.   Thomas mowed the dark-green grass¶ growing on the Fairy
                        circles, & segments of circles in my grass plot, which encrease in
                        number every year.

Sunday 8.
29 7/10½; SE.
Grey, sun, pleasant.

Monday 9.
29 7/10; 48, 65; SW.   Nightingale sings: Cuckoo is heard.
Warm & summer like.   Timothy the tortoise weighs 6 pd 11½ oz.

Tuesday 10.
29 6/10; E.
Bright, still, red even.

WALLINGFORD
Hot sun. Goslins on commons.
Black thorn blossoms.

Thomas in my absence planted beans, & sowed carrots, parsnips, cabbage-seed, onions, lettuce, & radishes.

Wednesday 11.
SE.
Hot sun, roads dusty.

OXFORD
Wheat looks well.
Men hoe their wheat, which is very forward, & fine.

Thursday 12.
E.
Fog, hot sun.

Thermometer at Fyfield 72! in the shade.

Two house-martins return to the nests under the eaves of my brew-house.

Friday 13.
E; 10.
Hot.

A great thunder-storm at Woodstock, & Islip: the Charwel much flooded, & discoloured. No rain at Oxford.

April 13. Prodigious was the damage done about the Kingdom on this day by storms of thunder, & lightening, & vast torrents, & floods, & hail. The town of Bromsgrove in Worcestershire, was quite deluged, & the shops & sitting rooms filled with water. A house was burnt at some place; & in others many people hurt, & some killed.

Saturday 14.
N.
Dark, shower.

One swift seen at S. Stoneham near Southampton.

Sunday 15.
E.
Fair, gale.

Monday 16.
E.
Fair, gale.

ALTON
Great bloom of cherries, pears & plums.

Tuesday 17.
29 2/10; E.
Rain, dark & moist.

SELBORNE
Saw a pair of Swallows at Alton.

Wednesday 18.
28 9/10; N; 56.
Rain, wet, & blowing.

Began to cut grass for the stable.

Thursday 19.
29 2/10½; N; 46.
Rain, wind & rain.

Redstart appears.
Some of the beeches in the hanger begin to look green.

Daffodils are gone: mountain-snow-drops, & hyacinths in bloom; the latter very fine: frittillaria's going.
    Vast flood at Whitney in Oxfordshire on the Windrush.

Friday 20.
29 8/10; 32; E.
Ice, clouds, & gleams.

Hyacinths are fine: tulips bud.

Saturday 21.
29 8/10; S.
Shower, sun & clouds,
gale.

No swallows yet seen here, & the martins have withdrawn themselves. Many Swifts seen at S. Stoneham.
Planted 4 rows of my own potatoes in the garden. Mowed the terrace walk.

Sunday 22.
29 6/10; S.
Shower, blowing.

Wild merise, or small cherry in fine bloom.

Monday 23.
29 4/10; S.
Sun, & gale.

A nest of young blackbirds destroyed by a cat in my garden. Several martins about the village.

Tuesday 24.
29 4/10½; N, SW; 59.
Rain, rain, gleam.

Lined the back of the cucumber-bed with hot dung: some fruit is in blossom. Dug the meadow-garden, very stiff & heavy.

Wednesday 25.
29 7/10; SW; W.
Gleams, & clouds, red
even.

Finished lining the bed, dug the flower-basons.
The first cucumber seems to be set.
Martins come.

Thursday 26.
29 8/10½; SW.
Sun, & clouds, gale
cool.

Two nightingales within hearing: cuckoos come round the village. Few swallows yet.

Friday 27.
29 8/10; SW.
Grey, gale, louring.

The middle Bantam hen sits in the barn.
Planted four rows of potatoes in the home garden.
Planted in the mead-garden eleven rows of potatoes, four of which were potatoes from Liverpool, sent to Dr Chandler by Mr Clarke. Planted in the mead four rows of beans.

Saturday 28.
29 9/10; W.
Louring, still, warm.

Made a third hand-glass bed for celeri in the home garden: the crops in the melon-ground are eaten by insects.

Sunday 29.
29 8/10; 58, 68; E,

NE.
Fog, dew, hot sun,
heavy clouds, cloudless,
sweet even.

Monday 30.
29 4/10; 53, 71; E, S.
Large dew, hot sun,
sweet even.

Men tye their hops. Dressing some of the borders.
Heavy thundrous clouds. Tulips blow.
On this beautiful evening came all at once seven Swifts, which
began to dash & play round the church.
Rain in April – 4 inch. 8 h.

MAY 1792

Tuesday 1.
29 7/10½; NW.
Sun, harsh, wind, cold
air.

White apple again shows much bloom.
Cut a good mess of asparagus.
Continue to dress border.
Chur-worm jars down at Dorton in swampy ground.

Wednesday 2.
29 9/10¼; 38; NW,
N.
No dew, harsh, cutting
wind.

Cut the leaves of Rhubarb for tarts: the tarts are very good.
Mrs Ben White, & her son Tom came from London.

Thursday 3.
29 9/10; 35; N.
Frost, ice, sun, harsh.

Cucumbers swell. Knobbed russets, royal russets, & nonparels
show good bloom.
Sent some of the leaves of the crocus's to Edm^d White; they make
good tyings for hops, being both tough, & pliant.

Friday 4.
29 6/10½; 41; N; 7.
Rain, rain, dark &
blowing, strong gales.

Began to use the lettuces under the fruit-wall.

Saturday 5.
29 8/10¼; N.
Sharp, cold showers,
cutting wind.

The foliage of trees, & the bloom are injured by the wind.
The bloom of apples is great.

Sunday 6.
29 8/10; N.
Severe, cutting wind.
Full moon.

The foliage of trees much injured by the wind.
Nightingales are silent.

During severe winds it is not easy to say how the Hirundines
subsist; for they withdraw themselves, & are hardly ever seen, nor

do any insects appear for their support. That they can retire to rest, & sleep away these uncomfortable periods, as the bats do, is a matter rather to be suspected than proved: or do they not rather spend their time in deep & sheltered vales near waters, where insects are more likely to be found. Certain it is that hardly any individuals of this Genus have been seen for several days together.

Monday 7.
29 7/10; 38; NE.
Sharp wind, sun,
louring, blood-red
sun set.

This harsh, uncomfortable weather has lasted now night & day for a week.
No swifts, & only one or two swallows, & Martins.

Tuesday 8.
29 7/10; 39; NE.
Dark, cloudless, &
sharp.

No dew for some days. The winds shatter the tender leaves of trees.
Swifts appear.

May 8. On this day 26 houses, besides a number of barns, stables, granaries, &c. were burnt down at Barton-Stacey near Winchester. Only ten or twelve houses were preserved, among which is the parsonage, a large farm house, & some others out of the line of the street. The people of Selborne subscribed £6 1s 0d on this occasion: the county collection was very large, & ample.

Wednesday 9.
29 8/10; NE.
Dark & harsh, still for
the first time since May
1st

No swifts. Chalk cart.
Nightingale sings again.
Wheat looks very yellow.
Cut a brace & an half of fine cucumbers.
Hops look yellow, & seem injured by the wind.

Thursday 10.
29 8/10¼; NE.
Dark & cool, hazy,
dark.

Peat-cart begins.

Friday 11.
29 8/10; 41; NE, SW.
Dark & sharp, louring.

Cut two brace of cucumbers. Saw one swift.
Sowed one row of scarlet kidney-beans.

Saturday 12.
29 9/10; 43; NE, S, E.
Dark, & still.

Sowed an other row of kidney-beans, in all a pint of scarlet.
Martins begin to build.

An army of caterpillars infest my young goose-berry trees, which were planted this spring: & the case is the same at Dr Chandlers. Thomas picked the trees carefully, & gave them a good watering.

Sunday 13.
29 7/10½; SW.

The shoots of the vines show rudiments of bloom in plenty.

Grey, sun, gleams.   Mr Ben White came.

Monday 14.
29 7/10, SW.   Cut two brace of cucumbers.
Wet, rain, dark.

Tuesday 15.
29 7/10; S.   The Dearling apple tree full of bloom.
Grey, gleams, louring   Ten or eleven swifts dash round the church.
& mild.

Wednesday 16.
29 4/10; SW; 61.   Martins abound. Mowed the grass-plot.
Wet, rain, rain, rain in
the night.

Thursday 17.
29 5/10¾; W; 47.   Sowed some Nasturtion seeds on the bank.
Rain, blowing.

                                           Mr Charles Etty returns from Madras well in health, & not lame
                                           from the accident of breaking his leg; but thinner than he was. He
                                           went first to Bengal, & so home in a Danish India man.

Friday 18.
29; 6/10; W.   Made a three-light annual bed: the dung was burnt for want of
Wet, blowing, dark.   turning. Strong wind. Mild.
                                           Cut two brace of cucumbers.
                                           The fern-owl, or eve-jar is heard to chatter in the hanger. So
                                           punctual are they!

Saturday 19.
29 6/10½; W.   Wind in the night.
Sun, wind, dark.   Sowed the annuals in the three-light frame.
                                           The middle Bantam Hen brought forth nine chickens.

Sunday 20.
29 5/10¾; 60; S, SE,   The missel-thrush has a nest on the orchard pear-tree. Warm, &
E.   thunder-like. Rain-bow. Grass grows. Loud thunder, & heavy
Sun, showers, clouds,   rain in the evening.
thunder & rain.

                                           May 20. The thunder of this evening burnt the barns, & out-
                                           houses of a farm between Gosport & Titchfield, & destroyed eight
                                           fine horses.

Monday 21.
29 6/10½; W; 47.   Honey-suckle against a wall blows: Columbine blows.
Dark, & warm,   Cut seven cucumbers. Haw-thorns blossom.
shower, sun, gale.   Fly-catcher returns, & appears.
                                           The cock missle-thrush sings on the tops of the tall firs.

Tuesday 22.
29 8/10; W.   A good dew.

Sun, sun & gale, cool.

Made two hand-glass beds for cucumbers.
The Fly-catcher comes to my vines, where probably it was bred, or had a nest last year.
It is the latest summer bird, & appears almost to a day! "Amusive bird, say where your hid retreat?"!¶

The white apples are out of bloom, being forward: the Dearling, a late keeping apple, but just in full bloom. So the earlier the fruit ripens the sooner the tree blossoms. The Dearling bears only once in two years, but then an enormous burthen. It has produced 10, & 13 bushels of fruit at a crop. The bloom this year is prodigious! the crop moderate, & the fruit small.¶

Wednesday 23.
30; N.
Dew, sun, pleasant.

Laburnum with it's golden tassels makes a beautiful show.
Sowed two rows of white kidney-beans.
Cut five cucumbers.

Thursday 24.
29 9/10; 40; SE.
White frost, cool, pleasant, chill.

The earliest orange-lily, & the fiery-lily blow.
Some mushrooms on the down.
The old speckled Bantam sits on eight eggs.

May 24. Tanner shot a hen Sparrow-hawk as she was sitting on her eggs in an old crow's nest on one of the beeches in the High wood. The bird fell to the ground, & what was very strange, brought down with her one of the eggs unbroken. The eggs of Sparrow-hawks, like those of other birds of prey, are round, & blunt-ended, & marked at one end with a bloody blotch. The hen bird of this species is a fine large hawk; the male is much smaller, & more slender. Hawks seldom build any nest. This Hawk had in her craw the limbs of an unfledged lark.

Friday 25.
29 4/10½; SE.
Red morning, dark, soft rain.

Red kidney-beans sprout.
Sorbus aucuparia, the Quicken-tree, or mountain ash full of bloom. The bunches of red berries would make a fine appearance in winter: but they are devoured by thrushes, as soon as they turn colour.

Saturday 26.
29 5/10; W; 44.
Gleams, & showers, & gale.

Thunder at a distance. Sowed two hand-glasses with cucumbers for the ridge crop.

Sunday 27.
29 ½/10; SE. Gleams, dark, heavy rain.

The missel-thrush has got young.

Monday 28.
29; SE, SW; 47.
Showers, showers.

Cut 4 brace of cucumbers.

Tuesday 29.
29 2/10; S; 32.
Wet, & windy,
blowing.

Wednesday 30.
29 4/10¾; S; 15.
Sun & clouds, shower,
yellow even.

Cut 4 brace & half of cucumbers.
Fern-owl jarrs.

My table abounds with lettuces, that have stood the winter;
radishes; spinage; cucumbers, with a moderate crop of asparagus.

Thursday 31.
29 7/10½; W.
Sun, fine dew, summer
weather.

Grass grows very fast.
Rain in May – 3 inch 0 hun.
Honey-suckles very fragrant, & most beautiful objects!
Columbines make a figure. My white thorn, which hangs over
the earth-house, is now one sheet of bloom, & has pendulous
boughs down to the ground.

JUNE 1792

Friday 1.
29 7/10; 58; SW.
Sun, summer weather,
wet.

M.ᵣ & M.ʳˢ Ben White left us, & went to Newton.
One of my low balm of Gilead firs begins to throw out a
profusion of cones; a token this that it will be a short-lived,
stunted tree. One that I planted in my shrubbery began to decay
at 20 years of age. Miller in his gardener's *Dictionary* mentions
the short continuance of this species of fir, & cautions people
against depending on them as a permanent tree for ornamental
plantations.

Saturday 2.
29 8/10½; N, N; 9.
Rain, rain, dark &
cool.

Mushrooms are brought to the door.
Sowed a long row of white kidney-beans. We have planted in all
one pint of white, & one pint of scarlet.

Sunday 3.
29 9/10; N.
Sun, strong, gale.

No may-chafers this year.

The intermediate flowers, which now figure between the spring, &
solstitial, are the early orange, & fiery lily, the columbine, the early
honey-suckle, the peony, the garden red valerian, the double
rocket or dames violet, the broad blue flag-tris, the thrift, the
double lychnis, spider-wort, monk's hood, & c.

Monday 4.
29 8/10; N.
Sun, strong gale.

Cut 4 brace of cucumbers. Hay making about London.
These strong gales shatter the foliage of the trees, & woods.

Monkshood by the garden pond.
WaRes.

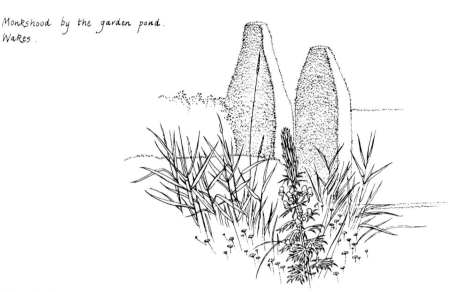

Tuesday 5.
29 7/10; 59; N.
Dark & harsh, heavy
clouds, mild.
Full moon.

One Fly-catcher builds in the Virginia Creeper, over the garden-door: & one in the vine over the parlor-window.
Between Newton and us we heard three Fern-owls chattering on the hill; one at the side of the High wood, one at the top of the Bostal, & one near the Hemitage. That at the top of the Bostal is heard distinctly in my orchard. Fern-owls haunt year by year nearly the same spots.

Wednesday 6.
29 6/10; 48; N, NE.
Sun, clouds, showers to
the SE.

Sowed a fresh made hand glass bed with cucumbers.
S^t foin begins to blow.
The mare lies out.

Thursday 7.
29 5/10; SE.
Clouds, heavy clouds.

Cut 5 cucumbers. Cinnamon-rose begins to blow.
Thundrous clouds. Copious dew.
Opened, & slipped-out the superfluous shoots of the artichokes.

Friday 8.
29 3/10; W; 47.
Rain, sun, gleams,
cool.

Began to prick out celeri.
Cut-off the cones from the balm of Gilead fir in such numbers that they measured one gallon & an half. So much fruit would have exhausted a young tree. The cones grow *sursum*, upright; those of the Spruce, *de orsum*, downward.

Saturday 9.
29 4/10; SW.
Clouds, & showers,
cool.

Pricked out more celeri; planted some rows of ten-weeks stocks; & sowed hardy annuals.

Sunday 10.
29 1/10; SW, S.
Dark, wet, rain.

Began to use green goose-berries.¶
House-martins, nesting in ready-built nests, hatch their young, & throw out the shells.

Monday 11.
29 2/10; SW.
Sun, showers, gleam.

MARELAND, ALTON
Nine fine coach-horses were burnt in a stable at Alresford.

June 11. Went, & dined with my brother Benjamin White at Mareland, to which he & his wife were come down for two or three days. We found the house roomy, & good, & abounding with conveniences: the out-door accommodations are also in great abundance, such as a larder, pantry, dairy, laundry, pigeon-house, & good stables. The view from the back front is elegant, commanding sloping meadows thro' which runs the Wey (the stream from Alton to Farnham) meandering in beautiful curves, & shewing a rippling fall occasioned by a tumbling bay formed by Mr Sainesbury, who also widened the current. The murmur of this water-fall is heard from the windows. Behind the house next the turnpike are three good ponds, and round the extensive outlet a variety of pleasant gravel walks. Across the meadows the view is bounded by the Holt: but up & down the valley the prospect is diversifyed, & engaging.

In short Mareland is a very fine situation, & a very pleasing Gentleman's seat. I was much amused with the number of Hirundines to be seen from the windows: for besides the several martins & swallows belonging to the house, many Swifts from Farnham up & down the vale; & what struck me most were forty or fifty bank-martins, from the heaths, & sand-hills below, which follow the stream up the meadows, & were the whole day long busied in catching the several sorts of *Ephemerae* which at this season swarm¶ in the neighbourhood of waters. The stream below the house abounds with trouts.

Tuesday 12.
29 4/10½; 38; SW;
48.
Showers, showers, cold & dark.

SELBORNE
Lime-trees show their bracteal leaves.
Mr Burbey has got eleven martins nests under the eaves of his old shop.

Wednesday 13.
29 2/10¼; 51, 58; SE;
46.
Rain, rain, rain.

Cold, & comfortless weather.
Grass grows. The ground is very wet.

Thursday 14.
29 7/10½; NW.
Sun, bright, & pleasant.

Pricked out more celeri, & planted out Savoys to stand the winter. Cut 4 cucumbers.

Friday 15.
29 9/10; 63; W, SW.
Summer weather.

Beat the banks; & planted cabbages in the meadow-garden. Six swifts.

Saturday 16.
29 8/10; 66; E.
Summer, hot sun, gale.

Planted some hand-glass plants in the frames of the fruiting cucumber-bed: cut down the lining, & worked it up with some grass-mowings.
Some young fly-catchers are out, & fed by their dams.

Sunday 17.
29 6/10½; 67; SW.
Summer, red even.

Elder-trees blow: the blossoms are solistitial.
Spotted martagons, roses, & corn flags begin to blow.
Saint foin fly, *sphynx filipendulae*, appears.

When the servants are gone to bed, the kitchen-hearth swarms with minute crickets not so big as fleas.
The *Blattae* are almost subdued by the persevering assiduity of Mʳˢ J. W. who waged war with them for many months, & destroyed thousands: at first she killed some hundreds every night.
The thermometer at George's fields Surrey – 82: on the 21, – 51.

Monday 18.
29 5/10½; NW, W.
Sun, wind, clouds, cool.

Made several beds for hand-glass cucumbers.
Cut 4 brace & half of cucumbers. The spotted Bantam hen brings-out seven chickens.
Took a black-birds nest the third time: the young were fledged, & flew out of the nest at a signal given by the old ones.

Tuesday 19.
29 4/10½; 51; NW, N.
Cold, dark & harsh.

Pinks, scarlet-lychnis & fraxinellas blow.
The narrow-leaved blue Iris, called Xiphium, begins to blow.

Wednesday 20.
29 4/10½; 48; NW.
Dark & sharp, red even.

Planted-out many cucumber-plants under the hand-glasses. The cold weather checks vegetation. Wheat spindles for ear.
Began to tack the vines: there is much show for fruit.

Thursday 21.
29 4/10½; 65; SW.
Sun, dark & cool.

Put sticks to some of the kidney-beans.
Longest day: a cold, harsh solstice!

Friday 22.
29 4/10; SW.
Showers, showers, bright, & cool.

The rats have carried away six out of seven of my biggest Bantam chickens; some from the stable, & some from the brew-house.

Black bryony and White bryony in Wool Lane
13 June.

Saturday 23.
29 5/10; SW.
Showers, windy,
showers.

Sunday 24.
29 6/10; 53; SW; 60.
Showers, showers,
heavy showers.

Thunder, & hail. A sad midsum.ʳ day.

When the *Blattae* seem to be subdued, & got under; all at once several large old ones appear: no doubt they migrate from the houses of neighbours, which swarm with them.

Monday 25.
29 8/10½; W; 27.
Dark & cool.

Put sticks to the kidney-beans: earthed out the bearing cucumber-bed. Annuals grow.

Timothy Turner sowed 40 bushels of ashes on Baker's hill: an unusual season for such manure!
    Wheat-ears begin to appear.
    Tryed for rats over the stable, & brew house with a ferret, but did not succeed.

Tuesday 26.
29 8/10¾; 59; SE; 19.
Rain, dark & mild.

Planted-out several basons of French marrigolds.

Wednesday 27.
29 8/10¼; 67; W; 19.
Rain, bright, warm,
fine red even.

Cut 4 brace, & half of cucumbers.

The late pliant sort of Honey-suckles, that do not make good standards, begin to show their yellow bloom: the more early are on the decline.
    Hung the net over the cherry-trees at the end of the house to keep off the magpies, which come to our very windows between three & four in the morning. The daws also from the church have invaded my neighbours cherries. Pies, & daws are very impudent!

Thursday 28.
29 8/10; 70; SW.
Sun, hot day, deep fog.

Began to cut our summer cabbage.
Glow-worms abound in Baker's hill.

Friday 29.
29 6/10; S; 12.
Wet, rain, rain, dark.

The *Hemerocallis*, day lily, begins to blow.
Straw-berries from the woods are brought; but they are crude, & pale, as might be expected. Cut-off the large leaves of the *Colchicum*, or meadow-saffron, now decaying: towards the end of August the blossoms, called by some naked boys, will shoot out, & make a pleasing appearance.

Saturday 30.
29 6/10; 61; W.
Sun, fine even.

The Saint foin about the neighbourhood lies in a bad way. Began
to cut the tall hedges.
Tyed-up pinks. Put sticks to the last row of kidney-beans.
Rain in June – 2 inc. 78 hun.

JULY 1792

Sunday 1.
29 7/10; 60; NW, SW.
Sun, cool, & shady,
cool & bright.

There is a natural occurrence to be met with upon the highest part
of our down in hot sunny days, which always amuses me much
without giving me any satisfaction with respect to the cause of it; &
that is a loud audible humming of bees in the air, tho' not one
insect is to be seen. This sound is to be heard distinctly the whole
common thro', from the Money-dells, to Mr White's avenue-gate.
Any person would suppose that a large swarm of bees was in
motion, & playing about over his head. This noise was heard last
week on June 28th
"Resounds the living surface of the ground:"
"Nor undelightful is the ceaseless <u>hum</u>"
"To him who muses . . . at noon."
    "Thick in yon stream of light, a thousand ways",
"Upward, & downward, thwarting, & convolv'd"
"The quivering nations sport" . . .

Thomson's *Seasons*.

Magpie.
Selborne High Wood.
July.

Monday 2.
29 6/10½; 61; SW.
Sun, louring & mild.

Planted the basons, & borders in the field with annuals.
Kidney-beans look well; but common beans run too much to haulm, & do not pod well.
Wheat begins to blow. Late orange-lily blossoms. Nuts begin to be formed on the hasels.

Tuesday 3.
29 5/10½; SW.
Grey, still & mild.

Planted more annuals along the borders of the garden.
Serapias latifolia blossoms in the hanger.

Wednesday 4.
29 5/¾; 61; SW.
Wet, dark & blowing, gleam.

Thursday 5.
29 5/10¾; 61; W.
Rain, rain, gleams.

Straw-berries brought, but not very well flavoured.
The Provost of Oriel, & Lady came.¶

Friday 6.
29 7/10; 61; NW.
Dark & still.

Gathered some cherries.
Mrs Eveleigh says, that the churring of the fern-owl is like the noise of a razor-grinder's wheel.

Saturday 7.
29 6/10¼; 64; SW.
Wet, summer, wet deep fog.

Put out more annuals.
Farmer Hoare's son shot a hen Wood-chat, or small Butcher-bird as it was washing at Well-head, attended by the cock. It is a rare bird in these parts. In it's craw were insects.

Sunday 8.
29 6/10½; SW.
Dark, mild, fog.

Thistles blossom: nasturtium blows.
Rasps begin to turn.

The Poet of Nature¶ lets few rural incidents escape him. In his *Summer* he mentions the whetting of a scythe as a pleasing circumstance, not from the real sound, which is harsh, grating, & unmusical; but from the train of summer ideas, which it raises in the imagination. No one who loves his garden & lawn but rejoices to hear the sound of the mower on an early, dewy morning.
"Echo no more returns the chearful sound"
"Of sharpening scythe" . . .
    Milton also, as a pleasing summer-morning occurrence, says,
"The mower whets his scythe"
                                                        L'allegro.

Monday 9.
29 6/10; 64; E, E.
Bright, dark & warm, yellow evening.

The Provost & Lady left us.
Thunder in the night, & most part of the day to the S. & SE.
Turned-out the cucumber-plants from under the hand-glasses.

Vines begin to blow.
Sweet Williams of last year in their seedling-bed made a beautiful appearance.

Tuesday 10.
29 6/10; 64; S, NW.
Wet, sun, dark & warm.

Guns fire at Portsmouth.
13 swifts playing round the church.

Wednesday 11.
29 4/10; 64; N; 92.
Rain, rain, rain.

Young swallows come out, & are fed by their dams.
A thoro' July rain.

Thursday 12.
29 3/10; 51, 61½; N; 77.
Wet & foggy, wet, & dark.

Great rain in the night. Sad hay-making!
My bloom of flowers injured by the rain.
The white apples make some show on the tree.
Planted out China asters: & red cabbage, & bore cole, & common cabbage, & Milan.

Friday 13.
29 5/10¾; 59; W, SW; 45.
Rain, sun, pleasant.

Rain in the night.
White lilies begin to blow.
Whortle-berries are offered at the door.
Cherries have little flavour.

Saturday 14.
29 8/10; 55; SW.
Sun & clouds, pleasant.

Planted more China-asters, & ten weeks stock.
Took away the cucumber-frames & lights.
The double roses rot in the bud without blowing out: an instance this of the coldness, & wetness of the summer.
Some H. martins that breed in ready-built nests bring out their young.
Potatoes blossom.

Sunday 15.
29 8/10; 65; S; SE.
Bright, summer, pleasant.

Golden-rod, & ferruginous fox-gloves blossom.
13 swifts.
Lime-trees blossom. Scarlet kidney-beans begin to blow. Rasps come in. Annuals grow.
Many swifts.

Monday 16.
29 5/10; S, SE, E.
Sun, hot, dark clouds, sprinkling, red, warm.

Distant thunder to the S. The thunder-cloud parted as usual before it reached us!
Farmer Corps brought me two eggs of a fern-owl, which he found under a bush in shrub wood. The dam was sitting on the nest; & the eggs, by their weight, seemed to be just near hatching. These eggs were darker, & more mottled than what I have procured before.

Tuesday 17.
29 4/10¼; 66; SW, S;
48.
Sun & clouds, yellow,
pleasant.

Much rain, & distant thunder in the night.

Wednesday 18.
29 5/10¼; 66; SW;
10.
Rain, sun & clouds.

Men cut their meadows. Mr Churton came.
Planted-out China asters, & annual sun-flowers.
Began to trench-out celeri.

Thursday 19.
29 6/10; 66; SW.
Fine morn, sweet day,
fine even.

My meadow is begun to be mowed.

Friday 20.
29 4/10; NE.
Dark, & mild, louring,
rain, rain, rain.

Trenched-out more celeri.
Simeon Etty brought me two eggs of a Razor-bill from the cliffs of the Isle of Wight: they are large, & long, & very blunt at the big end, & very sharp & peaked at the small. The eggs of these birds are, as Ray justly remarks, "*in omnibus hujus generis majora quam pro corporis mole.*"¶ One of these eggs is of a pale green, the other more white; both are marked & dotted irregularly with chocolate-coloured spots. Razor-bills lay but one egg, except the first is taken away, & then a second, & on to a third. By their weight these eggs seem to have been sat on, & to contain young ones.

Saturday 21.
29 5/10; 59; NW, W;
125.
Rain, rain, rain.

Made rasp, & curran jam, & jelly.
Much rain in the night. Blowing.
Artichokes come in. Much hay out.

Sunday 22.
29 7/10; 59; NE, SE.
Bright, pleasant, dew,
low fog.

The hand-glass cucumbers begin to shew male bloom. As things are so late this year, the interval between the failing of the early cucumbers, & the bearing of the late will be considerable.

Took the black bird's nest in the garden the fourth time: it contained squab young.

Monday 23.
29 6/10; 62; NE.
Vast dew, sun, sweet
even, vast dew.

Much Hay about.

Tuesday 24.
29 5/10½; SE, S.
Vast dew, sun, sweet

Preserved some cherries.
My meadow-hay was carried in decent order.

even, dew.

As we were coming from Newton this evening, on this side of the Money-dells, a cock Fern-owl came round us, & showed himself in a very amusing manner, whistling, or piping as he flew. Whenever he settled on the turf, as was often the case, M.ʳ Churton went, & sprung him, & brought him round again. He did not clash his wings over his back, so as to make them snap. At the top of the Bostal we found a bat hawking for moths. Fern-owls & Bats are rivals in their food, commanding each great powers of wing, & contending who shall catch the *phalaenae* of the evening.
The loud humming of bees, tho' none are to be seen, was again very audible on the down, from the money-dells almost to M.ʳ White's avenue.

Wednesday 25.
29 3/10½; 62; S, SW; 25.
Dark, wet, rain, rain, rain.

Gathered my first beans, broad ones: & dug-up my first potatoes, D.ʳ Chandler's sort from Liverpool. Swifts.

Thursday 26.
29; 3/10½; W.
Sun & clouds, shower, clouds.

Friday 27.
29 3/10; 61; SW, W; 14.
Showers, pleasant, heavy shower, gleam.

This cool, shady summer is not good for mens fallows, which are heavy, & weedy. Lettuces have not loaved, or bleached well this summer. Planted out more long rows of ten-weeks stocks. Planted out two more trenches of Celeri; in all six. Poultry moult.
Swifts.

Saturday 28.
29 4/10; W.
Showers, & gleams.

Everlasting pea blows.
Hay in a bad way.

†*Qui in primis in Ballia Ade Gordon capital Forestaris de Halsyesholte & Wolvemere & in ejus proencia & in proencia Rici de Westcot & Petri de Heghes Viridarior prdce Foreste sacramentum suum Diennt & sic proceperunt, videt, ad vadum de Ameresford &c. usq La Pleistow de Wateby – extra Parcum Istis de Venuz.¶* Perambulation of Aliceholt & Woolmer 28 Ed. i. from the original in the Tower – printed in Sixth Report of the Commissioners of Forests & Crown Lands 8 Feb. 1790. p. 33.
    In a perambul. II Car. i. it is "the *Pleystowe* of Whatleigh" ib. 36. "*usq Bakereswell & indi in Th'evene Path usq Hethorn & sic per candem Th'even Path*" in the former; is in the latter "from thence in the vene path also fernpath to Hathorn and soe by the same yᵉ vene path to Quernfors" Ec.

---

†Entry in an unknown hand: it is almost illegible.

Sunday 29.
29 3/10; 62; SW; 60.
Rain, rain.

Heavy showers. Apples fall much.

The well at Temple is 77 feet deep: 60 to the water, & 17 afterward. My well measures only 63 feet.

Monday 30.
29 7/10; 65; NW.
Fog, sun, clouds, soft & still.

Mr Churton left us, & went to Waverley.
Halo round the sun. Thunder.

Tuesday 31.
29 8/10½; 69; S, E;
19.
Rain, moist, warm, fog.

Rain in the night. Scarlet Martagons blow.
Finished cutting the tall hedges.
No swifts.
Rain in July – 5 inch. 16 hund.

Bakers Hill.
Wakes.
August.

AUGUST 1792

Wednesday 1.
29 9/10; 64; E.
Wet, sun, sweet day.

The old cucumber-bed bears again; but the fruit is not fine, & well-grown. Hot sun.

The young Hirundines begin to congregate on the tower. How punctual are these birds in all their proceedings!
   Floods out in several parts of the kingdom, & much hay & corn destroyed.

Thursday 2.
29 7/10; 75; NE.
Hot, summer weather, red even.
Full moon.

Fern-owls chatter on the down.
Sowed a crop of spinage to stand the winter.
Trenched a row of celeri in the field-garden; there are now seven long rows.

Two swifts. Young buzzards follow their dams with a piping, wailing noise.

Friday 3.
29 6/10; 75; NE, S.
Fog, vast dew! sultry,
vast clouds about,
thunder, dark, & hot.

First apricot: cut first hand-glass cucumber.

Saturday 4.
29 7 10½; E; 78.
Sun, sultry, vast
shower, gleam,
moonshine.

Distant thunder.

Sunday 5.
29 7/10½; 67; E.
Sun, hot, clouds, sweet
even.

The guns at the camp on Bagshot-heath were heard distinctly this evening.

Monday 6.
29 7/10; 69; E.
Vast dew, cloudless,
cool breeze, red even.

Sowed more endive, & lettuce.

Tuesday 7.
29 7/10¼; 69; NE.
Dew, sun, cloudless,
sweet even.

7. Several of my neighbours went up the Hill (this being the day of the great review at Bagshot heath) from whence they heard distinctly the discharges from the ordnance, & small arms, & saw the clouds of smoke from the guns. The wind being N.E. they smelled, or seemed to smell, the scent of the gun-powder. Wickham bushes, the scene of action, is more than 20 miles from hence. The crouds of people assembled upon this occasion were great beyond any thing usually seen at such meetings!

Wednesday 8.
29 8/10¾; 63, 66;
NE, S. Great dew, sun,
heavy clouds.

My lower wallnut-tree casts it's leaves in a very unusual manner. No wall-nuts; the crop dropped off early in the summer.

Thursday 9.
29 8/10; 72; S.
Dew, bright, hot &
still.

Men get-in their backward hay in good order.
Peat-cart interrupted by the rains, begins again.
Apricots ripen, & are good.

Friday 10.
29 8/10; 65, 70; SW.
Grey, sun, hot, clouds.

The hand-glass cucumbers bear, & show good vines.
Hops in bloom: the binds look clean, & free from insects.
Farmer Hewett began wheat-harvest down on the sands near the forest.

Saturday 11.
29 7/10½; 75; SW.
Sun, sultry, fiery red.

Apricots ripen: cucumbers bear.

Sunday 12.
29 7/10; 71.
Sun, sultry, grey &
warm.

Distant thunder.

The thermometer for three or four days past has stood in the shade at Newton at 79, & 80.

Monday 13.
29 6/10; 63, 74; NW.
Bright, hot, clouds.

Distant thunder.
Wall-nuts shed their leaves. Goose-berries wither on the trees.
Cut 72 cucumbers.
The honey-suckles glow with red berries, which are eaten by bull-finches, & red-breasts.
Green finches destroy the bore-cole seed.

Tuesday 14.
29 6/10½; NW.
Sun, hot, more cool.

Scarlet kidney-beans come in.
Housed two loads of peat.

Mrs J. White, after a long & severe campaign carried on against the *Blattae molendinariae* which have of late invaded my house, & of which she has destroyed many thousands, finds that at intervals a fresh detatchment of old ones arrives; & particularly during this hot season: for the windows being left open in the evenings, the males come flying in at the casements from the neighbouring houses wch swarm with them. How the females, that seem to have no perfect wings that they can use, can contrive to get from house to house, does not so readily appear. These, like many insects, when they find their present abodes over stocked, have powers of migrating to fresh quarters. Since the *Blattae* have been so much kept under, the Crickets have greatly encreased in number.

Wednesday 15.
29 7/10; SW.
Sun, warm, cool air.

Farmer Spencer begins wheat-harvest.
A smell of harvest prevails in the fields.

Thursday 16.
29 4/10; 65; SW.
Wet, gleams, dark &
moist.

Apricots good.
Cut 60 fine cucumbers.

Friday 17.
29 3/10½; SW, SE.
Sun, dark & warm.

Gathered more kidney-beans; some white ones.

Saturday 18.
29 3/10; E, N; 195.
Vast rain! rain, dark &
chill.

Black caps eat the berries of the honey-suckles.

Sunday 19.
29 5/10; 63; SW, NW.
Sun, shower, gleam,
clouds.

Naked boys, *colchicum*, appear.
Mich. daisies begin to blow.

Monday 20.
29 5/10; 61; SW.
Grey, shower, dark,
shower.

Thomas, in mowing the walks, finds that the grass begins to grow weak, & to yield before the scythe. This is an indication of the decline of heat.
Yucca filamentosa, silk-grass, blows with a fine large white flower. It thrives abroad in a warm aspect. Habitat in Virginia.

Tuesday 21.
29 2/10½; 64; SW.
Rain, rain, dark.

Vast rain. Bad harvest weather.
Cut 106 fine cucumbers.
Wheat-harvest becomes general.
Goose-berries, & currans gone.

Wednesday 22.
29 1/10; 60; SW; 102.
Rain, sun, showers.

Cut 52 cucumbers.
The seeds of the lime begin to fall.
Some wheat under hedges begins to grow.

Lime sets seed.
Selborne village.

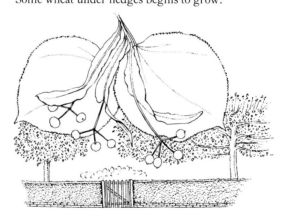

Thursday 23.
29 3/10¼; 62; SW,
W; 20.
Rain, showers, & wind.

Some wheat bound; & some gleaning.
I have not seen one wasp.

Friday 24.
29 7/10; 61; W.
Sun, shower, dark.

Wheat bound. Much gleaning.
John Berriman's hops at the end of the Foredown very fine.

Saturday 25.
29 5/10; 65; SW.
Showers, dark &
warm, rain.

Some pease housed in a wet condition.

My shrub, *Rhus continus*, known to the nursery men by the title of

Coccygria, makes this summer a peculiar shew, being covered all over with it's *bractaea paniculae filiformes*, which give it a feathery, plume-like appearance,¶ very amusing to those that have not seen it before. On the extremities of these panicles appear about midsumer a minute white bloom, which with us brings no seeds to perfection. Towards the end of August these panicles turn red & decay.

My large American Juniper, probably *Juniperus Virginiana*, has produced this summer a few small blossoms of a strong flavour like that of the juniper-berries: but I could not distinguish whether the flowers were male or female; so consequently could not determine the sex of the tree, which is diaecious. The order is *diaecia monadelphia*.

Sunday 26.
29 2/10½; 69; SW.
Showers, showers,
gleam, showers.

A fly catcher brings out a brood of young: & yet they will all withdraw & leave us by the 10.ᵗʰ of next month.

Monday 27.
29 5/10; 67; SW; 22.
Bright, fine day.

Cut 148 cucumbers.
Much wheat bound in small sheaves.

August 27. A fern-owl this evening showed-off in a very unusual, & entertaining manner by hawking round, & round the circumference of my great spreading oak for twenty times following, keeping mostly close to the grass; but occasionally glancing up amidst the boughs of the tree. This amusing bird was then in pursuit of a brood of some particular *phalaena* belonging to the oak, of which there are several sorts; & exhibited on the occasion a command of wing superior, I think, to that of the swallow itself.

Fern-owls have an attachment to oaks, no doubt on account of food: for the next evening we saw one again several times among the boughs of the same tree; but it did not skim round it's stem over the grass, as on the evening before. In May these birds find the *Scarabaeus melolontha* on the oak; & the *Scarabeaus solstitialis* at Midsummer. These peculiar birds can only be watched & observed for two hours in the twenty four; & then in a dubious twilight, an hour after sun-set, & an hour before sun-rise.

Tuesday 28.
29 6/10½; 64; E.
Vast dew, sun, soft
showers.

Men make wheat-ricks. Mʳ Hale's rick fell.
Vivid rain-bow.

Wednesday 29.
29 7/10; 61; NE, N.
Dark, & blowing,
blowing.

Mʳ Clement begins to pick hops at Alton.
Clavaria's¶ appear on the hanger.
Distant lightening to the southward last night.

Thursday 30.
29 6/10; 62; S; 8.
Dark, wet, fine even.

Farmer Ead of Rood begins hop-picking.
Wheat housed all day. Cut 151 cucumbers!
Ophrys spiralis, triple ladies traces, now blows in the long Lythe,
on the short Lythe, & on the S. end of the down.

Friday 31.
29 6/10; 57, 65; S, SE.
Vast dew, fog, grey,
dark & warm.
Full moon.

Many moor-hens on Comb-wood pond.
Kidney-beans abound.

SEPTEMBER 1792

Saturday 1.
29 5/10; 35.
Showers, showers,
showers.

Grass grows on the walks very fast.
Garden beans at an end.
Monthly roses now blossom very pleasingly.

Sunday 2.
29 5/10½; 65.
Showers, sun, fine
even.

Vivid rain-bow.

Sowed thirteen rods, or the twelfth part of an acre of grass ground
in my own upper Ewel-close with 50 pounds weight of Gypsum:
also thirteen rods in Dᵒ with 50 pounds weight of lime: thirteen
rods more in Dᵒ with 50 pounds weight of wood & peat-ashes: &
four rods more on Dᵒ with peat-dust.

    All these sorts of manures were sown by Broʳ T. W. on very
indifferent grass in the way of experiment.

Monday 3.
29 3/10; 62; S, SW.
Grey, dark, rain.

Cut 199 fine cucumbers!
Gil. White¶ came from Fyfield.

The well at Temple is 77 feet deep: 60 to the water, & 17
afterwards. My well measures only 63 feet to the bottom.

	Yards	feet
Goleigh well to the water is	55½	166:
to the bottom	57½	172½
Heards well to the water is	70⅔	212
to the bottom	83⅓	250

A stone was 4½ seconds falling to the water of Heards well; & 4
seconds to the water of Goleigh.
    The wells above were measured accurately by The Revᵈ
Edmund White on the 25ᵗʰ of August 1792, in the midst of a very
wet summer.
    Deep, & tremendous as is the well at Heards, John Gillman, an
Ideot, fell on the bottom of it twice in one morning; & was taken
out alive, & survived the strange accident for many years.

Only Goleigh, & Heards wells were measured by Mr E. White.

Tuesday 4.
29 3/10; 62; SW. 39.
Sun, showers, fair.

Hop-picking becomes general; & the woman have their gleaning in the wheat-stubbles.
Wheat grows as it stands in the shocks.

Wednesday 5.
29 6/10½; N, NW.
Wet fog, sun & clouds.

Wheat housed.

Thursday 6.
29 8/10; 60; W, SW.
Deep fog, sun, dark & heavy.

Gil. White left us.
Farmer Spencer finishes wheat-harvest.

Septr 6. The flying ants of the small black sort are in great agitation on the zigzag, & are leaving their nests. This business used to be carryed on in August in a warm summer. While these emigrations take place, the Hirundines fare deliciously by feeding on the female ants full of eggs.

Friday 7.
29 7/10; 63; SW.
Fog, dark & misting.

Good mushrooms on the down.
Hop-picking becomes general; & all the kilns, or, as they are called in some counties, <u>oasts</u> are in use. Hops dry brown, & are pretty much subject this year to vinny, or mould.

Saturday 8.
29 6/10½; 62; NW.
Wet, grey, wet, sweet afternoon.

Beeches begin to be somewhat yellow on their tops. Cut 135 cucumbers.

Sunday 9.
29 6/10; 59; 60; SW.
Vast dew, grey, sun, heavy shower, chill air.

Fly-catchers seem to be gone.

As most of the second brood of Hirundines are now out, the young on fine days congregate in considerable numbers on the church, & tower: & it is remarkable that tho' the generality sit on the battlements & roof, yet many hang or cling for some time by their claws against the surface of the walls in a manner not practised at any other time of their remaining with us. By far the greater number of these amusing birds are house-martins, not swallows, which congregate more on trees.
   A writer in the Gent. Mag. supposes that the chilly mornings & evenings, at this decline of the year, begin to influence the feelings of the young broods; & that they cluster thus in the hot sunshine to prevent their blood from being benumbed, & themselves from being reduced to a state of untimely torpidity.

Monday 10.
29 5/10; 60; W; 30.
Strong wind with showers, strong gale.

Cut 125 large fine cucumbers.

Tuesday 11.
29 7/10½; 48; NW.
Sun, & strong gale,
hail, & thunder, bright
& chill.

Nep. John White came from Salisbury.
My wall-nut trees are almost naked.
The grapes, of which there is a great crop, do not turn colour at
all. Some nectarines gathered, but they are not good.

Septem.ʳ 11. On this day my niece Anne Woods was married to Mʳ
John Hounsom, who encreases my nephews, & nieces to the
number of 59.

Wednesday 12.
29 4/10; SW; 16.
Blowing & wet, wet, &
windy, sad weather.

Began to light fires in the parlour.
Cut 25 cucumbers. J.W. left us.

Thursday 13.
29 5/10; 55; W.
Strong wind all night,
& this morning, sharp
wind.

Hops suffer, & kidney beans.
Bro.ʳ T. W. left us.
Hirundines hardly seen.

The stream at Gracious street, which fails every dry summer, has
run briskly all this year; & seems now to be equal to the current
from Well-head. The rocky channel up the hollow-lane towards
Rood has also run with water for months: nor has my great water-
tub been dry the summer through.

Friday 14.
29 3/10; S, W.
Rain, rain, vast rain.

From London three gallons of French brandy, & two gallons of
Jamaica rum.
Many apples & pears blown down.
The hop-pickers have been wet thro' twice.

Saturday 15.
29 9/10; 43; 45; N; 81.
Sharp, sun, pleasant,
sharp.

Cut 128 cucumbers.
Hop-women complain of the cold.
Some martins have broods not flown.

Sunday 16.
29 9/10½; 9/10; 38;
E, S.
White frost, sun, sun,
sharp air.

The cucumbers all cut down.
Some rock-like clouds.

Dʳ Chandler's Bantam sow brought him this last summer a large
litter of pigs, several of which were not cloven-footed, but had their
toes joined together. For tho' on the upper part of the foot there
was some what of a suture, or division; yet below in the soles the
toes were perfectly united; & on some of the hind legs there was a
solid hoof like that of a colt. The feet of the sow are compleatly
cloven. Mʳ Ray in this *Synopsis animalium quadrupedum* takes no
notice of this singular variety: but Linnaeus in his *Systema Naturae*
says, . . . "*Varietas frequens Upsaliae Suis domestici semper
monunguli: in ceteris eadem species.*"¶

Monday 17.
29 7/10; 55; SE, S.
Dark, wet, rain.

Gathered-in the white pippins, about a bushel: many were blown down last week. Oats housed.
Planted-out holly-hocks, & ferruginous fox-gloves.

As I have questioned men that frequent coppices respecting Fern-owls, which they have not seen or heard of late; there is reason to suspect that they have withdrawn themselves, as well as the fly-catchers, & black-caps, about the beginning of this month. Where timber lies felled among the bushes, & covert, wood-men tell me, that fern-owls love to sit upon the logs of an evening: but what their motive is does not appear.

Tuesday 18.
29 6/10; SW.
Bright, small showers,
wet.

Sowed a crop of brown Dutch lettuces, to be planted under the fruit-wall, where they are to stand the winter.
Oats. housed.

Wednesday 19.
29 3/10; 57; S, SE.
Rain, rain, warm, &
windy.

Hops become very brown, & damaged. The hop-pickers are wet thro' every day.
Many hirundines.

Thursday 20.
29 1/10; SW; W; 79,
41.
Rain, heavy rain,
gleam, rain-bow.

Much rain in the night.
The China asters are very backward, & hardly begin to blow.

Friday 21.
28 9/10½; 52; SW.
Cold, wet, & windy.

Kidney-beans injured by the frost on the 16th Hops very much damaged: bad weather for the pickers.

21. On this day Monarchy was abolished at Paris by the National Convention; & France became a Republic!

Saturday 22.
29 ½/10; 50½; W.
Sun, & wind, &
clouds.

In good seasons my grapes by this time have often been in great perfection: but now only here & there a berry begins to turn.

Sunday 23.
29 4/10; NW.
Bright, showers,
bright.

My Bantam chickens, which have been kept in the scullery every night till now for fear of rats, that carried away the first brood from the brew-house, went up last week to the beam over the stable.
    The earnest & early propensity of the *Gallinae* to roost on high is very observable; & discovers a strong dread impressed on their spirits respecting vermin that may annoy them on the ground during the hours of darkness. Hence poultry, if left to themselves & not housed, will perch, the winter thro', on yew-trees, & fir-trees; & turkies, & Guinea-fowls, heavy as they are, get up into apple-

trees; pheasants also in woods sleep on trees to avoid foxes: while pea-fowls climb to the tops of the tallest trees round their owner's house for security, let the weather be ever so cold or blowing. Partridges, it is true, roost on the ground, not having the faculty of perching; but then the same fear prevails in their minds: for through apprehensions from pole-cats, weasels, & stoats, they never trust themselves to coverts; but nestle together in the midst of large fields, far removed from hedges, & coppices, which they love to frequent/haunt in the day; & where at that season they can sculk more secure from the ravages of rapacious birds.

As to ducks, & geese, their aukward, splay, web feet forbid them to settle on trees: they therefore, in the hours of darkness & danger, betake themselves to their own element the water, where, amidst large lakes, & pools, like ships riding at anchor, they float the whole night long in peace, & security.

Monday 24.
29 ½/10; S; 63.
Rain, rain, gleam.

Vivid rain-bow. Warm abroad.

Tuesday 25.
29 5/10; 54; NW.
Strong gale, sun &
wind.

Lightening, rain-bow.
Men begin to bag hops. Celeri come in. Vine-leaves turn purple.

Wednesday 26.
29 8/10; 52; NW.
Sun & clouds, mild,
still.

The last gathered hops much injured. Barley grows in the fields.
Hopping at an end round the village.

Thursday 27.
29 6/10; S.
Grey, sun, wet.

Tyed-up about 30 endives: the plants all small this year.
Spinage thrives. Harvest over: the barley housed today looks sadly.
Swallows & martins; but they do not congregate.

Friday 28.
29 2/10½; S, SW; 79.
Rain, heavy rain,
gleam.

Timothy the tortoise, feeling the approach of cold weather, resorts to the spot where he usually hides, & sleeps in the sun under the warm hedge, tilting his shell an edge that it may take in every ray.

Saturday 29.
29; 53; S, E.
Rain, rain, vast rain.

Sunday 30.
29 2/10½; 60; SE; 90.
Dark, mild & still,
gleam.
Full moon.

Rain in the night. Some leaves of the Virginian creeper turn red.
Ivy blows.
Rain in Sept[r] – 5 inch. 53 h.

There is a remarkable hill on the downs near Lewes in Sussex, known by the name of Mount Carburn,¶ which over-looks that town, & affords a most engaging prospect of all the country round, besides several views of the sea. On the very summit of this exalted promontory, & amidst the trenches of it's Danish camp, there haunts a species of wild Bee,¶ making it's nest in the chalky soil. When people approach the place, these insects begin to be alarmed, & with a sharp & hostile sound dash, & strike round the heads & faces of intruders. I have often been interrupted myself while contemplating the grandeur of the scenery around me, & have thought myself in danger of being stung: & have heard my Brother Benjamin say, that he & his daughter Rebecca were driven from the spot by the fierce menaces of these angry insects.

In old days Mr Hay of Glynd Bourn, the Author of *Deformity*, & other works, wrote a loco-descriptive poem on the beauties of Mount Carburn.

OCTOBER 1792

Monday 1.
29 3/10; 63; SE.
Grey, shower, dark,
still & warm.

Ivy blows.
Timothy comes out on the grass-plot, & eats grass: a token that the weather is warm.

Tuesday 2.
29 3/10½; NE.
Dark, warm, & wet.

Wheat out at Buriton, Fraxfield, Ropley, & other places.

Octr 2. Flying ants, male & female, usually swarm, & migrate on hot sunny days in August, & Septemr, but this day a vast emigration took place in my garden, & myriads came forth in appearance from the drain which goes under the fruit-wall, filling the air & the adjoining trees, & shrubs with their numbers. The females were full of eggs. This late swarming is probably owing to the backward, wet season.

The day following not one flying ant was to be seen. The males, it is supposed all perish: the females wander away; & such as escape from Hirundines get into the grass, & under stones, & tiles, & lay the foundation of future colonies.

Wednesday 3.
29 5/10; 52½; NE; 19.
Dark & wet, grey.

Men begin to carry their hops to Wey-hill. Hirundines swarm around the Plestor, & up & down the street.

Thursday 4.
29 4/10; 48; E.
Cold air, dark, & still.

Friday 5.
29 3/10¾; E; 29.
Rain, dark & still.

Corn abroad almost spoiled.

Saturday 6.
29 4/10½; 53; E.
Dark, still, & moist.

Gathered in Cadillac, & Virgoleuse pears.
Many Hirundines; several very young swallows on the thatch of the cottage near the pound.
The evening is uncommonly dark.

Sunday 7.
29 5/10; NE.
Dark, wet, dark & still.

The crop of stoneless berberries is prodigious!

Among the many sorts of people that are injured by this very wet summer, the peat-cutters are great sufferers: for they have not disposed of half the peat & turf which they have prepared; & the poor have lost their season for laying in their forest-fuel. The brick-burner can get no dry heath to burn his lime, & bricks: nor can I house my cleft wood, which lies drenched in wet.

The brick-burner could never get his last makings of tiles & bricks dry enough for burning the autumn thro'; so they must be destroyed, & worked up again. He had paid duty for them; but is, as I understand, to be reimbursed.

Monday 8.
29 4/10¾; E, NE.
Grey, & sharp, gleams.

Gathered-in the Swans-eggs pears, a good crop.
Waggons set-out for Wey-hill with hops.
Wood-cock returns, & is seen.

Tuesday 9.
29 4/10¼; 46; NE.
Dark & sharp,
sprinklings, cold air,
wet.

Gathered-in the knobbed russetings a good crop, but the fruit is small. One swallow.

Octob.r 9. The sound of great guns was heard distinctly this day to the S.E. probably from Goodwood, where the Duke of Richmond has a detachment from the train of artillery encamped in his park, that he may try experiments with some of the ordnance.

Master Hale houses barley that looks like old thatch. Much barley abroad about the country, & some wheat.

Some pheasants found in this manour.

Wednesday 10.
29 4/10; 46; N, NW.
Dark & still, paths
steady.

Thursday 11.
29 5/10½; 46; NW.
Sun, bright & pleasant.

D.r Chandler mows the church-litton closes for hay. Farmer Parsons houses pease, which have been hacked for weeks. Barley abroad.
No swallows.

Friday 12.
29 1/10¼; 38; SE, S.

Gathered in the dearling apples: fruit small, & stunted.

White frost, sun, wind,   Endive comes in. No swallows.
& rain.

Saturday 13.
29; S; 36, 47.   No hirundines.
Red morn, sun, vast
shower, vivid rain-
bow, shower.

Sunday 14.
29 ½/10; SW.   Vast showers.
Rain, rain, rain.

Monday 15.
29 3/10; SW, W; 137.   Some swallows round the village.
Rain, rain, rain.   Vast showers.

Tuesday 16.
29 3/10¼; W; 27.
Showers, showers,
gleams.

Wednesday 17.
29 3/10¾; SW; 18.
Dew, sun, shower.

Thursday 18.
29 5/10½; W.   Mushrooms on the down.
Sun, bright & pleasant.

Friday 19.
29 5/10¼; NE, E, SE.   Made presents of berberries to several neighbours.
Sun, wet, rain.   Ring-ouzel seen in the Kings field.

Saturday 20.
29 3/10; 55; S.
Rain, rain, rain.

Sunday 21.
29 2/10; S.
Heavy shower, dark,
stars.

Monday 22.
29 6/10; 53; S; 87.
Showers, rain in the
night, wind & sun,
showers, still & bright.

Tuesday 23.
29 8/10½; 46; W,
NW.
Fine day, cloudless,
still, sweet moon-light.

Dᴿ Bingham & family left Selborne.

Wednesday 24.
30 ¾/10; 39; N.
Dark, white frost, small
wet, grey & still, moon
shine.

Men now sow wheat. The hanger looks very brown: leaves fall:
wall-nut trees naked some time.

Thursday 25.
29 8/10½; 44; NE.
Wet fog, gleams, grey.

Men sow wheat.
Nuts fall. Timothy lies under the hedge.

Friday 26.
29 6/10; NE.
Dark, shower, dark &
harsh.

Hired two old labourers to house my cleft billet-wood, which is
still in a damp, cold condition, & should have been under cover
some months ago, had the weather permitted.

Saturday 27.
29 6/10¼; 56; SE, S;
10.
Shower, sun, fine,
moonshine.

Some few grapes just eatable: a large crop.
Housed all the billet-wood. Leaves fall in showers.
A curlew is heard loudly whistling on the hill towards the
Wadden.

Octobᴿ 27ᵗʰ On this day Mᴿˢ S. Barker was brought to bed of a boy,
who advances my nepotes to the round & compleat number of 60.

Sunday 28.
29 6/10; 52; S, SW.
Shower, sun, soft, &
pleasant.

Thomas saw a polecat¶ run across the garden.

Monday 29.
29 6/10½; 55; 49; W;
28. Rain in the night,
sun, mild & pleasant.
Full moon.

Finished piling my wood: housed the bavins.¶
Fallows very wet.

Tuesday 30.
29 2/10½; S.
Wet, wet, vast rain with
wind.

Planted 100 of cabbages in ground well dunged, to stand the
winter.

Wednesday 31.
29 4/10½; W; 117.
Vast rain in the night,
gleams, sun.

Rain in Octobᴿ – 5 inch. 55 h.

NOVEMBER 1792

Thursday 1.
29 3/10; SW.
Dark, wind, rain, rain.

Friday 2.
29 8/10; 50; SW, S;   Gossamer, & insects flying.
40.
Lovely, soft day.

Saturday 3.
29 8/10; S.   Men sow wheat: but the land-springs break out in some of the
Sweet day.   Hartley-malm fields.
                                    Insects & gossamer.

Sunday 4.
29 8/10½; 57; SE.   The air swarms with insects.
Sweet, summer   Much barley, & oats out still in many places.
weather.

Monday 5.
29 8/10½; 45; SE.   Timothy comes forth.
Vast dew, deep fog,   Gossamer abounds. Men sow. Vast dew lies on the grass all day,
sweet day, cloudless.   even in the sun.

Tuesday 6.
29 8/10½; SE.
Deep, wet fog, dark, &
still.

Wednesday 7.
29 9/10¾; SE.   Men sow wheat in many places.
Dark, mild & still.

Thursday 8.
30 ½/10; SE.   Planted 3 quarters of an hundred more of cabbages to stand the
Dark, still & mild.   winter: dug-up potatoes; those in the garden large, & fine, those
                                    in the meadow small & rotting.

Friday 9.
29 9/10; 50, 53; SE.   Owl hoots; whether the barn, or wood owl, I know not.
Dark, still, & mild,
gleam.

Saturday 10.
29 8/10½; 51, 50; SE.   Several men here have finished sowing their wheat. This is the
Dark, still, & warm,   ninth dry day, wet fogs excepted.
wetish.

10. On this day my Brother Benjamin quitted South Lambeth, & came to reside at His House at Mareland.

Sunday 11.
29 7/10; 49; SE.
Wet fog, dark & still.

Monday 12.
29 3/10; SE.
Vast dew, sun, sweet
weather.

Planted in the garden 2 codling-trees, 2 damson-trees, & 22 goose-berry trees, sent me by Bro.ʳ T. W.
Many insects out.

Tuesday 13.
29 ½/10; 48; S, SE.
Rain, sun, mild, rain,
lightening.

Bantam hen lays.
Mʳ Ed. White & man brought a good fine young white poplar from his out-let at Newton, & planted it at yᵉ top of Parsons's slip, behind the bench; where it will be ornamental.

Wednesday 15.
29 4/10¼; 47; W.
Sun, sharp wind,
bright.

Timothy comes out.

Thursday 16.
29 6/10½; W.
Bright, sharp wind,
small shower, bright.

Vivid rain-bow.

Friday 17.
29 8/10½; 32; NW.
Frost, ice, bright &
sharp, frost.

Baker's hill is planted all over with horse-beans, which are grown four or five inches high. They were probably sown by jays; & spring up thro' the grass or moss. Many were planted there last year; but not in such abundance as now.

Sunday 18.
29 7/10; 38, 47; S.
Thaw, grey, & still,
wet.

Monday 19.
29 6/10¾; 49; W.
Grey, sun, wind,
clouds, wet, showers.

Water-cresses come in.

Tuesday 20.
29 9/10; 33; S.
White frost, sun, dark
& still.

Wednesday 21.
29 2/10½; SW.

Sent 3 bantam fowls to Miss Reb. White at Mareland, a cock &

Wet, driving rain with wind.

two pullets.

Thursday 22.
29 2/10½; W, NW.
Bright, rain in the
night, sharp wind,
shower, moon shine.

Timothy comes forth.

Friday 23.
29 6/10; N; 43.
Bright, shower, clouds.

Saturday 24.
29 9/10; 35; NE.
Sun, grey & still.

Saw a squirrel in Baker's hill: it was very tame. This was probably what Thomas called a pole-cat.

Sunday 25.
29 7/10; NE.
Grey, sun, & clouds.

Monday 26.
29 4/10½; 40; N.
Dark & still, & harsh, wet.

Timothy hides.

Tuesday 27.
29 5/10½; N.
Dark, & harsh.
Full moon.

Wednesday 28.
29 5/10; 42, 39; E.
Dark & harsh, wetish.

Thursday 29.
29 6/10½; NE.
Dark & still, fog.

This dry weather enables men to bring in loads of turf, not much damaged: while scores of loads of peat lie rotting in the Forest.

Friday 30.
29 6/10; 36; SE.
Dark, still & cold.

Finished tacking the vines, which have produced better bearing wood than could have been expected.
Rain in Novemr. – 1 inc. 65 h.

DECEMBER 1792

Saturday 1.
29 5/10; 37; NE.

Thomas started a hare, which lay in her form under a cabbage, in

Dark, & harsh.

the midst of my garden. It has begun to eat the tops of my pinks in many places.
The land springs, which began to appear, are much abated.

Sunday 2.
29 9/10½; 37; NE.
Dark & sharp.

This dry fit has proved of vast advantage to the kingdom; & by drying & draining the fallows, will occasion the sowing of wheat on many hundred of acres of wet, flooded land, that were deemed to be in a desperate state, & incapable of being seeded this season.

Monday 3.
29 9/10½; 31, 32;
SW, W.
Dark, & sharp, fog,
bright, rain.

Tuesday 4.
29 5/10; W.
Dark, fog, wind &
rain.

Timothy is gone under a tuft of long grass, but is not yet buried in the ground.

Wednesday 5.
29 3/10; 48, 53; W;
46.
Wet, rain in the night,
strong wind.

Timothy appears, & flies come out.

Thursday 6.
28 9/10; 50, 48; SW.
Wet & windy, strong
gales.

Friday 7.
29 7/10½; 33; NW.
Bright, & sharp,
clouds, sleet.

Took down the urns, & shut up the alcove.

Saturday 8.
29 9/10½; 31; W.
Frost, ice, bright.

Thin snow on the ground.

Dr Chandler brought a vast pear from the garden of his niece at Hampton which weighed 20 ounces, & ¾, & measured in length 6 inches, & ¾, & in girth eleven inches. It is the sort known by the name of Dr Uvedale's great Saint Germain.¶

Sunday 9.
29 5/10½; SW.
Strong wind, blowing.

Damage by the wind in some places.

Monday 10.
29 6/10½; W.
Strong gales.

Mr Taylor brought me a pine-apple, which was for the season, large, & well-flavoured.

Tuesday 11.
29 7/10½; NW.
Gale, pleasant.

Wednesday 12.
29 7/10; NW.
Grey, pleasant, wet &
dark.

Thursday 13.
29 4/10; NW, NE; 46.
Foggy & wet.

Friday 14.   NEWTON
29 5/10; 40; NW.
Grey, & mild, gleams.

Saturday 15.   SELBORNE
29 6/10¾; NW.
Grey, sun, pleasant,
yellow even.

Sunday 16.
29 9/10; S; 11.   The season has been so mild, that the *Antirrhinum Cymb.* still
Misty, warm & wet.   flourishes, & continues in bloom.

Monday 17.
29 7/10; 45; S.
Dark, still & mild.

Tuesday 18.
29 4/10; W.
Mild, dark, & wet.

Wednesday 19.
29 7/10½; 44; NW.   Flies come out in the windows.
Grey, sun, mild.

Thursday 20.
29 2/10½; SW.
Dark & wet, shower, a
short but violent gust,
lightening.

Friday 21.
29 7/10; 40; NW; 16.
Bright, & windy.

Saturday 22.
28 9/10; W; 20.
Strong gales with heavy
showers, hail, wind.

Sunday 23.
29 4/10; 32, 27; NW.   Freezing all day.
Hard frost, which did
not begin till after
six in the morning,
sun, frost.

Monday 24.
29 4/10; 27, 29; NW.   Covered the artichokes & rhubarb with litter, & the spinage, &
Frost, fair & still.   *Yucca filimentosa* with straw; & the few brown lettuces with straw.
                            M.ʳ Churton came.

Tuesday 25.
28 9/10; NW, SW.
Frost, frozen sleet,
sun, thaw, rain.

Wednesday 26.
28 9/10; W; 40, 3.   Bramblings are seen: they are winter-birds of passage, & come
Wet, snow, rain.   with the hen-chaffinches.
                          Nep. Ben White & wife came.

Thursday 27.
29 3/10; N.
Fair, sun, frost.

Friday 28.
29 5/10; W.
Sun, fair & mild.
Full moon.

Saturday 29.
29 5/10; 49; W.   B. White, & wife left us.
Fog, grey & mild.

Sunday 30.
29 8/10; 33; NW.
Sun, pleasant,
moonshine.

Monday 31.
29 8/10½; 30; NW.   Rain in Decem.ʳ – 2 inch 11 h.
Hoar frost, haze, thaw,
deep fog, frost.

Rain in 1792	inch.	h.
Jan.	6	7
Feb.	1	68
Mar.	6	70
Apr.	4	8
May	3	0
June	2	78
July	5	16
Aug.	4	25
Sep.	5	53
Oct.	5	55
Nov.	1	65
Dec.	2	11
	48	56

JANUARY   — 1793 —

Tuesday 1.
29 3/10½; S.
Frost, rain, wet snow,
rain.

SELBORNE

Wednesday 2.
29 5/10; N; 26.
Dark & wet, dark &
still, bright.

Thursday 3.
29 5/10; 28; SE.
Hoar frost, freezing,
rime, frost.

Friday 4.
29 4/10; 42; S; 33.
Rain, rain, gleams.

Venus is very resplendent.

Saturday 5.

Sunday 6.
29 8/10½; W.
Frost, bright sun, star
light, frost.

N. papers¶ mention snow to the northward.
On this day Mrs Clement was brought to bed of a boy, her ninth
child. My nephews and nieces are now 61.

Monday 7.
29 7/10; 42; E, S.
Swift thaw, warm, wet
fog, rain.

Nephew Holt White came.

Tuesday 8.
29 7/10; W; 107.
Sun, pleasant.

Much rain all night.

Wednesday 9.
29 7/10; E.
Frost, grey, mild.

Thursday 10.
29 3/10½; S, W.
Rain, rain, gleams,
rain.

M.ʳ Churton left us.

Friday 11.
28 9/10½; S.
Rain, sun, heavy
showers, lightening.

On this day came my Nep. John White of Sarūm with his bride,
late Miss Louisa Neave, who encreased my Nep. & nieces to the
number of 62.

Saturday 12.
28 8/10; W; 136.
Rain, gleams.

Vast rain in the night. Lightening.
Great stream in the cart-way.

Sunday 13.
29.
Fair, sun, mild.

Monday 14.
NE.
Dark, rain.

NEWTON
Snow-drops bud, & winter aconites blossom.
John White, & wife, & Holt White left us.

Tuesday 15.
29 8/10; NE.
Sleet, some snow.

Wednesday 16.
29 9/10; 32; NE.
Dark, frost & sharp,
frost.

SELBORNE

Thursday 17.
29 9/10½; 34; N.
Thaw, wet, sharp, &
harsh.

Turnip-greens come in.

Friday 18.
30 1/10; 32, 29; NE.
Frost, grey, bright,
frost.

Saturday 19.
30 1/10¼; 24; NE.
Hard frost, very white,
bright, & still, deep
fog.

Sunday 20.
30 1/10¾; 31; N,
NW.
Frost, rime on the
hanger, dark & still.

Lane in January
Selborne parish.

Monday 21.
30 1/10¼; 29, 35;
NW, SW.
Frost, thaw, still, &
dark.

Thrush sings, the song-thrush: the missle-thrush has not been
heard.

Jan. 21. On this day Louis 16ᵗʰ late king of France, was beheaded
at Paris, & his body flung into a deep grave without any coffin, or
funeral service performed.

Tuesday 22.
30 1/10½; 39; SW,
NW.
Thaw, dark & still,
mild.

Wednesday 23.
30; 37; S, SE.
Dark, mild, & still.

Thursday 24.
29 7/10½; SW.
Wet, rain, rain.

Friday 25.
29 8/10½; NE, E; 39.
Rain, dark & wet.

Snow-drops, daiseys, hepaticas, & ten weeks stocks blow.

Saturday 26.
29 9/10; SE.
Grey, sun, mild.

Mr Marsham, who lives near Norwich, writes me word that a
servant of his shot a bird last autumn near his house that was quite
new to him. Upon examination it appeared to him, & me, to
answer the description of the *Certhia muraria*, the Wall-creeper; a
bird little known, but some times seen in England. Ray, &
Willughby never met with it, nor did I ever find it wild, or among
the vast collections exhibited in London: but Scopoli had a
specimen in his Museum, & says it is to be found in Carniola.¶ It

Sunday 27.
29 9/10¾; SW.
Frost, sun, thaw, mild.

haunts towers, & castles, & ruins, & some times frequents towns, running up the walls of tall houses, & searching the crannies, & chinks for spiders, & other insects. Some of the internal wing-feathers are beautifully marked on the inner web with two white, or pale yellow spots; & the middle of the outer web edged with red. Two of these quills, drawn in water-colours, by a young Lady, & charmingly executed, were sent me by M:r Marsham in a frank: the pencilling of these specimens is truly delicate, soft, & feathery. It is much to be regretted that she did not draw the whole bird. The claws of this bird are strong & large, say Linnaeus, & M:r Marsham; & especially the hind claw.

Monday 28.
29 8/10; 50; W.
Great dew, sun, sweet day.

Bees come out, and gather on the snow-drops.

Tuesday 29.
29 5/10; SW.
Wet, fog.

Wednesday 30.
29 5/10; SW; 30.
Sun, cold shower, bright.

Rain in the night.

Thursday 31.
29 5/10; 35; SW.
White frost, sun, mild.

Rain in January – 3 in. 71 h.

FEBRUARY 1793

Friday 1.
29; SW.
Wet, rain, rain.

The Republic of France declares war against England, & Holland.¶

Saturday 2.
29; S; 15.
Wet, rain, rain, wind.

Sunday 3.
29 1/10½; SW; 50.
Rain, bright, sun.

A strong gust in the night blew down the rain-gage, which, by the appearance in the tubs, must have contained a considerable quantity of water.

Monday 4.
29; SW.
Grey, sun, starry.

Venus is very bright, & shadows.

Tuesday 5.

NEWTON

29 1/10½; 38; NW;   M.rs J. White set out for Kingston on Thames.
13. Fog.

Wednesday 6.
NW, SW. Sun, rain.   Rain in the night.

Thursday 7.
29 5/10.   Snow covers the ground.
Sun, snow melts.

Friday 8.   SELBORNE
29 2/10; W; 73.   War declared, & letters of Marque granted against the french
Showers, gleams.   Republic.¶

Saturday 9.
29 3/10; W.   First Bantam begins to lay.
Dark, sun, rain.

Sunday 10.
29 1/10; W.
Grey, sun, severe wind,
with flights of snow,
sleet, & hail.

Monday 11.
29 5/10; W; 18.   Paths get dry. Sowed a bed of radishes, & carrots under the fruit-
Grey, sun, sharp wind,   wall.
wet, rain.

Tuesday 12.
29 4/10; 45, 40; W.   M.rs J. White returns.
Sun, sharp wind.

Wednesday 13.
29 5/10¾; SW; 15.
Wet & foggy, moist
air.

Thursday 14.
29 4/10; SW; 19.
Rain, bright, sun.

Friday 15.
29 3/10¾; S.   Rain & hail in the night.
Dark, & moist, mild.   Made a seedling-cucumber bed: mended the frame, & put it on.

Saturday 16.
29 6/10; 33; N.   Sent some winter-aconites in bloom to D.r Chandler; & received

Bee visiting snowdrops.
January.

Sun, bright, red even, air cold.

back some roots of *Arum dracunculus*.
Tubbed, & salted-up a fine young hog, bought of Timothy Turner: weight – 9 Sc. 18 p. Price £4: 4s: 3d at 8s 6d per score.

Sunday 17.
29 6/10⅓; NE.
Grey, & still, hazy, wet.

Monday 18.
29 6/10; SW, NW.
Wet, gleam, bright.

Tuesday 19.
29 7/10½; 33; NW, NE.
Ice, white frost, fair, sweet day, gossamer.

Sowed first cucumber-seeds: ashed three parts of the great mead: dunged the annual basons.
Insects come forth.
Sowed half a barrel of American Gypsum, which was sent for in the autumn by Bro. Tho. on the fourth ridge of Tim. Turner's wheat, as you reckon from the walk in that field. The powder strewed about two thirds of the ridge from the Ewel S.E. ward.

Wednesday 20.
29 8/10; 30; NE, SW, S. Ice, very white frost, fair, fine day, fog.

Wheeled much dung into the garden.

Thursday 21.
29 8/10; 36; S.
Fog, sun, sweet day.

Dug the garden-plot in the orchard, & in the meadow: but the ground is very wet, & heavy.

Friday 22.
29 8/10½; 26; S.
Vast white dew, sun, fine day, wet.

Turned earth. Frost spoils the paths.
Cucumbers appear. Mended cucumber light.

Saturday 23.
29 8/10; SW.
Dark & moist, rain.

Crocus's begin to blossom.
Planted three rows of beans in the orchard.
Potted some cucumbers. Sowed some lettuces, & spinage in the border under the melon-skreen.

Mr White of Newton sprung a pheasant in a wheat-stubble, & shot at it; when, notwithstanding the report of the gun, it was immediately pursued by the blue hawk, known by the name of Hen-harrier, but escaped into some covert. He then sprung a second, & a third in the same field, that got away in the same manner: the hawk hovering round him all the while that he was beating the field, conscious no doubt of the game that lurked in the stubble. Hence we may conclude that this bird of prey was rendered very daring, & bold by hunger; & that Hawks cannot always seize their game when they please. We may further observe that they cannot pounce their quarry on the ground, where it might be able to make a stout resistance; since so large a fowl as a pheasant could not but be visible to the piercing eye of an hawk, when hovering over a field. Hence that propensity of cowring & squatting till they are almost trod on, which no doubt was intended a a a mode of security; tho' long rendered destructive to the whole race of *Gallinae*, by the invention of nets, & guns.

Sunday 24.
29 8/10; 46; SW.
Dark & mild, wet mist.

Wall-flowers blossom; crown-imperials sprout.

Monday 25.
29 3/10½; 45; SW.
Dark, warm, & wet.
Full moon.

Tuesday 26.
29 8/10¼; SW; 29.
Bright, gale, clouds.

Sowed more cucumber-seeds.

Wednesday 27.
29 6/10; SW, S.
Grey, & windy.

Carting-in three loads of hot dung, made an hand-glass celeri-bed, & sowed half of it.
Planted three rows of beans in the meadow plot. Paths dry.

Thursday 28.
29 6/10½; 39; W.
Some rain, bright, fine even.

Planted 50 good cabbage-plants: mended the bed planted in the autumn, & eaten in part by the hares.
Rain in February – 20 inch 32 h.

MARCH 1793

Friday 1.
29 2/10; S, W; 32.
Sad stormy wet day!

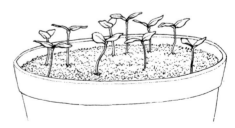

Cucumber seedlings.
Early May.

Saturday 2.
29 1/10½; SW.
Dark, & wet, rain,
stormy, fierce storm!

Sunday 3.
29 5/10; 36; W; 27.
Bright, strong gale.

Crocus's begin to make a fine shew.
The wind last night blowed off some tiles from my roof.

This storm did much mischief about the kingdom.
   We are much amused every morning by a string of Lord

Stawell's Hunters that are aired, exercised, & watered in a
meadow opposite to the windows of this house. There seem to be
two sets, which appear alternatly on the days that they are not
hunted. He has in all sixteen.

Monday 4.
29 6/10; SW.
Grey, sun, pleasant.

MARELAND

Tuesday 5.
29 5/10; S.
Fog, dark, rain.

Herons haunt the stream below the house, where the Wey
meanders along the meads.

Lord Stawell sent me a curious water-fowl, shot on Frinsham
pond, which proved to be the Shoveler, remarkable for the
largeness of it's bill. It is a species of duck, & most exactly
described by Mr Ray.
    Large wood-pecker laughs very loud.

Wednesday 6.
29 7/10; NE; 12.
Rain, gleam, grey.

Dogs-tooth violets blow. Wag-tails on the grass-plots:
they were here all this mild winter. Goldfinches are not paired.

Thursday 7.
29 8/10; 44; NE.
Grey, gleam, sharp air.

Trouts begin to rise: some angling takes place in this month. My
Brother's cucumbers are strong, & healthy.

My Brother's lambs frolick before the windows, & run to a certain
hillock, which is their goal, from whence they hurry back; & put
us in mind of the following passage in the Poet of nature:
. . . "now the sprightly race"
"Invites them forth; then swift, the signal given,"
"They start away, & sweep the massy mound"
"That runs around the hill" . . .¶
    Lady Stawell tells Mrs White that they have seen more
woodcocks & snipes at their table this winter than usual.

Friday 8.
29 9/10; NE.
Sun, & sharp wind.

Many red wings feeding in the meadow.

Saturday 9.
29 7/10½; NE.
White frost, ice, strong
sunshine, wind, sharp.

The sweet peal of bells at Farnham, heard up the vale of a still
evening, is a pleasing circumstance belonging to this situation, not
only as occasioning agreeable associations in the mind, &
remembrances of the days of my youth, when I once resided in
that town:¶ but also by bringing to one's recollection many
beautiful passages from the poets respecting this tuneable, &
manly amusement, for which this island is so remarkable. Of these
none are more distinguished, & masterly than the following:

Sunday 10.
29 5/10; NW.
White frost, thick ice,
severe wind, dark &
cold.

. . "let the village bells, as often wont,"
"Come swelling on the breeze, & to the sun"
"Half set, ring merrily their evening round."

. . . . . .
"It is enough for me to hear the sound"
"Of the remote, exhilerating peal,"
"Now dying all away, now faintly heard,"
"And now with loud, & musical relapse"
"In mellow changes pouring on the ear."
The village Curate.

Monday 11.
29 5/10; 40; NW.
Small snow, harsh, &
cutting!
some flakes of snow
falling.

Vast flock of Red-wings feeding in the meadow before the house.
There is a glade cut thro' the covert of the Holt opposite these
windows, up towards the great Lodge. To this opening a herd of
deer often resorts & contributes to enliven & diversify the
prospect in itself beautiful, & engaging.

Tuesday 12.
29 5/10; 29; E.
Hard frost, ice, bright
sun, cutting wind! rain.

Apricot begins to blow.
Red-wings, & starlings abound in the meadow, where they feed
in the moist, & watered spots.

Starlings by the pond
Wakes

Wednesday 13.
29 8/10; S; 24.
Rain, dark & moist,
gleam, fair.

During my absence Thomas parted-out my polyanths, & planted
them in rows along the orchard walk, & up the border of Baker's
Hill by the hot beds.
My Brother has a pigeon-house stocked with perhaps 50 pairs of
birds, which have not yet begun to breed. He has in the Yard
Turkeys, a large breed of ducks, & fine fowls. On the ponds are
geese, which begin to sit.

Thursday 14.
29 8/10¼; S.
Mild, summer-like,
soft evening.

Papilio rhamni, the brimstone butterfly, appears in the Holt.
Trouts rise, & catch at insects.
A dobchick comes down the Wey in sight of the windows, some
times diving & some times running on the banks.
Took a walk in the Holt up to the lodge: no bushes, & of course
no young oaks: some Hollies, & here & there a few aged yews:

no oaks of any great size. The soil wet & boggy.

Friday 15.
29 8/10; SW.
Frost, fog, bright, hot,
dark, appearance of
rain.

Timothy the tortoise comes forth, & weighs 6 pd 5½ oz.

Saturday 16.
29 1/10½; S.
Grey & mild, great
rain.

SELBORNE

On friday last my Brother, & I walked up to Bentley church, which
is more than a mile from his house, & on a considerable elevation
of ground. From thence the prospect is good, & you see at a
distance Cruxbury hill, Guild down, part of Lethe hill, Hind-head,
& beyond it the top of one of the Sussex downs. There is an avenue
of aged Yew-trees up to the church: & the yard, which is large,
abounds with brick-tombs covered with slabs of stone: of these
there are ten in a row, belonging to the family of the Lutmans. The
church consists of three ailes; & has a squat tower containing six
bells. From the inscriptions it appears that the inhabitants live to
considerable ages.

There are hop-grounds along on the north side of the turn-pike
road; but none on the south towards the stream. The whole district
abounds with springs.

The largest spring on my brother's farm issues out of the bank
in the meadow, just below the terrace. Some body formerly was
pleased with this fountain, & has, at no small expence, bestowed a
facing of Portland stone with an arch, & a pipe, thro' which the
water falls, into a stone bason, in a perennial stream. By means of
a wooden trough this spring waters some part of the circumjacent
slope. It is not so copious as Well-head.

Sunday 17.
28 7/10½; E.
White frost, sun, cold
wind, rain.

Timothy comes out.

Monday 18.
29 1/10; SW, NW; 86.
Rain, gleam, rain.

Rain in the night.
Turned out the cucumber-plants into the hills of the two-light
frame: the bed has been made a week last friday. Plants look well.

Tuesday 19.
29 5/10; SW; 25.
Rain, sun, soft.

Celeri comes up under the hand-glass.
Crocus's make a gay appearance still.
Daffodil blows. Timothy appears.

Wednesday 20.
29 4/10¾; 50; SW, S.
Wet, gleam, rain.

Planted 30 cauliflowers brought from Mareland; & a row of red
cabbages. The ground is so glutted with rain that men can neither
plow, nor sow nor dig.

Thursday 21.
29 6/10; 47; SW; 21.
Rain in the night, sun,
mild, & still.

Parted the bunches of Hepatica's that were got weak, & planted
them again round the borders.
Cucumbers thrive & look well.

Friday 22.
29 3/10; SW; 52.
Rain, rain, rain.

Saturday 23.
29 4/10; SW.
Some rain in the night,
sun, louring in the
west.

Sunday 24.
29 5/10½; E, N.
White frost, sun, rain,
rain.

This evening Admiral Gardner's fleet sailed from St Helens with
a fair wind.

Monday 25.
29 6/10¾; NE.
Rain, dark & harsh.

Tuesday 26.
29 6/10; NE; 54.
Snow & rain, harsh.

A sad wintry day!

Wednesday 27.
29 5/10; 33; NE.
Frost, fair, sharp.
Full moon.

Icicles.

Thursday 28.
29 4/10; 33; E.
Snow, fair, sharp.

Snow does not lie. Ice. Frost & icicles all day.

Friday 29.
29 5/10; 29; N.
White sharp frost, thick
ice: icicles, bright, gay
gleam.

Apricots blow: peaches & nectarines begin to open their buds.
Some thing again eats off the young celeri.

Saturday 30.
29 6/10; 28; N, NW.
White frost, thick ice,
bright & sharper, still.

Made a new hand-glass bed for celeri in the garden. The crocus's
still look very gay when the sun shines.

Sunday 31.
29 5/10¼; 34; N, SW.
Hoar frost, ice, bright
sun, grey & still.

Rain in March – 3 inch. 33 h.

APRIL 1793

Monday 1.
29 1/10½; S, SW; 50.
Rain & snow, rain.

In the mid counties there was a prodigious snow: some people
were lost in it, & perished.

Tuesday 2.
29 4/10½; 37; NW.
Dark & harsh, wet, fair
even.

The small willow-wren, or chif-chaf, is heard in the short Lythe.
This is the earliest summer bird, & is heard usually about the 20th
of March. Tho' one of the smallest of our birds, yet it's two notes
are very loud, & piercing, so as to occasion an echo in hanging
woods. It loves to frequent tall beeches.

Wednesday 3.
29 6/10; 35; S.
White frost, fair, still
day, beautiful evening.

Thursday 4.
29 6/10⅓; NE, N.
Mist, bright day, fine
gleam, cool wind.

Timothy Turner ashed great part of Baker's hill, & dunged one
part.
Wag-tail on the grass-plots.

Friday 5.
29 6/10½; NE.
Mist, sweet summer
weather.

The air smells very sweet, & salubrious.
Men dig their hop-gardens, & sow spring-corn.
Cucumber plants show rudiments of fruit.
Planted cuttings of currans, & goose-berries.

Saturday 6.
29 6/10¾; 45; NE.
Mist, cloudless, warm
sun.

Dug some of the quarters in the garden, & sowed onions,
parsnips, radishes, & lettuces.
Planted more beans in the meadow.
Many flies are out basking in the sun.

On the 6th of last October I saw many swallows hawking for flies
around the Plestor, & a row of young ones, with square tails,
sitting on a spar of the old ragged thatch of the empty house. This
morning Dr Chandler, & I caused the roof to be examined, hoping
to have found some of those birds in their winter retreat: but we
did not meet with any success, tho' Benham searched every hole,
& every breach in the decayed roof.

Sunday 7.
29 8/10½; NE.
Cold dew, bright, fine
even.

Hot sun, & cold air.
The chaffinches destroy the blossoms of the polyanths in a sad
manner. Cucumbers begin to show male-bloom.
Sowed a bed of carrots: the ground hard, & rough, & does not
rake fine.

Monday 8.
29 9/10; NE.
White dew, cloudless,
cold wind.

Tuesday 9.
29 8/10⅓; 35; NE.
White dew, cloudless,
cold wind.

Planted in one of the quarters of the garden, in ground well dunged, 8 long rows of potatoes. Carted in hot dung for the second cucumber bed.

April 9. Thomas Knight, a sober kind, assures us, that this day on Wish-hanger common between Hedleigh & Frinsham he saw several Bank-martins playing in & out, & hanging before some nest-holes in a sand-hill, where these birds usually nestle. This incident confirms my suspicions, that this species of *Hirundo* is to be seen first of any; & gives great reason to suppose that they do not leave their wild haunts at all, but are secreted amidst the clefts, & caverns of those abrupt cliffs where they usually spend their summers. The late severe weather considered, it is not very probable that these birds should have migrated so early from a tropical region thro' all these cutting winds, & pinching frosts: but is is easy to suppose that they may, like bats & flies, have been awakened by the influence of the Sun, amidst their secret *labebrae*,¶ where they have spent the uncomfortable foodless months in a torpid state, & the profoundest of slumbers. There is a large pond at Wish-hanger, which induces these sand-martins to frequent that district. For I have ever remarked, that they haunt near great waters, either rivers or lakes.

Wednesday 10.
29 8/10; 33; NE, N.
Harsh wind, frost, sun
& clouds.

Dug the asparagus bed, & cleared away the straw laid on. Farmers wish for a gentle rain.

Path in the Wakes garden.
Late July.

Thursday 11.
29 6/10; 32; N.
Hard frost, ice, dark,
sleet, wet, dark.

Some cucumber-fruit blows.
Hoed, & cleaned the alleys.

Friday 12.
29 4/10¾; 35; N.
Dark & harsh, sleet, &
hail, sharp wind.

Turned the heap of hot dung.
The ground is very dry, & harsh.

The Nightingale was heard this harsh evening near James Knight's
ponds. This Bird of passage, I observe, comes as early in cold
cutting springs, as mild ones!

Saturday 13.
29 3/10½; 33; N.
Frost, warm sun.

Sowed polyanth-seeds.
Bat out. This is the twelveth dry day.

Sunday 14.
29 5/10; 45; NW, W.
Grey, mild, harsh, sun,
sharp.

Monday 15.
29 3/10½; 32; W,
SW.
Hard frost, ice, gleam,
dark, shower.

Sowed fringed bore-cole, & Savoys, & leeks.
Made an hand-glass celeri-bed.

Tuesday 16.
29 6/10; 34; NW, N,
NW; 22.
Snow storms, hail,
gusts, sharp.

Made a hot bed for the two-light frame with lapped glass.

Wednesday 17.
29 3/10; 31; SW, S.
Hard frost, dark, rain,
rain & snow, rain, rain.

Thick ice on ponds!

Thursday 18.
28 9/10¾; W; 129.
Blowing, blowing.

Friday 19.
29 7/10½; NE; 10.
Showers of hail, &
sleet.

Gleams. Timothy, who has withdrawn himself for several days,
appears.

Saturday 20.
29 8/10; 35; N, SW, S,

Planted more beans in the meadow.

SE.
Hard frost, ice, warm
sun, cool even.

Cucumbers swell. Wall-cherries begin to blow.
The Cuckoo is heard on Greatham common.

Sunday 21.
29 8/10; S, SE.
Cold air, fine, summer
weather, sweet even.

Two Swallows seen at forest-side.

Monday 22.
29 7/10; 40; SE.
Brisk air, bright, red
even.

Began to mow the grass-walks.
Earthed the second cucumber-bed.

Tuesday 23.
29 4/10; SE, S, SW.
White frost, soft air,
cloudy.

Mowed the terrace. Cut the first cucumber.
Pulled the first radishes.
A swallow over my meadow.

Wednesday 24.
29 4/10; NW, NE.
Warm, gentle rain.

Crown imperials, & Fritillaria's blow.
When Thomas got-up to brew at four o' the clock he heard some
stone-curlews pass by over the house in their way to the uplands.
In the evening they flie over the village downwards, towards the
brook, & meadows, where they seem to spend the night.

Thursday 25.
29 5/10; 52; N, NW;
52.
Dark, still & mild.

Cut a brace of large cucumbers. Turned-out two pots of
cucumber-plants into their hills.

Friday 26.
29 3/10½; SW, NE.
Fair & pleasant.
Full moon.

Planted 25 good cauliflower-plants from Mareland.

Saturday 27.
29 1/10½; 45; E.
Grey, mild, & still.

Men begin to pole their hops. Mountain snow-drop blows. Cut a
large cucumber.
Sowed some cucumber-seeds in pots.

Sunday 28.
29 5/10; 58; N, NE.
Bright, summer
weather.

Wall-flowers full of bloom, & very fine.
Nightingale in my fields.

Monday 29.
29 4/10; SE, SW; 29.
Dark, rain, wind.

I have seen no *hirundo* yet myself.

Tuesday 30.
29; SE, S; 27.
Dark, rain, rain.

Saw two swallows at Gracious street.
Rain in April – 3 in. 19 h.
Sowed Columbines, two sorts; Scabius; Scarlet lychnis; Nigella;
10 weeks stocks; Mountain lychnis.

MAY 1793

Wednesday 1.
29; S, W; 73.
Blowing, shower,
gleam.

Great rain, wind, & thunder in the night.

Thursday 2.
29 4/10½; 44; W,
NW; 35.
Heavy showers.

Sad blowing, wintry weather.
I think I saw an house martin.
A pair of Swifts.

Friday 3.
29 9/10; NW.
Sun, & gale.

Timothy eats.
A pair of Missel-thrushes have made a nest in the apple-tree near
the fruit-wall. One young half-fledged was found in the garden.
Vines begin to shoot.

Saturday 4.
29 7/10¾; SW.
Grey, mild, clouds.

Hen red-start appears.
Some beeches begin to show leaves.
Sowed some fine Savoy seed from Newton.
Sowed fringed bore cole. Vines begin to shoot.

There is a bird of the black bird kind, with white on the breast,¶
that haunts my outlet, as if it had a nest there. Is this a ring-ouzel?
if it is, it must be a great curiosity; because they have not been
known to breed in these parts.

Sunday 5.
29 9/10; NW.
Shower, sun & gale,
cold air.

Damson, sloe-trees, & wild Merise blow.
Cock Redstart. House-martin appears.

There has been so little frost, that this *Antirrhinum Cymb.*¶
flourished & blossomed the whole winter thro', & is now very
thriving, tho' it usually dies about Xmas. So that, in mild times, it
is at lest a biennial with us, & may be perhaps of longer duration in
warmer regions.

Monday 6.
29 9/10; 49; N.
Grey, dark & still, wet.

Carted-in three loads of hot dung. Took down the linings of the
hot beds, & worked them up afresh with some hot dung.
Cut a large cucumber in the seedling-bed.

Tuesday 7.
29 8/10; N.
Dark & wet, showers.

The wall-cherries are much blown.

James Knight has observed two large field-fares in the high wood¶ lately, haunting the same part, as if they intended to breed there. They are not wild. A nest of this sort of bird would be a great curiosity!

Wednesday 8.
29 7/10½; NE, E,
SW.
Grey, shower, heavy
clouds
in the horizon.

Missel-thrushes feed on ivy-berries, now ripe.
M. thrushes do not destroy the fruit in gardens like the other species of *turdi*, but feed on the berries of missel-toe; & in the spring on ivy berries, which then begin to ripen. In the summer, when their young become fledge, they leave neighbourhoods, & retire to sheep walks, & wild commons.
Pears begin to blow.

Thursday 9.
29 8/10½; SW; 13.
Shower, sun & clouds,
shower, red sun-set.

Cut three cucumbers. Weed & dress borders.
Growing weather.
Black snails come forth.

The mag-pies, which probably have young, are now very ravenous, & destroy the broods of Missel-thrushes, tho' the dams are fierce birds, & fight boldly in defence of their nests. It is probably to avoid such insults, that this species of thrush, tho' wild at other times, delights to build near houses, & in frequented walks, & gardens.

Friday 10.
29 6/10; S, E.
Dark, sun & clouds.

4 swifts: few martins.

Saturday 11.
29 4/10½; SE, E.
Louring, moist, warm,
growing weather.

Cut two brace of fine cucumbers.
Dress borders. Mow the orchard.
Swallows begin to build: few house-martins yet.

Sunday 12.
29 6/10; 65; E.
Sweet, summer
weather.

The merise, or wild cherry in beautiful bloom.
A solitary hen red-start in the garden.
Early tulips blow.

Monday 13.
29 7/10; N.
Summer, gale, sweet
even.

Two nightingales sing in my outlet. Cut four brace of cucumbers. Foliage of trees expands very fast.
Made the three-light annual bed.
Peat begins to be brought in: it is in good condition. H. martin's build.
The old Bantam hen began to sit in the barn on eleven eggs.
The fern-owl, or churn-owl returns, & chatters in the hanger.

Tuesday 14.
29 8/10½; 60; N.
Bright, cool gale,
bright & cool.

Timothy travels about the garden.
Cut two brace & half of cucumbers.

Wednesday 15.
29 8/10¾; N.
Sun, & clouds, gleams,
dark.

Made an hand-glass seedling-bed for cucumbers.

Thursday 16.
29 8/10; 44; N.
Cold dew, sun &
clouds, red even.

Wall-honey-suckles begin to blow. The ten-weeks stocks, &
wall-flowers perfume the garden. Much peat carted in.
Sowed in the three-light annual frame African, & French
marigolds, China asters, pendulous Amaranths, Orange-
gourds.
Took the black birds nest a second time; it had squab young.

Friday 17.
29 7/10; 63; N.
No dew, thunder, small
shower.

Sowed a row of scarlet kidney-beans.
Thunder & lightening to the W. & S.W.
There was much rain, & hail at Emshot.
Set the second Bantam hen over the saddle-cup-board in the stable
with eleven dark eggs.

Saturday 18.
29 7/10; N.
Grey, small dew, dark
& louring.

Sowed an other row of scarlet kidney-beans.
Cut two brace of fine cucumbers.
Sowed an hand-glass with cucumbers for the ridge-bed.
Made rhubarb tarts, & a rhubarb pudding, which was very
good.

A man brought me a large trout, weighing three pounds, which he
found in the waste current at the tail of Bins pond, in water so
shallow that it could not get back again to the Selborne stream.

Sunday 19.
29 7/10½; 45, 56; N.
Cool air, frost, clouds,
& sun, bright.

The white apple-tree shews again, as usual, much bloom.
Wall-nut trees, & oaks begin to shoot.

Monday 20.
29 7/10½; 58; N.
White frost, bright day.

Cut two brace of fine cucumbers; & left one for seed.
The 10 weeks stocks, which stood the winter, make a fine show,
& are very fragrant.
Tulips blow.
Two nightingales sing in my outlet.

Avenue of Yews
Bentley Churchyard.

Tuesday 21.
29 7/10¾; N.
White frost, bright,
hazy.

Timothy eats much. Cut two cucumbers.
Few swifts to be seen.

Wednesday 22.
29 9/10; 45; N.
No dew, cold wind,
sun, cloudless.

The roads very dry.
Much peat carted.
Nep. Ben. White, & wife came.

Thursday 23.
29 8/10½; 58; N.
Haze, sun & sharp
wind.

Cut seven fine cucumbers.
Several swifts.

Friday 24.
29 8/10½; 58; N.
Fog, great dew, sun,
fine even.

The Fly-catcher, the latest summer-bird of passage, appears. It
usually comes on the 20.ᵗʰ

Saturday 25.
29 9/10; 44; N.
Haze, dark & harsh.
Full moon.

Cut down the greens of the crocus's; they make good tyings for
hops; better than rushes, more pliant, & tough.

Sunday 26.
29 9/10; 51; N.
Sun, white dew, hot
sun, red even.

The white pippin is covered with bloom.
Farmer Spencer's apple-trees blow well.
Nep. Ben White, & wife left us.

Monday 27.
29 8/10; 51, 61; N, E.
Hot sun, dark & warm.

Made a second hand-glass bed. Sowed a row of white kidney-
beans. Cut seven cucumbers.
Columbines blow.

The season is so cold, that no species of Hirundines make any
advances towards building, & breeding.

Tuesday 28.
29 5/10¼; NW, N.
Bright, sun & clouds,
cold air.

Grass-walks burn for want of rain.
Sowed an hand-glass with cucumber-seeds.
Ground much parched.

Wednesday 29.
29 5/10; N, W.
Sun & clouds, cold.

My weeding-woman swept-up on the grass-plot a bushel-basket of
blossoms from the white apple-tree: & yet that tree seems still
covered with bloom.
    29. Broʳ Benjⁿ & Mʳˢ White, & Mary White, & Miss Mary Barker
came.

Thursday 30.
29 7/10¼; 43½; N.

Fyfield sprung a brace of pheasants in Sparrow's hanger.

Cold wind, sun &
clouds, cold.

Hail-like clouds about.

Friday 31.
29 7/10½; N, W.
Cold air, sun, cold air.

Cut seven cucumbers.
Fern-owl chatters.
Rain in May – 1 inch. 21 h.

My great oak abounds in bloom, which is of a yellowish cast: the
young shoots usually look red.
    The house-martins at Mareland, in the few hot days, began to
build, but when the winds became cold again immediately
desisted.

Oak in flower.
Selborne.

JUNE 1793

Saturday 1.
29 6/10; S, S.
Sun & clouds, dark.

Timothy is very voracious: when he can get no other food he eats
grass in the walks.

Sunday 2.
29 4/10½; SE, SE.
Dark, soft rain, dark &
moist.

Fiery lily blows. A good rain at Fyfield, & a great rain at
Tidworth.
Hawthorn blows.
Cut 8 cucumbers.

Monday 3.
29 7/10½; SE.
Sun, mild & still.

The ground sadly burnt-up. Royal russets show much bloom.
Summer-cabbage comes in.

Bro.r Benj.n & I measured my tall beech in Sparrow's hanger,
which, at five feet from the ground, girths six feet one inch, & three
quarters.

Tuesday 4.
29 7/10; S.
Grey & mild, soft even.

Cinamon rose blows.
Many martins are gathering loam down at Gracious street, &
beginning to build.

Wednesday 5.
29 7/10; 67; SW.
Soft showers, golden
gleam, fog.

Laburnum blows: & peonies blossom.
The 10 weeks stocks of last year make a noble appearance, &
perfume the air.
Men's S^t foin burns, & dies away.
The farmers on the sands complain that they have no grass.

Thursday 6.
29 6/10; S, SE.
Dark, wet, rain.

Sowed two rows of large white kidney-beans: but the ground is so
hard, that it required much labour to render it fit to receive the
seed.
The old Bantam brought out only three chickens.
Mrs Clement, & children came.

Friday 7.
29 5/10½; SW.
Fair, sun with gale.

Watered well the white poplar at the foot of the bostal. Cut the
slope hedge in Baker's hill.
Made 6 hand-glass beds for late cucumbers.
The young Bantam hen brought out only two chickens.

Saturday 8.
29 7/10; 61; SW.
Grey, showers, fine
even.

Cut eight cucumbers.
Showers that wetted the blades of corn, & grass, but did not
descend to the root.
Ground very hard.
Planted out some cucumbers under the hand-glasses.

Sunday 9.
29 71/10; SW.
Sun & clouds, fine
even, cool.

Early orange-lilies blow.
Few chafers.

The water at Kingsley mill begins to fail. The land-spring in the
stoney-lane, as you go to Rood, stops. We draw much water for
the garden: the well sinks very fast.

Monday 10.
29 7/10¾; SW, W;
16. Showers, cool,
gleams, cold air.

Cut five cucumbers.

Tuesday 11.
29 6/10½; 61; SW.
Grey, sun, louring.

A man brought me a large plate of straw-berries, which were
crude, & not near ripe.
The ground all as hard as iron: we can sow nothing, nor plant
out.

Wednesday 12.
29 7/10; 62; N.
Bright sun, golden
even.

Cut eight cucumbers.
Mrs Clement & children left us.
Many swifts.

Thursday 13.
29 8/10½; 61; NE.
Shower, sun & cold
wind.

Cut ten cucumbers.
Provence roses blow against a wall. Dames violets very fine. Ten
weeks stocks still in full beauty.

Friday 14.
29 8/10; 48; NE.
Cold wind, dark,
gleams.

Cut four cucumbers.
Mr John Mulso¶ came.

Saturday 15.
29 8/10; 60; NE, SW.
Cold dew, sun, louring.

Men wash their sheep.
Mr John Mulso left us.

Sunday 16.¶

Travellers Joy.
Hollow Lane to Alton

NOTES

In order to avoid repetition the following abbreviations have been used:
GW = Gilbert White
NHS = *The Natural History of Selborne*

1784 Events and journeys

The Revd Ralph Churton was at Selborne over the New Year and left on January 10th. Gilbert spent the whole of March and a few days of April at South Lambeth. He was, however, ill during the early months of the year and was still unwell in April when his old friend Revd Andrew Etty, the Vicar of Selborne, died. Gilbert performed the burial service, his spirits depressed by this sad loss. He did not feel fully recovered in health for some time and missed his usual annual visit to Oxford.

During the pleasant weather of late May, Timothy the tortoise was lost, and found again a week later in the bean field, an incident which gave rise to a charming and thoughtful letter from Gilbert to John Mulso's daughter Hester, who stayed with her parents at the Wakes during the summer. There was also the unfortunate demise of two Madagascan tortoises brought back by young Charles Etty who returned to Selborne in the late summer. In May, Gilbert wrote to his niece Molly, his brother Thomas's daughter, that a Revd C. Taylor was the probable new Vicar of Selborne, but this gentleman did not take up the living until late September when, as predicted, Gilbert took on the curacy once more.

John Mulso was again at Selborne in November, and the Richardsons of Bramshott Place also paid a short visit. So did several of the White relatives, and Gilbert's niece/nephew count went up again in August with the birth of another great niece, reaching a total of 41. To some of his special correspondents among these nephews and nieces Gilbert writes with relaxed affection, signing himself 'loving friend' or 'loving uncle'. With Molly White he had an especially close relationship, based on mutual interests.

One of the excitements of the year was the passing over Selborne of Blanchard's air balloon and the account Gilbert made of it was sent to Molly and to his sister Mrs Barker. It was also published in a newspaper or magazine, a cutting of which was inserted in the Journal.

January	9.	A grey crow Hooded crows, or Royston crows as they are sometimes called (*Corvus cornix*), occasionally still appear in Hampshire.
	31.	Yellow wagtail Almost certainly the bird we now call the grey wagtail. In his list of species given in NHS Letter I to Daines Barrington, GW includes the yellow wagtail as one of the birds resident all year. In fact, the yellow wagtail (*Motacilla flava*) is a summer visitor to England, so GW's observations, made in winter, were probably of the grey wagtail *Motacilla cinerea* which has a yellow breast. The male grey wagtail differs from the female in having a black throat and being bright yellow when in breeding plumage. It is possible that GW mistook the male and female for different species.
February	14.	Thomas Thomas Hoar, GW's manservant, kept weather and temperature notes and occasionally the Journal notes when GW was absent. Six years older than his master, he was rememberd in GW's will as 'my old servant Thomas Hoar', and outlived him by four years.
April	5.	Timber cut . . . before barking time That is, before the bark had been removed for use in tanning.
	19.	Timothy The carapace of Timothy the tortoise, preserved in the British Museum, has been identified as that of a female of the species *Testudo ibera*.
	28.	Woodcocks . . . return . . . to the Eastern coast Most British woodcock are sedentary, though there is some internal movement. Continental birds arrive in autumn and there is a return movement in spring.
May	28.	Timothy the tortoise has been missing It was eight days before he was found, and GW elaborated the incident in a letter from Timothy to young Miss Hecky Mulso, daughter of his friend John Mulso.
June	5.	The hail storm This long account on an interleaved sheet appears in a slightly altered form in the NHS letter LXVI to Daines Barrington.
July	13.	Finished ripping, furring and tiling Ripping: removing the tiles of a building or roof and putting on fresh lathes; furring: the nailing on of thin strips of wood to rafters and beams to raise a surface ready for boarding or tiling.
	17.	Mr Charles Etty brought . . . two finely chequered tortoises The dismal deaths of

| | | young Charles Etty's tortoises here reported quite plainly seem to have brought home to GW the stress which these animals suffer during travel, knowledge which he incorporated into his 'Timothy' letter of August 31st – signed 'Your sorrowful Reptile'. GW was not so much of a scientist that he did not feel compassion for animals, a rare attribute in his time. |

		Latin translation 'Of an elliptical or egg-like shape, with more than half of it solid.' 'Of all the ones which I have ever seen, the most curved.'
	22.	Molly White's horse-chestnut tree Originally written as 'sycamore', but this was crossed out and 'horse-chestnut' inserted. In his letter to Molly dated 16th August GW calls it sycamore. Did Molly correct him after receiving the letter? Another letter to her dated 24th September mentions that a post was made with the detached bough.
August	6.	Tremella There are several observations on the appearance of the blue-green alga *Tremella nostoc*. The name *Tremella* is now used for a group of jelly-like fungi. *Nostoc* was named by Paracelsus and there are many references to its having been an emanation from the stars, but by the mid-18th century more rational descriptions of its origin were being sought, for example by Chambers.
	23.	Men turn their wheat in the grips To lie in grip: as the reapers left it in small heaps. 'The wheat after it is cut and lies in gripp does not lie so exposed for the sun and wind to dry the gripps after being fogged with wet.' (Lisle, 1722).
	25.	Apricot-tree . . . robbed of its fruit by a dog Perhaps more likely to be a fox, which is omnivorous. Some of the Earl of Selborne's pears on low espalier branches were eaten by foxes in 1986.
September	1.	My Nep: Edmd White & Mr Clement launched a balloon This was a period of
October	16.	intense interest in ballooning. Blanchard's balloon was a *Charlière* type (invented by Parisian physicist J. A. C. Charles), a balloon filled with hydrogen. It was in this type of balloon that Blanchard crossed the Channel in 1785. In 1784 he made a number of experiments in his balloon, and it was one of these, a flight which started out from Chelsea, that GW observed. The kind of balloon flown by Edmund White and Thomas Clement was hot air, not hydrogen – the kind in which the first flight with a man on board was made in the autumn of 1783.
September	25.	Sister Henry White and her daughter Lucy came Fifteen-year-old Lucy was brought to Selborne 'for a change of air'. GW perceived she was languid and had 'overgrown her strength . . . but no bad symptoms'. (Letter 19th October to Mrs Barker).
	29.	Took possession of the Selborne curacy '. . . after an intermission of 26 years', as GW remarked in his letter to Mrs Barker of 19th October – that is, since GW had last officiated as Curate at Selborne. The Revd C. Taylor, the new Vicar of Selborne, had been expected earlier but only took up the living on 26th September.
October	16.	The graphic letter in the newspaper 'from a Gentleman' and inserted in the Journal was from GW himself.
		'Set forth/Their airy caravan . . .' Quotation from Milton's *Paradise Lost* Book VII lines 427–30.
November	1.	Mr John Mulso was shot in the legs This unfortunate occurrence seems not to have resulted in serious injury, since it is not mentioned again either in the Journal or in any letters, and John Mulso was apparently fit enough to travel home nine days later.
December	13.	Shoveled out the bostal Sometimes spelt borstall, an 1888 definition gives a Saxon derivation for these names, applied in downs country to paths which wind up to the summits of hills; in this case a sloping path up the Hanger.

1785 Events and journeys

Early in the year the Revd Richard Yalden, Vicar of Newton Valence, died. He was a friend of long standing, not just of Gilbert but of the whole White family, and was much missed. His position at the Vicarage was taken by Gilbert's nephew Edmund, Benjamin White's son, who was also the nephew of the Revd Richard Yalden, Benjamin's first wife having been Ann Yalden, Richard's sister.

In April and May of this year, Gilbert stayed a month in South Lambeth where his two brothers Thomas and Benjamin resided. One of Gilbert's favourite nieces Molly (Mary White), daughter of his brother Thomas, married her cousin Benjamin, son of Gilbert's brother Benjamin, in June. Gilbert paid his regular visit in July to the Richardsons at Bramshott Place, and in August spent just over a week at Meonstoke with the Mulsos, leaving his Oxford sojourn until October.

This was a period of very hard weather. Following the great frost of December 1784, late frosts destroyed most of the garden crops and many other plants. There was then a considerable drought which caused even Gilbert's reliable well to become nearly dry and give bad water, and finally what little harvest survived the dry weather was swamped by massive rains in late summer and early autumn.

January	7.	Mr Blanchard . . . rode in a balloon This air voyage to France merited three exclamation marks – a rare distinction. It was considered a great feat at the time.
February	1.	A bat . . . dipping down and sipping the water This was very early for a bat to be flying, especially as it was a cold season. Possibly it was surprised out of hibernation.
May	15–21.	Misdated week. GW corrected Monday 15th and Saturday 21st but did not bother with the weekdays.
	29.	Coccus vitis viniferae This information was extended in the NHS Letter to Daines Barrington. The beetle is now known as *Pulvinaria vitis*. Mr. Lightfoot John Lightfoot accompanied GW's correspondent Thomas Pennant on a tour of Scotland in 1772, out of which experience Lightfoot wrote the celebrated *Flora Scotica*. He was also known for his study of insects.
June	4.	Miss White's sycomore See note for 22/7/84.
	19.	Oaks . . . ravaged by the caterpillars These would be the green oak roller *Tortrix viridiana*, one of the principal oak defoliators. The caterpillars of this moth feed until June inside rolled-up oak leaves, pupating within a folded leaf. They swarm in June and July, laying eggs on twigs. These eggs hatch out the following May.
August	12.	Black-caps This is more likely to refer to the bullfinch *Pyrrhula pyrrhula*, for which 'blackcap' is a country name, than the warbler we call by this name today.
	15.	Sam & Charles Samson and Charles White, the two elder sons of GW's brother Henry.
	16.	Gooseberries . . . eaten by the dogs See note on a similar occasion for 25/8/84, recalled by GW on 1/9/85.
September	8.	Parnassia Sites for this plant, rare in the south, have been recorded in Hampshire, though there are none there now. GW believed he had seen the grass of Parnassus, *Parnassia palustris*, in 1765 but had not been certain, though he had recorded it in flower several times since.
October	8.	Bror Henry, Bet and Charles Brother Harry, his wife Elizabeth and son Charles.
	12.	Well . . . so low The drought of this year seems to have affected the well more than in previous years.
November	11.	Celeri piped Celery with roughly hollow stems.
	13, 17.	Mr and Mrs Ben White GW's nephew Benjamin and the newly married Molly White.

1786 Events and journeys

The new year came in with the snow, which settled and drifted, the wind forcing it into the roof spaces and causing damage to ceilings, including those of the Wakes. In a letter in late January, Gilbert remarks that his gout is 'in a grumbling way'. His niece Jane Clements, married daughter of his brother Benjamin, came from Alton to Newton in the middle of the month with her young family to be inoculated against smallpox, as brother Harry's family had previously been in 1778. Gilbert's nephew Jack, now Dr Jack, was still at Alton. His widowed mother Mrs John White, who kept house for Gilbert at the Wakes, and Gilbert paid several visits to Alton during this year. Jack seemed to be making progress in Alton, but in October came news of a move back to Salisbury and better prospects.

Gilbert visited the Richardsons of Bramshott Place as usual in July. He spent ten days in August with the Mulsos in Meonstoke, and in October he paid a short visit to Oxford.

January	9.	Mr Churton left us Mr Churton's Christmas/New Year visits had become a regular event – he returned to Selborne this year on Boxing Day.
March	6.	birds are so distressed The suffering of the birds in this hard weather made a considerable impression upon GW who mentioned it also in a letter to his nephew, Sam Barker.
	30.	Mr Taylor and his bride The Revd Taylor was the newly married Vicar of Selborne. Mrs Taylor was a well-born and handsome woman whom Gilbert and the rest of the family at Selborne and Newton and Mrs Etty all found most agreeable. The Taylors had no intention of living at Selborne, so Mrs Etty retained her residence and GW his curacy.
April	20.	water ouzel The dipper – still a rare vagrant in Hampshire. This one recovered from its injury: see entry for 12th May, though there is no note as to whether it was

	.	returned to the wild.
	23.	grass-lamb Christmas-born lambs which have been out at grass and are now fit and ready for eating.
May	17.	Bantham sow Not a known usage, and apparently not a breed of pig, so possibly this was simply a general term for a small pig.
June	1.	Phalaena quercus See note for 19/6/85.
August	27.	swivel-gun A small gun or cannon mounted on a swivel which could be turned horizontally in any direction.
September	25.	niece Betsey Elizabeth White, brother Harry's daughter, born in 1767.
November	12.	Wolmer pond was sewed The pond was drained.
December		Accounts for 1783: These accounts appear to be the settlement with Mr Randolph, Rector of Faringdon, where GW had been Curate. The balance received on 13th September was paid in person since Mr Randolph was at Selborne at that time.

1787 Events and journeys

During this year Gilbert was much occupied with correcting the proofs of *The Natural History of Selborne* and getting his book through the beginning of the publishing process. One letter to his niece Molly concerning the order of some of the letters is particularly interesting. Sending on one of the Daines Barrington letters, he promises another 'which I shall also extract from my Journals'. This shows that he structured the NHS, putting in additions if necessary, and that it was not simply an artless selection of letters to his friends.

Gilbert made an Easter visit to Oxford in April and was away for a month at South Lambeth and London from mid-May, incidentally missing a visit from his friend the Revd Richard Churton who called at Selborne unexpectedly and found not only Gilbert but all his White friends away.

Towards the end of year, Gilbert and Mrs John White were looking after the young son of Molly and Ben White who was staying with his nurse at Selborne. In November Gilbert went to Fyfield to stay with his brother Harry and his family, returning to Selborne after ten days, and he paid a brief visit to nearby Newton just before Christmas.

The Journal for this year is written on blank pages ruled out manually, rather than in the usual printed volume.

February	23.	Cuckow . . . heard at Rolle in Switserland This and other notes of a similar nature are extracts from letters received from GW's friend Dr Richard Chandler.
March	16.	in a torpid state A house martin in torpor would have supplied factual evidence to support the theory that hirundines were a hibernating rather than a migratory species, a matter with which GW, like the naturalists of his day, was much occupied.
	20.	Monk's rhubarb See note for 31/10/87.
May	27.	Birds do not make nests so peculiar each to its species A most perceptive observation – often the skill of discerning birds' nests is lost with the passage of years. This was obviously not the case with GW, remarking here on the precise construction of nests in his sixty-seventh year.
June	11.	Quail A rare enough sight anywhere nowadays, let alone in South Lambeth, though in the late 18th century this was still a rural village separate from London, as many of GW's other observations testify.
July	8.	Hops are diecious plants Dioecious: having the male and female reproductive parts on separate flowers on separate plants. It was usual to plant female hops only, as is largely the custom on Continental Europe. GW suggested that this practice might be at least partly responsible for the uncertainty of hop harvests and advocated that perhaps just a few male plants should be planted. He returns to the subject in 3/8/91 when he notes that the male flowers are producing pollen and female flowers coming into bloom in Mr Hale's hop garden. The crop of hops is increased if the flowers are fertilised and the hop flavour is stronger, which it seems suits English beers better than the lighter ones, and has recently been a matter of dispute in the European markets and the EEC.
	20.	Sam White entered . . . at Oriel College Samson, the eldest son of GW's brother Harry, was following in his uncle's footsteps at Oxford.
September	15.	a dog & a bitch of the Chinese breed This description is substantially reproduced in NHS Letter LVIII to Daines Barrington. Almost certainly it refers to the Chow, a breed of the Spitz group with spiky hair, pointed ears and muzzle and tail curled over the back – the same group as huskies and elkhounds. A characteristic of the breed is the blue tongue. Kamschatdales Kamschatka is a peninsula in NE Asia in the USSR.

October	2.	The quantity of potatoes . . . prodigious In the NHS Letter XXXVII to Daines Barrington dated 8th January 1778, GW wrote: 'Potatoes have prevailed in this little district, by means of premiums, within these twenty years only; and are much esteemed here now by the poor, who would scarce have ventured to taste them in the last reign.'
	31.	Monk's rhubarb Strictly, this name applies to *Rumex alpinus*. But in this species it is the leaves only that may be used cooked or in salads, whereas on this date GW clearly describes using the stalks in tarts. He is probably growing the culinary rhubarb, *R. x cultorum* or *R. rhubarbarum*, which became available in the 18th century. However, on 1st June 1789 GW describes monk's rhubarb as 7 ft high, and in full bloom on the 22nd May in the following year. *Rumex alpinus* does not flower until July, and this sounds more like the ornamental rhubarb, *Rheum palmatum*. In later years (7th May 1791 and 18th May 1793) he refers simply to 'garden rhubarb' or just 'rhubarb'.
	21.	William Dewye: See note 26/4/89.
November	7.	The Fyfield Comedians The childen of Harry and Elizabeth White and their friends.
	16.	Norway rats These are now known as the common or brown rat, *Rattus norvegicus*. They are thought to have been introduced to Britain about 1728–29 in ships from Russia. They extended their range in the 18th century, spreading across Europe, and replacing the black rat as the commonest species.
December	24.	Bantham fowls . . . flew over the house Bantams are renowned for their flightiness.
	27.	Musca domestica This shows extraordinary tolerance towards an insect usually regarded as a pest.

1788 Events and journeys

In January, the woodcutters moved into the Selborne Hanger for the second time to fell some of the mature beech. 'If my niece does not come, and see the remains of that sweet pendulous covert next summer, she will scarce be able to conceive how lovely and romantic it once had been,' Gilbert wrote to Molly White in January. By August, Harry White was noting in his journal 'Selborne Hanger dreadfully denuded and ye grand Hanging Wood facing Bro: White's garden horribly mangled.'

During February Gilbert was busy with his Index ('an occupation . . . full as entertaining as that of darning of stockings'). Molly was doing an excellent job editing the *Natural History*. Molly's son was still at Selborne; Gilbert affectionately called him 'the learned pig', referring to the famous pig of the time who was said to be learning to read and write, but remembered now only in the little nursery rhyme 'Come hither little piggy-wig, Come and learn your letters . . .' Both child and book were apparently doing well, as Gilbert wrote in March: 'In return for your care of my brat, I have pleasure to inform you that your boy is perfectly well and brisk.'

Both Molly and Gilbert's brother Benjamin had stayed at Selborne early in the year. Other visitors included brother Thomas, and Mrs Harry White and two of her daughters. In August, Harry White himself came to stay, bringing some others of his large family. Gilbert wrote at the beginning of December to the Revd Richard Churton on the subject of his friend's regular winter visit to Selborne: 'Pray come on 24th for if you cannot be as regular in your migrations as a ring ousel or a swallow, where is the use of all your knowledge?'

March	23.	Holes . . . bored by bank-martins The migration or hibernation of hirundines was a theme to which GW frequently referred, and a question which he never finally resolved. With martins, especially those that were hatched late in the season, he seemed to be more inclined to accept the idea of hibernation. This is discussed in the NHS Letter XXXVI of 1777 and Letter LV of 1781 to Daines Barrington.
April	19.	The voice of the Cuckoo is heard in the land An echo of *The Song of Solomon* adapted from 'The voice of the turtle . . .'
May	15.	Sheared my mongrel dog Rover Hair from animals such as cows and goats helps to bind old-fashioned plaster mixtures. This is especially useful when going over lathes and reduces cracking and shrinkage. Owners of old listed buildings are sometimes advised to follow this practice; the coarse hair from zoo animals such as yaks and camels has proved particularly effective. GW was uneasy (January 1778) when his plasterer added wood ash to make the plaster set more quickly but modern opinion is that this (then common) practice is acceptable, but that neither coal ash nor brick dust should be used.
	25.	Latin translation 'And drive the struggling steers amongst the very vineyards.' (Virgil): *Georgics II*, 356–7)

June	6.	Pottle A liquid measure equivalent to half a gallon.
	9.	The stalks and ribs of the leaves . . . embossed with large tumors These excrescences are the galls of the aphid *Pemphigidae bursarius*, still a common poplar gall insect.
	14.	Bro. Benjamin has in his grounds 77 rows of Lucerne In the agricultural books of the 17th and 18th centuries this is usually written as 'la lucerne'. It is the leguminous plant *Medicago sativa*. Also known as 'purple medick' and 'clovergrass', it was recommended as a fodder plant. In 1762, the *Gentleman's Magazine*, a publication which the White brothers both read and contributed to, noted that 'one acre of Lucerne can maintain three or four horses' – one of Benjamin's rows kept a horse for 24 hours.
	25.	Latin translation 'So thick the pointed hail leaps pattering upon the roofs.' (Virgil: *Georgics I*, 449)
July	12.	Latin translation 'Mark, too, when in the woods many a walnut tree shall clothe herself in flower, and shall droop her fragrant boughs. If fruits prevail, likewise shall corncrops follow, and with great heat shall come great threshing.' (Virgil): *Georgics I*, 187–190)
	.	Nux Authorities seem to think that the *nux* in question is the almond rather than the walnut.
	14.	Piped . . . pinks To pipe: to propagate pinks by taking cuttings or slips, removing them at a joint in the stem.
	15.	Jennetings An apple now usually called Joaneting. It is a dessert variety which ripens early (another name is June-eating) and has been known since before 1600.
	20.	John Philips (1676–1709), author of several poems famous in their time amongst which *Cyder*, written in 1709, was one of the best known. It was a poem written in imitation of Virgil's *Georgics*, celebrating the cultivation, manufacture and virtues of cider, and it provided a model for Thompson's *The Seasons*.
	28.	S. Loe A member of the Loe family who kept a record of measurements and observations.
August	9.	in old July According to the old calendar. On 3/9/52 Britain and her dominions adopted the Gregorian calendar.
September	9.	lime-tree . . . a wild tree The small-leaved lime, *Tilia cordata*, is a native tree and found growing wild. It was also part of coppice woodland. This species has been recorded in the vicinity of Selborne.
October	4.	Latin translation 'And every fertile tree which at the season of early bloom had decked itself in the promise of fruit, when, in autumn, its time was fully come, bore a fruit for every flower.' (Virgil: *Georgics IV*, 142–143)
	18.	The pound This appears to have been an enclosure for temporarily confining stray animals situated near the Plestor, the small green in front of the church. The pound field, which is mentioned two days later, is the field roughly triangular in shape situated to the south-east of land belonging to the Wakes, across which runs the path leading to the zig-zag.
	28.	my meridian line A line traced on the ground to indicate a position of the meridian which is determined by observation of positions of the sun.
November	1.	six yeoman prickers A pricker is a tracker looking for 'pricks', or footprints.
December	16.	perforated stopple The stopper of a container perforated to allow a gas or liquid to pass through.

1789 Events and journeys

In the January and February issues of the *Gentleman's Magazine*, Gilbert's brother Thomas added his own complimentary reviews of *The Natural History of Selborne* to the many which had already appeared. The book had a warm and appreciative reception, though Gilbert's pleasure in its success must have been marred by the shock of his brother Harry White's death on 27th December 1788. Gilbert did not go to Fyfield though he made efforts to establish some kind of security for his brother's family by writing letters trying (unsuccessfully, as it turned out) to get young Samson White appointed to his father's Fyfield living. On a positive note, his nephew John ('Gibraltar' Jack) was 'on his way to become the first medical man in Salisbury'.

The success of the *Natural History* brought new correspondents, among them the young George Montagu, who was later to become a respected ornithologist.

Gilbert was away from home at South Lambeth and London between 19th June and 4th July, but other than this he was scarcely absent from Selborne. He had, however, his usual generous portion of visitors: Mr Richardson from Bramshott, his niece Mrs Clement and her husband and three children, brother Thomas, Molly and her son and husband, Mr and Mrs Sam Barker, and also Thomas, the son of his old friend John Mulso.

January	1.	Timothy begins to sink his well In a letter to Thomas Barker dated 8th January, GW reported 'failure of water is remarkable. The ponds are all dry, and most of the wells in the village & among the rest my own.'
	3.	blue rag Probably not a welcome find: '. . . this rag is rugged and stubborn', as GW wrote in NHS Letter IV to Thomas Pennant. The blue ragstone is found in shallow strata in the Selborne greensand and, being durable, was used for paths, stables and dry walls.
	10.	Great speckled diver or loon The great northern diver *Gavia immer* – other names are speckled diver or loon. The name 'sprat loon' more often refers to the red-throated diver, or in Norfolk to the black-throated diver. This is a bird which is seen in southern counties only rarely and in winter, its summer breeding range being north of the British Isles, though there are a few breeding records from the north-west of Scotland.
	14.	A Goosander, & a Dun diver GW correctly notes the male and female merganser *Mergus merganser*, thought by many earlier naturalists to have been two species because of their differences in plumage.
	15.	frost . . . entered the ground about 12 inches A remarkable depth for frost to penetrate.
March	27.	Violets smell Their presence was noted six days previously, but the weather had been gloomy. Sweet violets yield their scent most strongly in sunlight, and after the severe frost there seems to have been sun on this day.
April	26.	certificate people The couple in question had a certificate or letter from their native village which testified to their good character and promised to take them back if they became a charge on their adopted parish. Also known as registered, or testimonial persons. See also entry for 21/10/87.
May	10.	Chrysomelae oleraceae The turnip fly was first noted in 1772, but here it is given a full description.
		Latin translation 'One that jumps using its very thick rear legs: the jumping "chrysomela" is dangerous to young plants and to delicate leaves.'
	17.	Latin translation 'A mouse ravages my borders and is feared by the tenant as much as a Calydonian boar.' (Martial: *Book XI Epigram XVIII*, lines 17–18).
June	11.	strawberries cryed about A reference to the tradition of singing wares, which was developed into an art in London at this period. Such cries inspired Herrick's *Cherry Ripe* and Weeke's beautiful musical arrangement of a number of cries.
	23.	pottle See note for 6/6/88.
July	19.	slidder A word often used by GW, and here defined.
	23.	Carduus crispus A synonym for the welted thistle, *Carduus acanthoides*, not now regarded as a sub-species as formerly.
August	8.	Two poor half-fledged fern-owls GW's local fame as a naturalist seems to have led a number of people to bring unwelcome gifts such as this. The nightjar was a species GW had observed closely and as he noted in a letter to Robert Marsham in 1791, 'I have thoughts of sending a paper to the RS [Royal Society] respecting the fern owl; and seem to think that I can advance some particulars concerning that peculiar migratory, nocturnal bird, that have never been noticed before.' He put it off, though mentioning it again in 1792, and never wrote it.
		chine Backbone. GW originally wrote 'backs', then wrote in 'chines' above, but perhaps neglected to make up his mind which word he preferred since he did not cross one of them out.
September	23.	the King's coronation The 22nd September was the anniversary of King George III's coronation.
October	3.	land-rail The corncrake, *Crex crex*, a bird mentioned several times but here fully described. A summer migrant, wintering in Africa, it is now uncommon in the British Isles owing to the destruction of its habitats and changes in agricultural practice.
	30.	toached the inside of the tiling To toach or torch: in plastering, to point the inside joints of roof slates laid on lath with lime-hair plaster.

November	3.	awakened from sleep See note for 23/3/88.
	26.	mows A heap of unthreshed corn stored in a barn.
	29.	Housed 8 cords of beech billet A cord is strictly 128 cubic feet; in practice a pile of cut wood about 8 × 4 × 4 feet. A billet is wood cut for fuel.
December	8, 9.	leash of hares Three of the same kind of animal, usually hounds, foxes or, as here hares.

1790 Events and journeys

Apart from a short stay at Newton Valence, Gilbert did not leave Selborne until April when he travelled to Oxford for a few days. At the end of the month, his friend Dr Chandler came to live in Selborne with his baby son and his wife, who was to give birth to their second child only a few days after they moved in. During this year, Gilbert acquired a new correspondent in Robert Marsham (1708–97), a gentleman whose interest in arboriculture set Gilbert to examine the trees of his neighbourhood, some of which he had planted himself.

In Salisbury his nephew John (Jack) White continued to prosper. Mid-year saw Gilbert in South Lambeth and London for just a over a month. The latter half of the year brought almost continual visits from one member or another of the White family. There was another period of drought in the autumn and winter and Gilbert's well was almost dry for months, until rain fell again in late November.

December brought a sad letter from John Mulso, informing his friend of his wife's death. Mulso himself was in poor health and this was the last letter that Gilbert was to receive from his old correspondent.

January	10.	A ripe wood-strawberry Unusually late, although the winter had been relatively mild. The wild strawberries' fruits are rarely seen after the beginning of August, although the form known as the alpine strawberry will continue to flower and fruit until checked by hard frosts, especially if they are in a sheltered spot.
March	7.	Torricellian tube The barometer, named the Torricellian tube after Evangelista Torricelli, the Italian physicist and mathematician (1608–47) who discovered the principle of the mercury barometer.
	15.	A vast snake A large grass snake – a species severely in decline in Britain in the 20th century, like most other native reptiles.
	20.	That noise in the air of some thing passing This is a remarkable observation of the stone curlews' spring arrival by a man who suffered from deafness, at a time when it was not scientifically established that many birds perform a great part of their migratory flight during the night hours.
	21.	Sand-martins are the most early among the hirundines This observation is taken for granted now by bird watchers.
	21.	Latin translation 'Its mouth has a stretched snout which is bristly, very long and bivalve.'
	28.	house . . . over-run with a kind of black beetle The cockroach *Blatta orientalis* was common in the warmer parts of America but James Rehn (Academy of Natural Sciences, Philadelphia), who was something of a cockroach detective, established that it came to America from Africa on slave ships. He suggested also that it arrived in Europe on Phoenician vessels. However, the accepted time of introduction into Europe is the 16th century, again from trading ships, but it spread only slowly.
April	3.	Geffrey Whitney's Emblemes Whitney brought to England the 'emblem book', so popular on the Continent. His book, published in 1586, contained 248 emblems: verses usually consisting of one or two six-line stanzas prefixed by a device or woodcut and motto. Some of the emblems were original, others borrowed from other writers; they were intended to provide pieces of wisdom or knowledge for the readers to reflect upon.
	20.	Latin translation 'Odd numbers, please God.' (Virgil: *Eclogues 8*, 75).
	29.	Doctor Chandler, & Lady came to the parsonage house The doctor, his wife and their baby son had a terrifying journey home from Rolle in Switzerland, braving both the dangers of navigating the Rhine and their passage through revolutionary Europe. Dr Chandler had previously asked GW to look about for a house for the family – one possibility had been a town house at Alton.
June	1.	ordinary barrels, buckets &c Unexceptional barrels and buckets, that is, those of no great quality.
	21.	Geffrey Whitney See note for 3/4/90.
July	4.	Now this maxim . . . of place and convenience This paragraph was added eleswhere on the same page, the link being marked by an asterisk.

	25.	infusion of the blossoms of the lime tree Lime tissane is still an esteemed herbal remedy in France.
	27.	Honey-dews The sweet, sticky substance found on the leaves and stems of trees and plants, which is the excreta of aphids, was formerly believed to be a natural phenomenon in origin like the dew. Its connection with aphids was not fully understood until the following century.
	31.	Phil. Trans *Philosophical Transactions* was the title of a learned publication of the Royal Society begun in 1665.
August	7.	Latin translation 'Sorrowing images of ivory shed tears in our temples and brazen statues break into sweat.' (Virgil: *Georgics I*, 480).
	14.	Harvest bugs bite the ladies These insects are particularly irritating during the late summer and early autumn. Some people are extremely allergic to their bites, which are common in bracken or brambly areas.
	23.	staddle Sometimes referred to as staddle stones or rick staddles, this is a platform of stone or timber upon which a rick is built to raise it off the earth and prevent rats' entry.
September	19.	Shear-water This bird was almost certainly blown inland by a summer gale. Notes of gales about Selborne occur a few days later.
	21.	Mrs Clement . . . to be inoculated Some years before, the Barker family had been successfully inoculated against smallpox, a practice strongly advocated by Lady Mary Wortley Montagu as early in the century as 1717. Following their example, Jane Clement (daughter of Benjamin White) and some of the Chandler family were also inoculated, apparently with success.
	25.	there the snake throws . . . In this paragraph GW can be seen at his best, demonstrating his gift of lucid observation and experimentation. Latin translation 'The slippery snake sloughs off its skin on thorns.' (Lucretius: *De Rerum Natura*, 4,61)
	30.	Mrs Brown Nee Sarah Barker, daughter of GW's sister Anne and Thomas Barker. She was married to Edward Brown of Stamford in Lincolnshire.
October	2.	A curious bird Thomas Bell, an early editor of White, believed this bird to have been a strange cross between a blackcock – the male grouse – and a pheasant.
	3.	Newton vicarage house . . . 600 feet higher than S Lambeth This calculation is about right.
	20.	spring-keepers The freshwater shrimp, probably *Gammarus pulex*, the commonest of the three British species.
November	11.	Fyfield A dog evidently named after the home parish of GW's late brother Harry. A cock-dog (or cocker or cocking dog) is one, usually a spaniel, trained to raise game birds.

1791 Events and journeys

In January Gilbert wrote that 'the rains this winter have been prodigious', and he even included a rain chart copied from the Journal for this year in a letter dated February 1792 to his niece Mary Barker, noting that the fall between the 13th and 19th November was 5·1 inches. Three of the five trips Gilbert made during the year were to nearby Newton Valence for one or two days. He was in Oxford at Easter and spent a month at midsummer travelling from Bramshott Place, visiting Edmund White at Godalming, then moving on to London and South Lambeth.

On his return to Selborne he was unwell, suffering from 'a feverish disorder' and also from a urinary illness he calls 'gravel'. However, at the end of the year he is writing to Marsham about sending a paper on the fern-owl (nightjar) to the Royal Society with informaton which had not previously been observed.

An earlier letter to Marsham notes with satisfaction that Edward Jenner's original observations on the behaviour of the nestling cuckoo had received some corroborative support from his correspondent's friend Lord Suffield. Jenner's work caused a tremendous outcry and disbelief. Another correspondent of Gilbert's, George Montagu, later wrote a well-substantiated account of the way the cuckoo ejects other eggs or fledglings, vindicating Jenner, who was a doctor as well as an ornithologist and known for his pioneering of the practice of vaccination in Britain.

In September of this year Gilbert's old friend and long-standing correspondent John Mulso died.

January	21.	the planet Jupiter Venus was what GW had originally written and subsequently corrected.
February	1.	gross-beaks Hawfinches, *Coccothraustes coccothraustes*, one of the most elusive
March	3.	of our breeding birds. They are not now numerous, and estimates of populations in
	20.	the past are extremely unreliable because of the shy behaviour of the species. At

present they are widely but sparsely distributed in Hampshire. An exceptionally large flock in the New Forest was reported to Guy Montford who wrote a monograph on the bird during the years of the Second World War, and it seems likely that a similarly unusual flock inhabited the environs of Selborne in the winter of 1791. Not having been mentioned previously, the hawfinch now features in several Journal entries.

As for the apricot buds, though hawfinches have been observed to take fruit buds this is more characteristic of bullfinches, which were also seen in Selborne gardens, and are mentioned by GW on 7th February and again on 20th March.

April	2.	Hannah White Twenty-one year old daughter of Benjamin White, sister of Molly,
	12.	now Mrs Ben White, who accompanied her on this trip to Selborne – though not up the Hanger to the alcove before breakfast on the 12th.
June	1.	Chur-worm jars A name for the mole cricket (*Gryllotalpa gryllotalpa*); also called eve-chur.
		Bay the stream To dam or divert the stream
	9.	No rain . . . gardens & fields much parched A year of extremes, this low June rainfall of .91 inches was followed by a July record of 5.56 inches.
	24.	Selburne GW sometimes varied the spelling of place names, rendering Selborne as Seleburne or Selburne, an older form of the name.
July	9.	pomgranade The pomegranate, *Punica granatum*, can survive as an outdoor plant in the milder areas of Britain's south and west.
	14.	bat of the largest sort The noctule bat, *Nyctalis noctula*, was first observed in Britain by GW.
	31.	Latin translation 'Sometimes, although rarely, it visits England during the autumn; however, it does not spend long here nor nest here.'
August	7.	a picture of a mule pheasant This was the painting mentioned on 2nd October 1790.
September	6.	A swift still hovers A very late bird, mentioned by GW in a letter to Robert Marsham in December.
	12.	When Autumn scatters . . . From Thomson's *Seasons*; extracted from *Autumn*, lines 834–46.
December	20.	white, and a yellow wagtail The white wagtail, which GW also describes as the grey and white, is the pied wagtail, *Motacilla alba yarrellii*. A very few of the European race of white wagtails *Motacilla alba alba* breed in Britain. For yellow wagtail, see note 31/1/84.

1792 Events and journeys

Gilbert made only three trips away from Selborne during this year: to Oxford in April for several days, a single day in June spent at Mareland near Alton with his brother Benjamin and his wife, and another day at Newton Valence in December. In November, Benjamin left South Lambeth and came to live at Mareland, 'a beautiful seat between Alton and Farnham, late the residence of Mr Sainesbury, Uncle of Mrs Edmund White, and agent to Lord Stawell.'

The weather of 1792 reached extremes of warmth and wet, and Gilbert wrote of the 'sad wet summer & autumn in our hay, or fallows, our corn & our forest fuel which lies rotting in the moors of Woolmer.' Nevertheless, there were as usual visits from many of his relatives, including his namesake, Harry's son Gilbert. At Christmas, with his customary regularity, Mr Churton arrived to spend the festive season with his old friend.

January	17.	Antirrhinum Cymb The ivy-leaved toadflax, *Cymbalaria muralis*, is a perennial which dies back in winter but revives in all but the hardest frosts.
February	4.	Crocus blows, gossamer floats This was entered by mistake in the Journal for 7th January. The two dates are both at the foot of the page position (that is, on a Saturday).
	9.	9 score A weight of 20 or 21 lb, used usually in weighing pigs or oxen.
March	17.	Lord Stawell This was Lord Stawell of Alice Holt, with whom GW was on friendly terms. He shared an interest in natural history, called sometimes at the Wakes and in October 1790 sent GW the curious pheasant (see note for 2/10/90) and other curiosities.
	23.	Crown imperials bud for bloom, & stink much The glossy, bright breen leaves of these plants have a foxy smell.
April	7.	Thomas mowed the dark green grass The grass just inside a fairy ring is typically a richer green in colour where the roots have benefited from the nutrients produced by

	.	the fungi which caused the ring. The Thomas here is Thomas Hoar, not GW's brother.
May	22.	Amusive bird . . . A line from GW's own poem *The Naturalist's Summer Evening Walk*.
		crop moderate, & fruit small Evidently written in at a later date.
June	10.	began to use green goose-berries Traditionally, small early green gooseberries are picked in June. This thins the bushes for the sweet dessert crop.
	11.	swarm 'Abound' written first in manuscript and then crossed out.
July	5.	Provost of Oriel, & Lady Dr and Mrs Eveleigh.
	8.	Poet of Nature James Thomson, with reference to his poem *The Seasons*. He was a favourite poet of GW's, who often quoted him.
	20.	Latin translation 'In all the members of this species the eggs are larger than one would expect given the size of their bodies.'
	28.	Latin translation The two entries for this date, in someone else's handwriting, are almost illegible and seem to be unintelligible. They cannot therefore be given a rational translation.
August	25.	Latin translation 'Slender, fibrous tufts.'
		feathery, plume-like appearance This is the reason why *Cotinus coggygria* is now known as the smoke tree. GW's came in 'a large cargo of shrubs and flower roots from Brother Thomas in London.'
	29.	Clavarias A group of club fungi without gills, which are fleshy and branching. GW is possibly referring to the one now known as *Clavariadelphus pistillaris*, which grows in beech-woods.
September	3.	Gil. White GW's nephew, Harry White's third son, born in 1771.
	16.	Latin translation 'The usual variety of domesticated Upsalian swine always has its toes joined together: in other members of the species one sees the same thing.'
	30.	Mount Carburn Mount Caburn.
		species of wild bee Possibly *Bombus lapidarius*, which nests in large colonies underground, usually in a mouse hole, and resents disturbance.
October	28.	polecat *Mustela putorius*, but see entry for 24/11/92.
	29.	bavin A bundle of brushwood. Technically it differs from a faggot in that it is secured with one band instead of two.
December	8.	Dr Uvedale's great Saint Germain An ancient variety of pear, named after Dr Uvedale who lived at Enfield at about 1690.

1793 Events and journeys

Although this was the last year of Gilbert White's life, he did not suffer a lingering malady. His Journal entries show him to have been quite active both in mind and body. He was at Newton Valence for three days in February, and early in March he spent an enjoyable and energetic twelve-day period with his brother Benjamin at his new home Mareland. Benjamin and Mrs White repaid the visit in May and several other relatives also came, including Gilbert's nephew Benjamin and Molly White, and his nephew John (Jack) White, who had recently married, came with his wife to spend three days at Selborne. There was also John Mulso, the son of Gilbert's old friend, who stayed overnight on 14th June.

The Journal entry for 15th June notes young John Mulso's departure. On this day also Gilbert wrote a letter to Robert Marsham which was quite lengthy and discursive but which mentions his having been 'annoyed this spring with a bad nervous cough, and a wandering gout, that have pulled me down very much', and he ends 'the season with us is unhealthy.' On 16th June there is no Journal entry. The doctor was summoned from Alton the following day, and visited daily thenceforth until 26th June, which was the day of Gilbert White's death.

It was his specific wish that he should be buried with a simple ceremony in the churchyard at Selborne, a place where he had often remarked on the swifts and martins and the yew tree where a pair of nuthatches once bred.

January	6.	N. papers Newspapers?
	27.	Scopoli had a specimen in his Museum . . . found in Carniola G. A. Scopoli 1723–88, Italian naturalist. Carniola is in present-day Yugoslavia.
February	1.	War declared, and letters of Marque granted Britain had been neutral until France
	8.	had declared war (actually on 31st January, not 1st February). This expensive and damaging war was not finally to end until 1815. Letters of marque gave licence to make reprisals on the subjects of a hostile state for injuries alleged to have been done by the enemy's army – in fact, a licence to pirate.
March	7.	'now the sprightly race . . .' Thomson's *Seasons*, 'Spring', lines 835–8. See also note for 8/7/92.

	8.	I once resided in that town This observation would seem to confirm the idea that GW had been at school at Farnham.
April	9.	Latin translation Lairs.
May	4.	blackbird . . . with white on the breast Most likely a partly albino bird.
	5.	Antirrhinum Cymb. See note for 17/1/92.
	7.	field-fares in the high wood Almost certainly late leavers. Fieldfares now breed in Scotland, even in some northerly parts of England, but the earliest breeding record is 1967.
June	14.	Mr John Mulso The son of GW's lifelong friend John Mulso, who had died in 1791.
	16–22.	The dates and month for this week and the heading 'Selborne' were written into the Journal, but GW made no further entry.

Well-head

GLOSSARY · INDEX

Included in this glossary/index are words or ideas which might perplex the modern reader: scientific names, unfamiliar common names, archaic or idiomatic terms, and names of people and places. Some species may be mentioned frequently so only the first date reference has been given, unless another entry is particularly significant or is accompanied by reference to a note¶, in which case this date is also given.

In order to avoid repetition the following abbreviations have been used:
GW = Gilbert White
NHS = *The Natural History of Selborne*

Entries are indexed as they appear in the text, with their date. Then follows the present-day common name and scientific name, with other names used by Gilbert White shown afterwards in brackets.

Examples
Churn-owl: 5/7/89 Nightjar *Caprimulgus europaeous* (Fern owl, goatsucker, eve-jar)

i.e. The bird referred to by Gilbert White as 'churn-owl' is now known as the nightjar, scientific name *Caprimulgus europaeus*. On other occasions Gilbert White refers to this bird as the fern-owl, goat-sucker or eve-jar, so these names are shown in brackets. If a species is referred to by an out-of-date scientific name only, that would be the index entry, and it would appear thus:

Antirrhinum cymbalaria: 17/12/85, 17/1/92¶ Ivy-leaved toadflax *Cymbalaria muralis*

i.e. The plant Gilbert White identifies as *Antirrhinum cymbalaria* is the ivy-leaved toadflax, present-day scientific name *Cymbalaria muralis*.

An entry may appear with a note mark ¶ beside the date, as in the last example. This indicates that there is further information to be found in the *Notes* for that date.

Brimstone butter-fly: 7/4/85, 9/4/89 *Gonepteryx rhamni*
Broccoli, purple: 21/4/85 *Brassica oleracea*
Brown, Mrs: 20/8/84, 30/9/90¶ GW's niece Sarah, daughter of his sister Anne and Thomas Barker,
    married Edward Brown of Stamford, Lincs.
Bullace: 1/5/88
Bullfinch: 14/2/86 *Pyrrhula pyrrhula* (Black-cap)
Bunting: 15/6/88
Burbey, Mr: 11/1/87 Kept a shop in Selborne
Burgamot, autumn: 1/10/84 Pear variety (also spelt Bergamot)
Bustard: 16/11/87 Great bustard *Otis tarda*
Butcher-bird, red-backed: 23/5/87, 20/6/87 Red-backed shrike *Lanius collurio* (Flusher)
Butter-cup: 18/5/86 *Ranunculus bulbosus*
Butterfly, brimstone: 7/4/85, 9/4/89 *Gonepteryx rhamni*
Butterfly, brown: 7/4/85 Meadow brown *Maniola jurtina*
Buzzard: 2/8/92 *Buteo buteo*
Buzzard, honey: 12/9/87 *Pernis apivorus*
Cabbage: 26/4/84 *Brassica oleracea*
Cadilliac: 5/10/84 A variety of pear (Cadillac)
Caltha palustris: 14/4/86 Marsh marigold
Campanula, pyramidal: 30/7/85 Chimney bellflower *Campanula pyramidalis*
Candy-tuft: 15/4/91 *Iberis umbellata*
Cane, Mr: 26/11/86 Basil Cane, cousin of GW, Curate of Ludgershall, Wiltshire, 7 m northwest of
    Andover
Canterbury bells: 16/4/89 *Campanula medium*
Carduus crispus: 23/7/89¶ Welted thistle (syn, *Carduus acanthoides*)
Carduus lanceolatus: 23/7/89 Spear thistle *Cirsium vulgare*
Carduus nutans: 23/7/89 Musk thistle
Carduus palustris: 23/7/89 Marsh thistle *Cirsium palustre*
Carp: 12/11/86 *Cyprinus carpio*
Carpenter, John: 24/4/84 The Selborne cobbler
Carrots: 28/4/84 *Daucus carota*
Catsup: 28/8/86 Ketchup: sauce or condiment (Catchup)
Cauliflower: 21/6/86 *Brassica oleracea*, Botrytis group
Cedar of Libanus: 4/2/85 Cedar of Lebanon *Cedrus libani*
Celeri: 4/6/84, 11/11/85¶ Celery *Apium graveolens*
Certhia: 15/9/86 Treecreeper *Certhia familiaris*
Certhia muraria: 25/1/93 Wallcreeper *Tichodroma muraria* (Wall-creeper)
Certificate people: 26/4/89¶
Chafer: 17/5/85 Maybug or cockchafer and summer chafer *Melolontha melolontha* and *Amphimallon
    solstitialis*
Chaffinch: 14/11/86 *Fringilla coelebs*
Chamomile, wild: 12/6/89 Mayweed, corn chamomile *Anthemis arvensis* and stinking chamomile *A.
    cotula*
Chandler, Dr: 27/2/86, 29/4/90¶ Dr Richard Chandler, traveller and antiquarian, friend and
    correspondent of GW. Vicar of Wordham and East Tisted, nr Selborne
Chardon: 13/6/90 Cardoon *Cynara cardunculus* (Chardoon)
Charles: 15/8/85¶ GW's nephew Charles White, second son of his brother Henry from Fyfield
Chase, Miss and Miss Rebecca: 12/2/89
Chaumontelle: 1/10/84 Pear variety (Chaumontal)
Chawton: 18/7/87 A village 3 m from Selborne
Cherries, wall: 3/5/84 Edible varieties of *Prunus*
Chest-nut, edible: 24/4/84 chestnut *Castanea sativa*
Chestnut, horse 22/7/84¶, 1/6/90 *Aesculus hippocastanum*

White, Henry (Harry) Holt: 19/11/85, 9/10/86 GW's nephew, one of his brother Thomas's twin
   sons born in 1763
White, Holt: 25/8/91, 7/1/93 GW's nephew, one of his brother Thomas's twin sons
White, John: 4/9/90 GW's nephew from Salisbury, son of his deceased brother John whose widow
   kept house for GW
White, Lucy: 25/9/84¶ GW's niece, daughter of his brother Henry
White, Mary: 29/5/93 GW's niece, daughter of his brother Benjamin
White, Molly: 22/7/84 GW's niece, daughter of his brother Thomas
White, Mrs: 7/7/88 GW's sister-in-law who had kept house for him since the death of his brother
   John
White, Ned: 14/3/90, 17/1/91 GW's nephew Edward, son of his brother Henry
White owl: 3/2/87 Barn owl *Tyto alba*
White, Rebecca: 16/11/89 GW's niece, daughter of his brother Benjamin
White, Sam: 20/7/84 GW's nephew, son of his brother Henry
White, Thomas: 5/6/84 GW's brother from South Lambeth
White, Thomas Holt (Tom): 19/11/85, 9/10/86 GW's nephew, one of his brother Thomas's twin
   sons born in 1763
White-thorn: 1/6/84 Hawthorn *Crataegus monogyna* (*Crataegus oxyacantha*)
White-throat: 1/5/84, 14/9/87 *Sylvia communis*
Whiting: 7/10/88 *Merlangus merlangus*
Whitney, Geffrey: 3/4/90¶
Whortle-berry: 13/7/92 Bilberry *Vaccinium myrtillus*
Widgeon: 26/12/85 Wigeon *Anas penelope*
Willows: 26/5/86 *Salix* spp.
Willow-wren, large shivering: 18/4/85 Probably the wood warbler *Phylloscopus sibilatrix*
Willow-wren, smallest: 15/4/85 Chiff-chaff *Phylloscopus collybita* (Chif-chaf)
Willughby: 10/1/89 Francis Willughby, author of *The Ornithology*, published in 1678
Wind-hover: 12/9/87 Kestrel *Falco tinnunculus* (Kestril)
Winter aconite: 16/1/85 *Eranthis hyemalis*
Wood-chat: 7/7/92 Woodchat shrike *Lanius senator* (Small butcher bird)
Wood-cock: 28/4/84¶, 11/11/85 *Scolopax rusticola*
Wood-lark: 25/5/86 *Lullula arborea* (*Alauda arborea*)
Wood-owl, brown: 2/2/87 Tawny owl *Strix aluco*
Woodpecker: 23/3/91 Green woodpecker *Picus viridis*
Wood-pigeon: 5/11/84 *Columba palumbus* (Stock dove, *Columba oenas*)
Wood-ruff, 25/5/85 Woodruff *Galium odoratum*
Wood-sorrel: 22/4/89 *Oxalis acetosella*
Wood-straw-berry: 15/7/84, 10/1/90¶ Wild strawberry *Fragaria vesca*
Woods, Anne: 8/7/88, 11/9/92 GW's niece, daughter of his sister Rebecca and Henry Woods of
   Chilgrove
Woods, Edmund: 12/6/84, 8/7/86, 23/6/91
Woods, H.: 8/7/88 GW's nephew Henry, son of his sister Rebecca and Henry Woods of Chilgrove
Worm, slow: 28/1/88 *Anguis fragilis*
Worms: 19/11/86 Earthworms *Lumbricus* spp.
Wornil: 8/8/89 Warble or swelling on the back of cattle caused by the maggots of the warble fly,
   Hypoderma bovis
Worry bree: 8/8/89 *See* wornil
Wren: 3/9/84 *Troglodytes troglodytes*
Wren, golden-crowned: 15/9/86, 2/8/87 Goldcrest *Regulus regulus* (Golden-crested wren)
Wren, large shivering willow-: 18/4/85 Probably wood warbler *Phylloscopus sibilatrix*
Wren, laughing: 26/4/85 Willow warbler *Phylloscopus trochilus* (*Regulus non-cristatus medius*)
Wren, smallest uncrested willow-: 15/4/85, 16/3/88 Chiff-chaff *Phylloscopus collybita* (Small
   uncrested, chif-chaf)
Wry-neck: 6/4/87 *Jynx torquilla* (*Jynx sive torquilla*)

Timothy among the chicory.
Wakes herb garden.

BIBLIOGRAPHY

Bunyard, Edward	*A Handbook of Hardy Fruits* (2 vols., 1920)
Britten, J. & Holland, Robert A.	*A Dictionary of English Plant Names* (1886)
Chinery, Michael	*A Field Guide to the Insects of Britain and Northern Europe* (Collins, 1973)
	Collins Guide to the Insects of Britain and Western Europe (Collins, 1986)
Clapham, A. R., Tutin, T. G. & Warburg, E. F.	*Excursion Flora of the British Isles* (3rd ed., 1981)
	Flora of the British Isles (2nd edition, 1962)
Galpine, John Kingston	*The Georgian Garden – An Eighteenth-Century Nurseryman's Catalogue.* Introd. by John Harvey (Dovecote Press, 1983)
Harvey, John	*Early Nurserymen* (Phillimore, 1974)
	Early Gardening Catalogues (Phillimore, 1972)
Hitt, Thomas	*A Treatise of Fruit Trees* (1757)
Holt-White, Rashleigh	*Life and Letters of Gilbert White* (1901)
Miller, Philip	*The Gardener's Dictionary* (1731 etc.)
Parkinson, John	*Paradisi in Sole Paradisus Terrestris* (1629)
Ray, John	*Catalogus Plantarum Anglicae* (1677)
	Historia Plantarum (1686–1704)
	Synopsis Methodica Stirpium

	Britannicarum (3rd ed. by J. J. Dillenius, 1724)*
Rye, Anthony	*Gilbert White and his Selborne* (1970)
Smith, A. W. revised by Stearn, William T.	*A Gardener's Dictionary of Plant Names* (1972)
South, Richard	*The Moths of the British Isles* (Frederick Warne, 1961)
Stearn, William T.	*Botanical Latin* (2nd ed., 1973)
Vilmorin-Andrieux	*The Vegetable Garden* (1905)

The following editions of Gilbert White's works have been consulted or referred to:

Natural History and Antiquities of Selborne edited by R. Bowdler-Sharpe (1900–01), Sir William Jardine (1890), E. M. Nicholson (1929), Richard Mabey (1977).

Gilbert White's Journals edited by Walter Johnson (1931).

The Garden Kalendar included in the Bowdler-Sharpe edition of the *Natural History of Selborne* (see above).

---

*Facsimile edition with Introduction by William T. Stearn, published by the Ray Society 1973.